Race:

SCIENCE AND POLITICS

Race:

SCIENCE AND POLITICS

BY RUTH BENEDICT

INCLUDING

The Races of Mankind

BY RUTH BENEDICT AND GENE WELTFISH

(Fulton)

THE VIKING PRESS · NEW YORK

Contents

FOREWORD TO THE COMPASS EDITION

by Margaret Mead

RUTH BENEDICT wrote this book during her sabbatical leave from Columbia University in 1939, as part of the responsibility of the scientist as citizen. Europe lay under the threat of a spreading Nazi racism, and the need for understanding the problems that underlie racism was becoming ever clearer in the United States. As an anthropologist, and an anthropologist closely associated with Franz Boas, who had waged a lifelong battle on behalf of scientifically based recognition of the unity of the human race, Ruth Benedict felt there could be no more urgent use of her few months away from a heavy teaching load than to place the problem in scientific perspective for educated laymen.

She was not a physical anthropologist nor was she primarily concerned with the biological questions which are the special domain of the students of human biology. Rather she was a cultural anthropologist who believed that through knowledge—especially knowledge of the history and functioning of human cultures, viewed comparatively —man might attain greater control over his own destiny and shape the world in which he lived closer to his aspirations for freedom and democracy.

This book presents the core of Ruth Benedict's approach to the question of the human consequences of racial discrimination. During the years that followed there was a series of widely diffused activities, all based on this book: the pamphlet *The Races of Mankind,* first published as a Public Affairs pamphlet in 1943; an animated color film, *Brotherhood of Man,* initiated by the United Automobile Workers, CIO, and produced by United Productions of America; and a book called *In Henry's Backyard,* published by Henry Schuman, based on the film. Ruth Benedict was given three awards in connection with her work on race, which in their timing reflect the kind of penetration her work achieved: from the National CIO Committee to Abolish Racial Discrimination, November 1944; from the New York Committee of the Southern Conference on Human Welfare, March 1948; and, four years after her death in 1948, an award in communication (given specifically for the film *Brotherhood of Man*) by the Institute of Design of the Illinois Institute of Technology, 1952.

In 1945 a new edition of *Race: Science and Politics* was issued, and the foreword written specially for it in March of that year (not included in this edition) reads strangely today. The war had not yet ended; the countries with racism as a special tool still dominated men's fears; the United States was associated with the Soviet Union and with China as allies; Japan was an enemy; the whole host of new countries which have combined their new national identity with various militant forms of racism were not yet born. Ruth Benedict could speak of racism almost as a special disease of part of the white race, heavy on a Christian conscience. Today we see racism rearing its ugly head in Asia and Africa, not as wartime propaganda but as part of these new nations' attempts to find their nationhood. The world setting has altered, and the need for men to

recognize their membership in one race has been immeasur-
ably deepened by the possibility of a war of extinction, for
which racial antagonisms might provide the tinder.

Meanwhile the United States in its inter-racial situation
has been confronted with a new version of the age-old contrast between the ideal and the actual, vulnerable now not
only to the prophet at home, but also to the propagandist
abroad. As our own failures and confusions became significant for our position as a nation, national pressure to set our
house in order has increased. In every community in the
United States, North and South, large and small, the advocates of change need backing from science, from history,
from ethics, for the day-by-day skirmishes over schools and
churches, employment and housing. Of these, Ruth Benedict
wrote, in her foreword to the 1945 edition of this book: "In
race attitudes the behavior of the employer, the union member, the neighbor on our block, the waiter in the restaurant,
the customer in the grocery store add up to the only total
there is or can be. . . . For the dominant race cannot have
freedom for themselves unless they grant it without regard
to race or color. As Booker T. Washington once said, 'To
keep a man in the ditch, you have to stay there with him.' "

Since this book was written, there have been twenty
years of human experience and scientific work to widen
the context of its usefulness. We know a great deal more
about innate human behavior, about the origins of trust
and distrust, and about the importance of small children's
being in an atmosphere of security when they encounter
strangers, especially strange-looking strangers. We know a
great deal more about the extent to which each human
being is dependent upon developing a positive identity, as
an individual whose sex and physical type, nationality and
family, occupation and life history are matters for pride,
and how deep the damage is if on any of these points the

individual must assume instead a negative identity. We have had to struggle with the question of whether a sufficiently great threat to the survival of any society would automatically evoke from the citizenry of that society the kind of behavior necessary to save it. And when we have asked this question and studied it in the light of our knowledge of the behavior of living creatures in general and of man in particular, we have been forced to recognize that human beings have spent their entire existence as Homo sapiens developing devices by which one group—the more successful—survived at the expense of another, and that we have as yet only the insights of the prophets of man's unity to guide us in dealing with a world that is either safe for all or safe for none.

Since this book was written the conscience of mankind has been affronted and confronted with the details of what it meant to live in a concentration camp under Hitler, of the terrible loss of human dignity resulting from the responsible and even benevolent attempts to deal with groups of uprooted human beings—the Japanese Americans, the hundreds of thousands of refugees from each side resulting from conflict between Moslem and Hindu, Nationalist and Communist China, Arab nations and Israel. We have come to see the sufferings springing from persecutions on the grounds of color or imputed race as part of a terrible pattern of political attempts to immobilize, or eliminate, or eradicate whole groups of human beings.

The very conception of "the human race"—made up of men and women of African and Asian, European, American, and Australian stock, which in 1940 seemed such a broad and encompassing category—has now shrunk almost to neighborhood terms, with the inclusion in contemporary human consciousness of space exploration and the possibility that men, in man-made space ships, may set out to look for, and possibly find, other forms of life which might rob our cherished humanity of its special uniqueness. We spoke of "the earth" when this book was written. Now we speak of "Earth."

Such rapid changes in human consciousness, changes which do not even allow for the birth of a new generation to take over ideas which the parent generation finds difficult to learn, require every possible kind of assistance from the human scientist. This is what Ruth Benedict meant this book to be, a kind of handbook for those who carried a pilgrim's staff in their hands on the steep journey into an unknown world. She left her own scientific labors, the detailed analysis of the records of disappearing ways of life which she sought to preserve to enlighten and delight future generations of men, to go out into public places, to write, to speak, to sit all day on committees and in conferences, that the people of the United States might learn to treat all other men as members of the human race. This book is the most permanent record of this devoted activity —more needed today than when it was written.

September 1958

Race:

SCIENCE AND POLITICS

PART ONE. *Race*

I. RACISM:

THE "ISM" OF THE MODERN WORLD

As EARLY AS the late 1880's a French pro-Aryan, Vacher de Lapouge, wrote: "I am convinced that in the next century millions will cut each other's throats because of 1 or 2 degrees more or less of cephalic index." On the surface it appears a fantastic reason for world wars, and it was certainly a reason new under the sun. Was he right? What could it mean? The cephalic index is the quotient of the greatest breadth of the head divided by its length, and some tribes and peoples over the world run to high indices and some to low. Narrow heads are found among uncivilized primitives and among powerful and cultivated Western Europeans; broad heads are too. Neither the narrow heads of the whole world nor the broad heads stack up to show any obvious monopoly of glorious destiny or any corner on ability or virtue. Even in any one European nation or in America men of achievement have been some of them narrow-headed and some broad-headed. What could it mean that "millions will cut each other's throats" because of the shape of the top of their skulls?

In the long history of the world men have given many

reasons for killing each other in war: envy of another people's good bottom land or of their herds, ambition of chiefs and kings, different religious beliefs, high spirits, revenge. But in all these wars the skulls of the victims on both sides were generally too similar to be distinguished. Nor had the war leaders incited their followers against their enemies by referring to the shapes of their heads. They might call them the heathen, the barbarians, the heretics, the slayers of women and children, but never our enemy Cephalic Index 82.

It was left for high European civilization to advance such a reason for war and persecution and to invoke it in practice. In other words, racism is a creation of our own time. It is a new way of separating the sheep from the goats. The old parable in the New Testament separated mankind as individuals: on the one hand, those who had done good and, on the other, those who had done evil. The new way divides them by hereditary bodily characteristics—shape of the head, skin color, nose form, hair texture, color of the eyes—and those who have certain hallmarks are known by these signs to be weaklings and incapable of civilization, and those with the opposite are the hope of the world. Racism is the new Calvinism which asserts that one group has the stigmata of superiority and the other has those of inferiority. According to racism we know our enemies, not by their aggressions against us, not by their creed or language, not even by their possessing wealth we want to take, but by noting their hereditary anatomy. For the leopard cannot change his spots and by these you know he is a leopard.

For the individual, therefore, racism means that damnation or salvation in this world is determined at conception; an individual's good life cannot tip the balance in his favor and he cannot live a bad life if his physical type is the right sort. By virtue of birth alone each member of the "race" is high caste and rightly claims his place in the sun at the expense of men of other "races." He need not base his pride upon personal achievement nor upon virtue; he was born high caste.

From this postulate racism makes also an assertion about race: that the "good" anatomical hallmarks are the monopoly of a pure race which has always throughout history manifested its glorious destiny. The racialists have rewritten history to provide the scion of such a race with a long and glamorous group ancestry as gratifying as an individual coat of arms, and they assure him that the strength and vigor of his race are immutable and guaranteed by the laws of Nature. He must, however, guard this pure blood from contamination by that of lesser breeds, lest degeneration follow and his race lose its supremacy. All over the world for the last generation this doctrine has been invoked in every possible kind of conflict: sometimes national, between peoples as racially similar as the French and Germans; sometimes across the color line, as in Western fears of the Yellow Peril; sometimes in class conflicts, as in France; sometimes in conflicts between immigrants who arrived a little earlier and those who came a little later, as in America. It has become a bedlam.

Where all people claim to be tallest, not all can be right. In this matter of races, can the sciences to which they all appeal judge among the babel of contradictory claims and award the decision? Or is it a matter of false premises and bastard science? It is essential, if we are to live in this modern world, that we should understand racism and be able to judge its arguments. We must know the facts first of race, and then of this doctrine that has made use of them. For racism is an *ism* to which everyone in the world today is exposed; for or against, we must take sides. And the history of the future will differ according to the decision which we make.

WHAT THEY SAY

In this there is nothing new: that when a philosopher cannot account for anything in any other manner, he boldly ascribes it to an occult quality in some race.

> Walter Bagehot, *Physics and Politics*. New York, D. Appleton and Co., 1873, p. 2.

The White race [today read *Nordics*] originally possessed the monopoly of beauty, intelligence and strength. By its union with other varieties [read *Alpines, Mediterraneans*] hybrids were created, which were beautiful without strength, strong without intelligence, or if intelligent, both weak and ugly.

> Arthur de Gobineau, *Essay on the Inequality of Human Races.* Translated by Adrian Collins. New York, G. P. Putnam's Sons, 1932, p. 209.

List of physical characteristics of the genuine Teuton:

The great radiant heavenly eyes, the golden hair, the gigantic stature, the symmetrical muscular development, the lengthened skull (which an ever-active brain, tortured by longing, had changed from the round lines of animal contentedness and extended toward the front), the lofty countenance, required by an elevated spiritual life as the seat of its expression. . . .

> Houston Stewart Chamberlain, *The Foundations of the Nineteenth Century.* New York, Dodd, 1912, Vol. I, p. 535.

What racists say of their own race:

Judgment, truthfulness and energy always distinguish the Nordic man. He feels a strong urge toward truth and justice.

... Passion in the usual meaning of the rousing of the senses or the heightening of the sexual life has little meaning for him. ... He is never without a certain knightliness.

Hans F. K. Gunther, *The Racial Elements of European History*. Translated from the second German edition by G. C. Wheeler. London, Methuen & Co., Ltd., 1927, pp. 51, 52.

In mental gifts the Nordic race marches in the van of mankind.

Bauer, Fischer and Lenz, *Human Heredity*. Translated by Eden and Cedar Paul. New York, Macmillan Co., 1931, p. 655.

What racists say of other groups:

Many intellectuals are trying to help the Jews with the ancient phrase, "The Jew is also a man." Yes, he is a man, but what sort of a man? The flea is also an animal!

Goebbels, reported in *Time*, July 8, 1935, p. 21.

If non-Nordics are more closely allied to monkeys and apes than to Nordics, why is it possible for them to mate with Nordics and not with apes? The answer is this: it has not been proved that non-Nordics cannot mate with apes.

Herman Gauch, *New Foundations for Research into Social Race Problems*. Berlin, 1933. Cited by J. Gunther, *The Nation*, February 5, 1935.

People who live in glass houses: Opinions about our ancestors:

FIRST CENTURY B.C.: Do not obtain your slaves from Britain because they are so stupid and so utterly incapable of being taught that they are not fit to form a part of the household of Athens.

Cicero to Atticus.

ELEVENTH CENTURY: Races north of the Pyrenees are of cold temperament and never reach maturity; they are of great stature and of a white color. But they lack all sharpness of wit and penetration of intellect.

Saïd of Toledo (a Moorish savant), quoted in Lancelot Thomas Hogben, *Genetic Principles in Medicine and Social Science*. New York, A. A. Knopf, Inc., 1932, p. 213.

II. RACE: WHAT IT IS NOT

CHINESE HAVE a yellowish skin and slanting eyes. Negroes have a dark skin and wide flat noses. Caucasians have a lighter skin and high thin noses. The color and texture of the hair of these peoples differ as much as do their skin and noses. These are outward and visible signs by which we recognize race; they are racial characteristics. In briefest possible definition, race is a classification based on traits which are hereditary. Therefore when we talk about race we are talking about (1) heredity and (2) traits transmitted by heredity which characterize all the members of a related group. The first necessity in discussing race is to outline what race is *not*. A great deal of the confusion about race comes from confusing hereditary traits with traits which are socially acquired.

In the first place, race and language are not the same. This should be obvious, for not all who speak Arabic are Arabians and not all who speak English are of the White race. Nevertheless the confusion occurs constantly.

A man's hereditary features and the language he speaks depend upon two different sets of circumstances. His hereditary anatomy depends upon his remote ancestors, and his language depends upon the speech he heard when he was a

9

child. From the point of view of human morphology these two are not even related, for whatever the inherited conformation of his oral cavity and vocal cords, a child learns to speak any language spoken about him, and children with the same oral conformation speak languages with the most different sounds. If not even a man's speech organs account for the language he speaks, still less do racial features like skin color, cephalic index, eyes, and hair determine his mother tongue. The Negroes in America speak English or Spanish or Portuguese or French, depending upon the language of the country in which they live; and Negroes without white blood speak these languages as readily as the light-brown. According to their associations they speak with the intonations of the poor white of the area or of the privileged minority. And this is not a situation which is new in the world. So the primitive Manchus who came from the Siberian tundras have for centuries spoken in China a pure Chinese, and the Arabic language was spread after the ninth century over immense areas of northern Africa among peoples of Negroid blood.

When the people of one race speak the same language and that language is spoken only by that one race, as among some primitive tribes, this is not because the two are interdependent but because they both depend on a third circumstance. This circumstance under which both physical form and language take shape and become unique is isolation. In prehistoric times the world was sparsely populated, and in isolated regions both physical type and language might become different from those in any other part of the world. The process is so simple that it is the more remarkable that it did not happen oftener than it did. The principal reason why it did not was that isolation was so often broken. When two peoples became thoroughly intermingled by conquest or intermarriage, their descendants were racially one mixed type; but they spoke one or the other language.

There was also another factor which operated in history from the earliest times. Racial types maintain themselves over longer periods and over greater areas than language does; people of the same racial type commonly speak several languages which cannot be reduced to a common linguistic family. In the early history of mankind this must have been even truer than it is today, for widespread languages, like Bantu and Polynesian, were once restricted to small groups and have spread far and wide only in comparatively recent times; in parts of the world like the Caucasus and like aboriginal California the early condition still survives. Languages in these latter areas stop short at the margins of one valley, but the racial type is the same over great areas. From earliest times, therefore, language and race have had different histories and different distributions; in the modern world they are shuffled like suits in a pack of cards.

In spite, however, of the impossibility of arguing from race to language or from language to race, race and language are constantly confused. *Aryan,* the term now used in Germany for the preferred race, is the name of a group of languages which includes the Sanskrit of ancient India and languages of ancient Persia; and *Aryan* has also been commonly used as a term covering a much larger group of languages, the Indo-European, which includes not only Sanskrit and Old Persian but German, English, Latin, Greek, Armenian and Slavic. In whichever sense *Aryan* is used, it is a language term and has no reference to a peculiar German racial heritage. Because of the ludicrous inapplicability of the first sense of the word *Aryan,* the Nazis, when they selected the term, were obviously thinking of it in the latter sense of *Indo-European.* But the people speaking Indo-European languages have no unity of racial type either in skin, in eye or hair color, in cephalic index or in stature.

The foremost student of the Aryan languages in the last

century, Max Müller, exposed the fallacy vigorously even in the 1880's—a fallacy which had already become current through the writings of Thomas Carlyle, the English historian J. R. Green, and the French racialist Count de Gobineau. "I have declared again and again," Max Müller writes, "that when I say Aryas (Aryans) I mean neither blood nor bones nor hair nor skull; I mean simply those who spoke an Aryan language. When I speak of them I commit myself to no anatomical characteristics. To me an ethnologist who speaks of Aryan race, Aryan blood, Aryan eyes and hair, is as great a sinner as a linguist who speaks of a dolichocephalic [narrow-headed] dictionary or a brachycephalic [broad-headed] grammar." [1] Nevertheless, as we shall see in discussing the history of racism in Europe, the list of sinners has increased rather than diminished since Max Müller's time.[2]

The fundamental reason why language cannot be equated with race is that language is learned behavior, and race is a classification based on hereditary traits. Language is only one special instance of how learned behavior varies in mankind without relation to physical type. It was not only the Chinese language that the Manchus learned in China; they took over Chinese architecture, the forms of Chinese family life, Chinese ethics, Chinese literature, Chinese food. It is not only the English language that American Negroes use; they become Baptists and Methodists and Pullman car porters. Instead of learning, as in Africa, the elaborate technicalities of "throwing the bones" for divination, they learn the technicalities of reading and writing; instead of the complexities of *mankala*, the intricate peg-game of Africa and the Near

---

[1] *Biography of Words and the Home of the Aryaans*, London, 1888, p. 120.

[2] I have myself in this volume used *Slav*, which refers to languages, as a racial term. There is no word in popular usage which designates this group in biological terms.

East, they learn to shoot craps. Their culture becomes American.

For culture is the sociological term for learned behavior, behavior which in man is not given at birth, which is not determined by his germ cells as is the behavior of wasps or the social ants, but must be learned anew from grown people by each new generation. The degree to which human achievements are dependent on this kind of learned behavior is man's great claim to superiority over all the rest of creation; he has been properly called "the culture-bearing animal." He does not grow wings or fins to cross the seas; he builds ships and airplanes, and the building and operating of these are culturally transmitted. He does not grow fangs and claws to kill his enemy; he invents gunpowder and Maxim guns. This non-biological transmission is a great advantage in that it allows for much greater adaptability to circumstances, but it progressively lessens the importance of biologically transmitted behavior.

This elementary truth is essential for the understanding of race. Race is biologically transmitted, and among the social insects and to a lesser degree among the carnivores their tastes in food, their ways of obtaining it, their aggressiveness or lack of aggressiveness in assuring their own survival are also biologically transmitted. That "the leopard cannot change his spots" means that the leopard, because he belongs to a certain species, will always be found stalking the jungle for his prey. But in man the great aggressors of yesterday become the mild peace-lovers of today. In the ninth century Scandinavians were the feared aggressive Vikings of the sea; in the present generation they are the peaceful non-aggressive exponents of co-operatives and the "middle way."

Even more commonly, at the present time yesterday's non-aggressors become today's aggressors; their race has not changed, but their behavior has. Japan has a history of peace and non-aggression that cannot be matched in the Western World. During the first eleven centuries of her recorded history she was engaged in only one war abroad. Indeed this sole conflict ended in 1598, and from that time until 1853, when Japan opened her doors to intercourse with the world outside, the building of all ocean-going boats was forbidden by imperial decree to make certain that Japan would preserve her policy of isolationism. The ceremoniousness, the light-heartedness, the aesthetic appreciation of the Japanese were traits that passed current as their essential qualities. Since 1853 they have fought five times overseas and are well on their way to becoming one of the most aggressively warlike nations of the world. In the human race no centuries-long existence free from conflict as the lamb's guarantees that the next generation may not become the lion.

There is another aspect of this fact that race and culture are distinct. In world history, those who have helped to build the same culture are not necessarily of one race, and those of the same race have not all participated in one culture. In scientific language, culture is not a function of race.

The more we know about the fortunes and the vicissitudes of any civilization, the less it proves to be the peculiar off-spring of an unmixed race. This is true even far back in pre-history, and an eminent archeologist has said that the great social truth made clear by archeology is that culture lives on and maintains itself though the race perish; either as conquerors or as peaceable settlers a new racial type carries on the old ways of life of the conquered or earlier occupants of the land. The archeologist looking back over the long centuries sees, not the destruction of that civilization when one racial carrier was superseded, but the continuity of its history in the hands of one racial type after another. The growth of human civilization in the European Paleolithic (Old Stone)

Age has cultural, but not racial, continuity. The culture which Neanderthal Man possessed was after his disappearance carried forward by Cro-Magnon man, given new embellishments by men of the later Old Stone Age, and elaborated by the races of the New Stone Age. Only the last two types are racially ancestral to modern man. This lack of racial continuity in one small corner of Europe during prehistory is better established for Europe than for other parts of the world because the archeology of Europe is better known, but all that research into prehistory is uncovering in Africa, in Asia, and in Central America tells the same story.

This story has been repeated in Western civilization since the dawn of history and the evidence of it constantly accumulates. A century ago the historian of Western civilization was content to begin with Greece, but today this is inadequate. Historical study has unrolled a longer history under our eyes. Greece was the inheritor of earlier Oriental civilizations and its early culture owed much to Egyptian influences. Essential cornerstones of our civilization are the inventions of other races. Perhaps we describe this civilization of ours as built on steel and gunpowder. But steel was invented either in India or in Turkestan, and gunpowder in China. Perhaps we prefer to identify our Western culture by its printing presses and literateness. But paper and printing were both borrowed from China. Our economic life with its great concentration of population is based on the cultivation of grains and of animals which are Neolithic inventions from Asia; corn and tobacco were first domesticated by the American Indian. Our control of Nature is overwhelmingly dependent on mathematical calculations. But the so-called Arabic system of notation which is essential to all complicated mathematics was unknown in Europe in the Roman era; it was invented in Asia and introduced to our civilization by the Moors. Algebra was a method of calculation also borrowed by Europeans from Asiatic peoples.

Wherever we look, the truth is forced upon us that many different races have contributed to the growth of our culture, and that when we hold culture as the constant, race is a variable. The White race was once the borrower, as today Japan is. The White race spent long centuries at the process and Japan a few decades, but by that token some literalists could argue the racial superiority of the Japanese over the White race.

When we look at the fact of cultural-racial separateness from the other side, this time holding race constant, we find that the culture of any one race is of many degrees of complexity. While certain groups of a given race forge ahead and set up great states or build great cities which are architectural triumphs or carry out great public works, other groups of the same race may remain primitive nomadic herdsmen. A race does not move forward as a whole. So some groups of Arabs built up great states under sultans with regal splendor, the arts and sciences flourished, and they were in the vanguard of the civilization of their day. Other members of the same race were simple Bedouins following their herds from pasturage to pasturage. Similarly the primitive Amur River tribes of Siberia or the Yukaghir of the Siberian tundras are of the same race as the civilized Chinese. The Malay race also has its half-wild primitive tribes of the coastal Malay Peninsula and at the same time its centers of high civilization. Race is not a touchstone by which civilized people can be separated from uncivilized. Rude people of barbarian ancestry have shown themselves to be abundantly able to adopt the highest extant civilizations and to contribute to their development.

The Manchus were a rude and unnoted nomadic Tungus tribe, but first through contact with the Mongols, and later by their conquest of China in the mid-seventeenth century, they became the ruling dynasty of a country unsurpassed in riches and glory at that period. Wherever we look—to the Malays, the Manchus, the Mongols, the Arabs, or the Nordics—the same story repeats itself over and over.

The Nordics belong to this list, and no one need quarrel with the extravagant claims that have been made for their "manifest destiny" if these same claims are allowed also for all other rude peoples who have come to participate ably in the building of civilization. When, however, the Nordics are singled out as a peculiar instance and their participation in civilization credited to their racial type and not to the universal processes of history, it is easy to recognize the special pleading. It is closer to actual history to speak of them as Hooton does—as "the raw-boned ruffians from the North," [1] whose irruptions shattered the peace of early Europe—or to call attention, as Hankins [2] does, to the fact that they "destroyed civilizations more frequently than they created them." The point to note, however, is that they were a group with certain inherited features, and that though they were once rude, they later became exponents of a great civilization; their former rudeness in no way disqualified them from participating ably in its development.

History cannot be written as if it belonged to one race alone. Civilization has been gradually built up, now out of the contributions of one race, now of another. When all civilization is ascribed to the "Nordics," the claim is the same one which any anthropologist can hear any day from primitive tribes—only they tell the story to themselves. They too believe that all that is important in the world begins and ends with them; the creator gave to them exclusively in the beginning all that is good and at their downfall will destroy the world. We smile when such claims are made by a rude and

---

[1] Hooton, Earnest A., *Up from the Ape*, New York, 1931, p. 525.

[2] Hankins, Frank H., *Racial Basis of Civilization*, New York, 1926, p. 350.

tiny American Indian tribe or a naked Papuan of New Guinea, but ridicule might just as well be turned against ourselves. After all, the world of these tribes extends but a little way beyond their borders and folk tales serve them for history; their exaggerated claims are the result of ignorance. But when the same crude provincialism is put forward learnedly in our day, it is still a childish primitive error maintained in the face of all that historians have ascertained and in the face of modern knowledge of the whole extent of the globe.

Provincialism may rewrite history and play up only the achievements of the historian's own group, but it remains provincialism; it is not history. The lesson of history is that pre-eminence in cultural achievement has passed from one race to another, from one continent to another; it has embraced not whole "races" but certain fragments of an ethnic group which were for certain historical reasons favorably situated at the moment. Peace had been achieved for a certain period, or freedom from exploitation for certain groups. All those of the race who were within the range of these conditions profited by them, and the arts of life were advanced; individuals of whatever race rose to the opportunity and have often left their names enrolled in history. It has happened in Mesopotamia, in China, in India, in Egypt, in Greece, in Rome, and in England. Obviously no racial type has a monopoly of high culture.

It behooves us, therefore, to study race historically and biologically and anthropometrically without expecting race to account for all human achievements. Race is a scientific field of study. But human history is a vastly more complicated thing than a mere record of the distribution of anthropomorphic measurements, and cultural achievements are not mechanically transmitted and guaranteed by any racial inheritance.

WHAT THEY SAY

Since biological change occurs slowly and cultural changes occur in every generation, it is futile to try to explain the fleeting phenomena of culture by a racial constant. We can often explain them—in terms of contact with other peoples, of individual genius, of geography—but not by *racial* differences.

R. H. Lowie, *An Introduction to Cultural Anthropology.* New York, Farrar and Rinehart, 1934, p. 9.

The growth and spread of civilization has gone on with a serene indifference to racial lines. All groups who have had an opportunity to acquire civilization have not only acquired it but also added to its content. Conversely, no group has been able to develop a rich or complex culture when it was isolated from outside contacts.

Ralph Linton, *The Study of Man.* New York, D. Appleton-Century, 1936, p. 54.

If we can once thoroughly convince ourselves that race, in its only intelligible, that is, biological, sense, is supremely indifferent to the history of languages and cultures, that these are no more directly explainable on the score of race than on the laws of physics and chemistry, we shall have gained a viewpoint that allows a certain interest to such mystic slogans as Slavophilism, Anglo-Saxondom, Teutonism and the Latin genius, but quite refuses to be taken in by any of them.

Edward Sapir, *Language.* New York, Harcourt, Brace and Co., 1921, pp. 222–223.

The role of Nordics in history:

The racists say:

It is only shameful indolence of thought, or disgraceful historical falsehood, that can fail to see in the entrance of the Germanic tribes into the history of the world the rescuing of agonizing humanity from the clutches of the everlastingly bestial.

> Houston Stewart Chamberlain, *The Foundations of the Nineteenth Century*. New York, Dodd, 1912, Vol. I, p. 495.

The historians say:

The material culture of the Nordics was not originally superior to that of the Danubian peasants or the megalith-builders; in Transylvania they appear frankly as wreckers; in the ancient East and the Aegean they appropriated and for a time impaired older and higher civilizations.

> V. Gordon Childe, *The Aryans*. New York, A. A. Knopf, Inc., 1926, p. 207.

Even in a political and military sense no convincing case can be made for Nordic supremacy during the medieval period.

> H. E. Barnes and H. David, *The History of Western Civilization*. New York, Harcourt, Brace and Co., 1935, Vol. I, p. 446.

They do not like each other's languages:

French

The native or acquired difficulty among the Germans of getting the nervous centers of the *medulla oblongata* to carry out the orders of the cerebral centers regarding syllabic sound-production—they say *fa* and *pa* for *va* and *ba*—is a pathological fact still observable in our own day.

> Honoré Joseph Chavée, *Bulletin d'Anthropologie Sociale*, 1873, p. 505, quoted by Jacques Barzun, in *Race, A Study in Modern Superstition*. New York, Harcourt, Brace and Co., 1937.

German

The Nordic race alone can emit sounds of untroubled clearness whereas among non-Nordic men and races the pronunciation is impure, the individual sounds confused and more like noises made by animals.

> Herman Gauch, *New Foundations for Research into Social Race Problems.* Berlin, 1933, p. 165.

Summary:

The so-called racial explanation of differences in human performance and achievement is either an ineptitude or a fraud.

> Arnold Joseph Toynbee, *A Study of History.* London, Oxford University Press, 1934, Vol. I, p. 245.

III. MAN'S EFFORTS TO CLASSIFY HIMSELF

IN ALL MODERN SCIENCE there is no field where authorities differ more than in the classifications of human races. Some have separated races on the basis of geographical distribution, some on the basis of skin color, some on the basis of cephalic index, some on a combination of several traits. Some have divided mankind into three races, some into seventeen, some into thirty-four. Some have made primary an ethnic group which another authority has made secondary. This lack of agreement is not a matter of scientific perversity but is due to the facts of human history and the known principles of biology—two subjects which we shall discuss in the following chapters. But first it is necessary to consider the material on which any classification of human races must be based and the categories that are in use.

Racial classification of the human species has an honorable background. Similar classification in botany and zoology has progressed from the crude eighteenth-century categories of Buffon to the more basic ones, established in modern use, which group living forms to show genetic relationships and to indicate evolutionary sequence.

The scientist has before him the results that have been attained in the study of living forms other than human, and he knows the pitfalls of superficial resemblances. In zoology a classification is considered artificial if, for instance, it classes a whale with fishes simply because whales swim; the classification is basic when it classes a whale with mammals, whose processes of reproduction and need for breathing air into their lungs the whale shares. For the study of mammals, it is necessary to subordinate many obvious physical differences that appear among mammals, and to consider together not only whales, whch swim like fishes, but also bats, which fly like birds. Whales and bats moreover must be studied alongside hoofed animals and men, for they are all mammals.

Students of human races, therefore, hoped to establish classifications of man which were more than superficially descriptive and which might have a validity such as the classification of mammals has.

Before the time of Darwin the basis for such classification was fundamentally different from that used today. In those days the question at issue was polygenesis (many origins) versus monogenesis (one origin). The position stated in the Bible and accepted by the Church was that all men were sprung from Adam, and this position was traditional in pre-Columbian Europe. The voyages of discovery, however, and the widening of the world under man's eyes made another possibility attractive, for how was one to account for yellow men and black men and red men without a number of special acts of creation? We must remember that in those days nobody knew how widely the yellow race varied within itself, or the black race, or the red; nor was it known how these groups shaded off one into another. The races were seen as a series of contrasted pictures like those in our own elementary geographies.

There were monogenists who believed that climate had produced these varieties of mankind. Among these the most famous was the Baron de Montesquieu, whose *Spirit of Laws* was published in 1748. There were also the polygenists who believed that these varieties were separate "thoughts of God" and unrelated one to another. Geoffroy St. Hilaire in the French Academy in 1830 argued against the monogenist Cuvier, who derived all races from Noah through his three sons, Ham, Shem, and Japheth, and Goethe's excitement over this debate shows well the place this controversy had in contemporary thought. "What do you think of the great event?" he exclaimed to a friend of his. "The volcano has broken out, everything is in flames, and it's no longer something going on behind closed doors. You cannot imagine what I felt on hearing the news of the meeting." [1]

Even before Darwin there were learned students who challenged this idea that each race was a separate entity. The first great anthropologist, Theodor Waitz, argued against it on the basis of physical measurements of different races. He showed that racial stereotypes failed to correspond to the facts; the yellow man or the red man included whole series of types, some of them more like Europeans, for instance, than they were like other groups of their own race. Waitz wrote without knowledge of Darwinism, though his *Anthropology* was published in the same year as the *Origin of Species,* and we must therefore not credit Darwinism alone with dealing the death blow to this old controversy. Nevertheless Darwin's idea of species and the interpretation he gave to the anatomical similarities between man and the higher apes deprived the controversy of any point. It threw the whole argument into a wider context, and in this context all the primates, including all races of man, became branches of one family tree.

Since Darwin, all racial studies have had a different back-

---

[1] *Gespräche mit Eckermann* III, p. 240, quoted by Jacques Barzun in *Race, A Study in Modern Superstition,* New York, 1937, p. 63.

ground from the earlier controversies. They accept the family tree to which all mankind belongs and attempt to determine in how far human varieties have biological significance.

It was immediately evident that mankind did not include a series of fully developed species, the proper criterion for which was, according to Darwin, sterility or the production of sterile offspring if they were crossed. Nothing was more obvious than the fact that fertile children were born from the mating of even the most extreme types of the White race with the most extreme types of Negro or Mongolian; intermixture of different ethnic groups had occurred constantly in history and was occurring at an increasing rate as men became more mobile in a world where transportation facilities were more ample.

The idea of species, however, underlay all the thinking of the period, and if human varieties could not be separated one from another by mutual sterility, the criteria must be found in some physical characteristics. To serve as racial criteria these characteristics must be present in the whole race in some fashion peculiar to that race alone, as, for example, extremely dark pigmentation, frizzy hair, and a certain form of broad, flat nose are found nowhere but among Negroes. A whole range of characteristics have been studied and used as racial criteria in this sense, and the results of these studies are necessary for a modern understanding of race.

Skin Color

The racial difference that at once arrests attention is skin color. The wall paintings of ancient Egyptians used four pigments for the complexions of the four peoples they knew; red for themselves, yellow for their enemies in Asia, white for people from the north, and black for Negroes. This classification has been reduced by one and given a Greek terminology. Its value consists in that it is the most generalized category into which human beings are zoologically divided:

 Leucodermi—white-skinned
 Xanthodermi—yellow-skinned
 Melanodermi—black-skinned

In general usage this classification corresponds to the division into Caucasoid (white), Mongoloid (yellow), and Negroid (black); these are the obvious and striking human varieties. Further physical characteristics, as we shall see, can be associated with these three groups. They have each a large geographical range, and represent real differentiations.

Skin color, of itself, however, has very limited scientific use as a criterion of these primary races. The range in each group is very large and some groups of Whites are darker than some Negroes. Broca, the French physical anthropologist, used thirty-four shades of skin color and Deniker nine. Differentiation into shades is a help in one direction but it makes the overlapping even more serious.

The superficial character of skin color as a criterion of race becomes a serious difficulty when the question is one of assigning problematic groups to the primary races. Are the Australians Negroid because their skin color is nearest the range for Negroes; are light-colored Armenian types Caucasoid because theirs is nearest the range for Whites? All students agree that such arguments are superficial.

Skin color, therefore, as a means of differentiating the ethnic groups of man with the widest geographical range has some advantage if it is loosely applied. As a scientific criterion it has a gross rather than a specific usefulness.

Eye Color and Eye Form

Eye pigmentation is commonly recorded in physical measurements of populations but it does not identify an individual as a member of a particular race. Dark eyes are common to all human races and cannot therefore be used to differentiate them. Even more special types of eye color, such as blueness, have never been found coextensive with a whole ethnic group.

Eye form appears in racial descriptions primarily in reference to the "slanting" eyes typical of yellow-skinned Asiatics. It is called the Mongoloid eye, and the slant-eye appearance is caused by a fold of skin, the epicanthic fold, which covers the inner angle of the eye. It occurs in infancy among many Whites but does not usually persist into adulthood; it occurs among some Negroes and is characteristic of some American Indians (also Mongoloids) though most of these latter do not have it.

Hair Color and Hair Form

Dark hair color, like dark eyes, is so widely distributed among mankind that it does not serve to define race, and, as with blue eyes, even the special trait of blond hair does not run uniformly through any ethnic group.

Hair form can also be classified. There are three major types:

Leiotrichy—straight lank hair (e.g., Chinese, Eskimo)
Cymotrichy—wavy hair (e.g., inhabitants of Europe, India, Australia)
Ulotrichy—wooly or frizzy hair (e.g., Negroes, Melanesians)

These differences in hair appearance are due to the form of the individual hair as seen in cross section under a microscope; straight hair is round, wooly hair extremely oval, and wavy hair falls in between.

Again like skin color, these different hair forms are found in ethnic groups of wide geographical distribution, and when used as characteristics of these major groups they have descriptive value. The trouble with them as racial traits is that they cross-cut races as described in other terms. Because Australian blackfellows have smooth wavy hair, like that of Europeans, they are not therefore Europeans, nor are the Eskimos Chinese because they have straight lank hair. Smooth wavy hair is typical of Europe, Egypt, and the Asiatic peoples who live from the eastern Mediterranean down to and including India, and is therefore characteristic of peoples who are unlike in other physical traits. Hair form nevertheless has a certain value in the study of the distribution of races, and no one doubts, on other grounds as well as hair form, that the dark Melanesians of western Oceania —for instance, the natives of the Solomon Islands—are genetically related to African Negroes.

Shape of the Nose

Physical anthropologists have paid considerable attention to measuring the types of human nose. There are two chief categories:

> Leptorrhine—narrow nostrils (e.g., European, Eskimo)
> Platyrrhine—flat broad nostrils (e.g., Negroes, Tasmanians)

Besides these, various descriptions of the nose bridge are in use: concave, convex, aquiline, or straight.

Here again, though certain extreme nose shapes are found only in certain groups in the world—certain broad flat forms among certain Negroes and certain narrow aquiline ones among certain Caucasians—even these do not identify a man who on other counts is a Negro or a Caucasian, both races having a great range of nose shapes.

Stature

Bodily height is the extreme case of a physical trait which, though it is also hereditary, is easily modified by environment. Many studies have demonstrated that stature as well as body weight is influenced by diet, sickness, and other conditions of life. It is therefore in most cases not a reliable index of genetic relationship. A good exception to this rule is the case of the pygmies, among whom stature is clearly hereditary and can be used for zoological classification. In other cases, however, even when stature is hereditary, tall groups jostle short groups within each race as it is defined in other terms. The tallest and the shortest group measured are both Negro, and even on the remote island of Tierra del Fuego, an extremely tall American Indian tribe is the neighbor of an extremely short tribe. Stature is a very fallible racial criterion.

Cephalic Index

The cephalic index is the ratio of the maximum breadth to the maximum length of the head seen from on top, and is expressed in a percentage. This aspect of the head has been arbitrarily divided into three types:

Dolichocephalic—narrow-headed, with cephalic index under 75

Mesocephalic—medium-headed, with cephalic index 75–80

Brachycephalic—broad-headed, with cephalic index over 80

Of all human measurements, the cephalic index is the commonest in physical anthropology and the data on it in a given population are the most often available. This is because it is definite and easy to measure, and because, with certain allowances for the thickness of the skin, it can be used in measurements of skulls as well as of heads of living people.

The cephalic index does not serve to distinguish the White race from the Mongoloid nor from the Negro, nor has it any constant value for any primary race. For instance some American Indian groups have the narrowest skulls ever measured and some the broadest skulls, and these are groups which, judged by other characteristics, fall together into one race. Similarly, the cephalic index distinguishes between certain sub-groups of the White race rather than having a constant value for all Caucasians. In other words, a graph of the cephalic index shows peaks and valleys *within* large groups otherwise similar and is chiefly used to describe small local variations.

These are the most important anatomical features which have been used as racial traits. There is also, in a somewhat different field, the study of blood groups. Knowledge of blood groups arose from experience in the transfusion of blood, when it was found that the blood from certain persons was fatal to some others. It was discovered that at least four blood types could be differentiated, and this held out high hopes to students of races. The technique of determining the blood type is simple, and the very first work on races showed that one blood group was concentrated among Asiatic Mongoloids, another in Western Europe and a third among American Indians and Eskimos, who are Mongoloid in the usual classification.

Blood types are strictly hereditary and very stable; any individual having a blood type A, for example, must have had an ancestor whose blood type was A. Therefore when different blood types are present in any population, it is one of the surest signs of mixed ancestry. But even such isolated races as the aboriginal Australians have a high percentage of blood group A, which is that most characteristic of Western Europe. And in Europe 10 to 30 per cent of the population everywhere have blood type B, which is that most characteristic of India and Eastern Asia. The evidence from the study of blood groups emphasizes in the strongest possible manner the great amount of biological mixture that must have taken place from the earliest times.

We are now prepared to understand some of the problems that have increasingly faced those students of human races who have attempted to establish biologically valid categories of mankind. No one doubts that the groups called Caucasoid, Mongoloid, and Negroid each represent a long history of anatomical specialization in different areas of the world; but great numbers of individuals cannot be assigned to one or another of these races on the basis even of several of the above criteria. There are Whites who are darker than some Negroids; dark hair and eyes are common among all races; the same cephalic index is found in groups of the most diverse races; similar hair form is found among ethnic groups as distinct as native Australians and Western Europeans; blood groups do not define races.

Racial differentiation might, nevertheless, depend upon certain combinations of these anatomical characteristics. But these traits are not co-extensive. If a student takes skin color first, he will have in Sweden, for instance, a considerable number of fair-skinned individuals. If he adds fair hair and blue eyes to this first category, he will have to cut down his group numerically. He may then add tall stature and again rule out many individuals. By adding narrow-headedness he eliminates certain others. He has now a tall, blond-haired, blue-eyed, fair-skinned, narrow-headed group. But it is a series of individuals, not the population of Sweden. Retzius, who measured thousands of army recruits in Sweden, a country which is famous for the combination of character-istics we have just enumerated, found that only 11 per cent conformed to this description, and this in spite of the fact that three of his criteria—fair skin, blue eyes, and blond hair—are all aspects of one type of pigmentation and might be expected to occur together. If he had added other an-atomical criteria his group would have been smaller yet.

In order to understand the significance of such a situa-tion, let us imagine that a zoologist listed five traits which distinguished a variety of black bears. He then measured the group which of all groups in the world was most char-acterized by these traits and found that only 11 per cent conformed. He would certainly decide one of two things: either he had chosen traits which were too variable within the group to be definitive, or the group was the result of mixture with other varieties, and could not serve as an origi-nal type.

In exactly similar fashion the physical anthropologist has to consider these two possibilities. The traits he has selected may have been suggested merely from his own superficial experience and not be the ones which characterize Sweden. Since, as we have seen, dark hair, dark eyes, and not-fair skin are characteristic of the human race as a whole, the opposite traits of blond hair, blue eyes, and fair skin which occur in Sweden arrest his attention. Extreme features al-

ways stand out unduly, whatever they are. But this sus-
ceptibility of his to blondness, which caused him to set up his
criteria in this way, was obviously not a function of the
actual composition of the Swedish population but of the
strangeness of blond features in comparison with the darker
coloring of other human groups. It was a shot in the dark
which was not borne out by measurements.

On the other hand, the physical anthropologist has to consider a second possibility: his 11 per cent who are tall, fair,
blue-eyed, yellow-haired, narrow-headed may represent an
original pure type which has been attenuated by intermarriage and "swamped" by other immigrants, but it may still
be a true representative of a pure original race. In this case
the physical anthropologist has to square his interpretation
with the biological laws of heredity; specifically he has to
take account of what is technically known as independent
segregation, that is, how inherited items from both ancestral
lines, whether hair color or intelligence, split up in any such
intermingling of blood and get sorted out in new combinations in the offspring. (See pp. 56–60.) Inheritance always
works in this way. Hence, once mingling has occurred, no
individual samples can represent the original race *in toto,*
even though there are living individuals in whose veins its
blood still runs.

Whether the physical anthropologist measures Swedes or
Algerians or Chinese or Greeks, the same difficulty presents
itself. Over and over again he discovers the obvious consequences of the great intermixture that has occurred, or he
discovers that the universality of the "ideal" type he set out
to investigate in a given group is an illusion. If he compares
his findings in his own group with those of another investi-
gator in a different group—comparing, for example, Swedes
with Sicilians—he finds that none of his traits are utterly
lacking in individuals of the other group. The statistical

distribution is different; that is all. He set out to isolate an anatomical variety of mankind as he would isolate a species of birds, but the facts he has gathered prove only that the human situation does not correspond to the situation among birds.

The physical anthropologist, therefore, has no recourse but to give up the parallel with birds and dogs, and to work out some classifications which correspond to the facts he has accumulated. When he does this, he has to say: In great areas of the world certain anatomical specializations have occurred in mankind and of these the most definite are the Caucasoid, Mongoloid, and Negroid. In exactly the same manner, but to lesser degree, specialization has occurred also in more restricted areas, but showing in many respects, as in that of the cephalic index, numerous identical forms in all primary races. These anatomical specializations are old and were clearly marked at the dawn of history; high cultural development, however, is recent and appears now in one area of the world, now in another. It does not follow the fortunes of any one of these races, whether we use the term in the sense of the three major stocks or in the sense of small subdivisions of these. (See pp. 14–18; 91–95.) The present distribution of bodily form in the world can be understood only by virtue of our historical knowledge of the migrations of peoples from the earliest Paleolithic to the present day (chapter IV), and this disproves the existence of "pure races" in any center of Western civilization.

We are left, therefore, with the task of describing, first, the major human stocks, and then an indeterminate number of local specializations. In the major stocks the characteristics are of course quite generalized since they must overspan so many local variations within the stock.

The Caucasian is relatively hairy, has smooth (wavy to curly) hair, minimum prognathism (jaws projecting beyond the plane of the face), a fairly high, thin nose, and straight eyes. (N.B. Caucasians have no characteristic cephalic index or body height, no specific hair color or eye color; their noses may be Roman or concave; even the color of their skin is extremely variable.)

Mongoloids have very little facial and body hair, and their head hair is lank and straight. (N.B. Skin color varies too widely to admit of definition; the slant eye is local and among American Indians is absent except sporadically; cephalic index covers the whole known human range; nose form also runs from Roman to concave.)

The Negroid type has the darkest skin range, kinky hair, thick lips, frequent prognathism, a flat nose. (N.B. The body height of Negroes is extremely variable, including the tallest and shortest groups known, and their cephalic index is also variable though narrow-headedness is general.)

Boas has suggested that it is ethnically more correct to reduce even these three primary stocks to two, the Mongoloid and the Negroid, and to place the Caucasic type as a local specialization of the Mongoloid. He points out that this would do least violence to the facts in accounting for the Caucasic traits of the Ainu, an aboriginal group of Japan. All observers have commented upon the likeness of the Ainu to the White race, not only in skin color but in their hairiness, which is the trait that sets them most conspicuously apart from the surrounding Mongoloids. If this type represented by the Ainu and the Whites were potential among Mongoloids, the likeness of Ainu and Whites would represent two conspicuous parallel developments without having to be accounted for by a hypothetical migration.

Before the dislocations following the discovery of the New World, the three present-day major stocks were each distributed around a major body of water: the Caucasians around the Mediterranean, the Negroids around the Indian

Ocean, and the Mongolians around the Pacific. Specifically Negroid peoples are characteristic not only of Africa but of the Western Pacific, the Oceanic Negroids being called Melanesians, literally, "black islanders." The Mongoloids were distributed not only in Asia but through the length and breadth of the New World, those of the New World being the American Indians.

It is clear also that no scientific purpose is served by speculating about the allocation of doubtful peoples to one or another primary stock. It only happens that Caucasian, Mongoloid, and Negro have the widest distribution in the world and the most definite anatomical traits. "Three" is not a sacred number which rules that the history of these three stocks is older than, or different from, other groups now marginal. As more physical characteristics are considered, more and more groups have to be differentiated. The Australian aborigines, or even the Bushman-Hottentots, may be representative of now marginal groups which were once widely distributed over the world. On the other hand the Polynesians may be a well-marked variant due to racial crossing at some remote period. If human zoology pointed to an original fixed series of pure races, it would be important to get an answer to these questions; since, however, all evidence points in the direction of progressive and local variations upon one human theme, these questions become biologically of little importance.

These progressive and local specializations in physical traits occurred not only in the primary races and in other distinctive races, like the Polynesian and Australian; they occurred also within each widespread race, differentiating sub-groups, now in regard to cephalic index, now in regard to height or hair color or complexion. In the most commonly used classifications based on anthropomorphic measurements, the Caucasians of Europe fall into three subdivisions: Nordic, Alpine, and Mediterranean. The Nordics, in Northern Europe, have frequent blond pigmentation, tall stature, and narrow-headedness. Nordics are found in Russia, Finland, Estonia, Lithuania, Scandinavia, Holland, Belgium, Germany, France, and England. The Alpines, in Central Europe, have variable body build, usually stocky, medium pigmentation, and broad-headedness. They are predominant in Germany and France and extend into the central highlands of Europe and as far east as eastern Rumania. The Mediterraneans, in Southern Europe west of the Adriatic, have light body build, somewhat darker pigmentation, and the narrow-headedness of the Nordic. These distributions refer to concentrations only, for the populations of Europe all include significant numbers of individuals who conform to types whose concentration is in another area. Nevertheless, the distribution of cephalic index measurements, for instance, is marked. These distributions of physical type run roughly horizontal across the European map; they do not differentiate present nations of Europe like Germany and France, which both include a northern strip in which the Nordic type occurs and a much wider strip in which Alpines predominate.

The Mediterranean and the Alpine types both include many peoples outside of Europe.

The Alpine sub-group extends, in Asia as well as in Europe, through a belt north of the Mediterranean peoples. They are therefore sometimes called Eurasiatics. In the words of an authority who has most recently written on European physical anthropology, Carleton Coon: "The geographical extent of the Alpine racial type is enormous, reaching from France to China. Throughout this extent it maintains a nearly constant form, in stature, in the dimensions of the head and face, in pilosity, and in general morphological features." [1]

The Mediterranean sub-race includes the Hamites, who form the bulk of the population of Egypt, and the Semites, so called from the language they speak. The Bedouins of Arabia are, in Coon's phrase, "of pure Mediterranean race," [2] and the same authority places in this group Irano-Afghans of Persia and Afghanistan.

The lack of any correlation between race and sovereign states is obvious. The individuals who plan the policies of Germany or France or who shout together in the streets over a national victory in war are united not by the similarities of their cephalic indices or by any common family tree, but by the fact that they read the same newspapers and will be called upon to die for the same flag. An Alpine individual of Germany will not feel mystic kinship and common cause with the fierce Georgians of the Caucasus or the Tadjiks of Russian Turkestan though they all belong on one branch of the human family tree, nor will an Italian Mediterranean with a Bedouin. Both Alpine and Mediterranean sub-groups form majorities in communities of vastly different cultural complexity, and, unless indoctrinated by racialists, they do not split up into warring parties on the basis of different physical types.

The actual distribution of physical types in the world, and especially in Europe, cannot be understood without some review of historical migrations and conquests and intermingling of peoples, and to such facts we must turn in the next chapter.

---

[1] Coon, Carleton, *The Races of Europe*, New York, 1939, p. 646.
[2] *Ibid.*, p. 623.

WHAT THEY SAY

Races as irreducible categories exist only as fictions in our brains.

Jean Finot, *Race Prejudice*. Translated by Florence Wade-Evans. London, Constable & Co., Ltd., 1906, p. 317.

The different races of man are not distinguished from each other by strongly marked, uniform, and permanent distinctions, as are the species belonging to any given tribe of animals. All the diversities which exist are variable, and pass into each other by insensible gradations.

J. C. Prichard, *Natural History of Man*. London, H. Baillière, 1855, p. 473.

The bones of a stunted Nordic are almost indistinguishable from those of an overgrown and muscular Mediterranean. The Nordic is supposed to have a longer and narrower face, larger brow ridges, and a more sloping forehead, a longer, narrower and higher nose, and a more boldly jutting chin. But I do not believe that any physical anthropologist can with certainty distinguish the skeletal remains of the taller individuals of the Arab sub-race of Mediterraneans from those of a Nordic.

E. A. Hooton, *Up from the Ape*. New York, Macmillan Co., 1931, p. 526.

IV. MIGRATION

AND THE MINGLING OF PEOPLES

MIGRATION IS AS OLD as mankind. Somewhere in the Old World our arboreal ancestors gradually reached the human level and man began his first and most spectacular migration. Neanderthal Man seems to us now a defenseless, ape-like creature, but he had at least fire and stone tools. During the early glacial periods he spread from Asia into Europe and occupied a great part of it. But Neanderthal's migrations were as nothing compared to those of the early forms of Homo sapiens which followed him. Gradually but irresistibly, by the beginning of historic time, man had occupied the whole round earth. He had not accepted Land's End barriers, but had pushed into the New World in the region of Bering Strait and had occupied the continents of the Americas from Alaska to Tierra del Fuego. With the simplest savage equipment—no boats, no agriculture, no breeding of animals—he even reached Australia and maintained himself in its punishing deserts.

No other animal form has so spectacular a history, no other has established itself under so many environmental extremes. It would be reasonable to suppose that defenseless early man, in accommodating himself to a damp equatorial forest or to a barren arctic tundra, would have grown himself a different body, that his organs would have assumed different forms; in other words, that he would have differentiated into species, as the deer family is represented by the reindeer and the elk in the subarctic and by different varieties of true deer in the temperate and tropical zones. The marvel is that man's physical form remained stable, and that, instead, he was able to survive under all these difficult conditions by virtue of his inventions—ways of building houses, ways of clothing himself, ways of procuring food. His one physical adjustment which may have survival value is skin color; dark pigment has been shown to act as a filter against the actinic rays of the sun, which in large quantities are harmful to man. Specialization in dark pigmentation therefore would be an advantage to tropical people. The other human specializations, like differences in the shape of the skull, lank or curly hair, even short or tall stature, do not in themselves show any survival value and seem from this point of view almost irrelevancies.

From another standpoint these specializations, however, are anything but irrelevancies. Man is much more interested in himself and his varieties than he is in any other series of facts, and differences which pass unregarded when they hold between various breeds of mice, are, between various breeds of man, the occasion of persecution and deportation. Nevertheless from the zoological standpoint they remain surprisingly small and arbitrary.

To understand the map of physical differences we have to turn to the facts of history. The dramatic spread of mankind over the whole world had two aspects: first, that of man's gradual infiltration into all parts of the world; and, second, that of his localization and isolation in relatively permanent occupation of certain areas. Man, that is, was not only spectacularly mobile, but he also settled down. The world during the Stone Age was sparsely populated, and a group that established itself in one territory might remain in occupation of it for centuries. During all that time no alien peoples might press upon it; the group might breed and die for generations, a world unto itself. Whether the total group which made up this "world" was large or small, this meant inbreeding, and under primitive conditions the group was often very small indeed. No two people in the tribe, under such conditions, could marry without having whole series of ancestors in common, and therefore anatomical traits which seldom appeared elsewhere might by this inbreeding even become the rule. Curious specializations occur. The Lapps have a ridge along the middle line of the palate, and the Inca of Peru specialized in an interparietal bone in the skull. These are anatomical minutiae which arose originally by mutation (see p. 62) and have been made common in these corners of the world by inbreeding of family lines.

Such an area, where a settled inbreeding group becomes differentiated from other groups in secondary characteristics, has been called "an area of characterization." [1] Thus Eastern Asia was an area of characterization for the slanting eye, and a great region extending from India to Western Europe an area for smooth wavy hair. Under very early human conditions, when the tempo of migration was much slower than it is today, people in some areas of characterization bred together for so many centuries that they must have approached racial purity. Geneticists count that with the strictest inbreeding for some seventeen generations—which would mean today the continuous inbreeding of some strain since before Columbus was born—they can get a strain which satisfies genetic requirements of purity; it would

---

[1] Haddon. A. C.. *Wanderings of Peoples,* London, 1912, p. 47.

breed true. To get this strain in the laboratory they cross only descendants of one pair and are satisfied with nothing less. Such inbreeding must always have been rare in human societies, but there may well have been an approximation to it in some undisturbed areas, and these conditions, however they fell short of ideal requirements, favored diversification of bodily form among the human race.

But areas of characterization occur in exactly similar fashion after such groups have interbred one with another. Permanence of occupation was always being disturbed either by climatic changes or by pressure of other tribes, and when this occurred and two hitherto isolated groups came into contact, we know from the physical measurements of their descendants that they mixed. It used to be thought that at least Homo Sapiens had not mixed with Homo Neanderthalis, his more apelike predecessor in Europe. But intermediate skeletons have been unearthed which are believed to show that even these most divergent of known human forms interbred, and some students have now identified traces of Neanderthal inheritance in modern European races. Certainly all racial types since that time have interbred whenever they came together in the same region. The countries of such interbreeding became again areas of characterization; out of the hereditary traits contributed by the component groups, a group arose which differed from all these ancestors, but had certain stable anatomical traits.

The world today still has areas of characterization in which new human types have only recently been stabilized. Several such areas have been studied and they are indubitable, for we know the parent races that went into the mixture and the length of time it has taken to produce the new stable variety. Such a modern instance, to be comparable to earlier ones, must be an area where the offspring of racially distinct parents have interbred. The necessary isolation may be geographic, as on Pitcairn Island, where descendants of six English sailors, the mutineers of the famous *Bounty,* and of the Tahitian (Polynesian) women who accompanied them in their desperate escape from civilization have lived and been inbreeding since 1790. Oftener the isolation is social and the mixed bloods come to form an intermarrying group distinct from the native community or that of the Whites. This has happened among the Bastaards in South Africa, where descendants of Boers and native Hottentot women have maintained themselves as an inbreeding group and in the course of several generations have developed a stable type which differs from that of either ancestral group. The same thing is happening today among the Anglo-Indian groups in India, even in great urban centers.

The first and essential step toward understanding race in the world today is the recognition of the fact that these areas of characterization are unlimited in number. There certainly existed in earlier times many areas of characterization, the representatives of which are not found today, though their "blood" is now inextricably mingled in various degrees in surviving races. It is impossible to reconstruct their original physical type. Their skeletons have perished or, even if some are extant, many traits used in racial differentiation are irretrievably lost. From certain other areas of characterization, hordes spread out and established themselves over two continents; under favorable conditions they multiplied, bred with the previous occupants of distant parts, and formed new areas of characterization.

Within the area of characterization, we must remember, there had to be a certain permanence of occupation and inbreeding. The situation is so different in urban centers of Western civilization today that we are usually unaware of its implications. These vast concentrations, drawn from every corner of the earth, and their members ready to move on to new pastures tomorrow, are new to human history. They do not give the conditions under which racial types readily become fixed. Such conditions are represented, rather, by the peasant population of much of Europe—people rooted in the land they cultivate, and inbreeding within narrow confines. Our cities might become areas of specialization if national and international machinery broke down and every man's life were safe only within the walls of Berlin or London; if this persisted for generations their heterogeneous populations of the moment would, in course of time, become homogeneous, that is, something that would warrant the name of a stable race.

An understanding of the distribution of racial types in the world is possible only against this background of multiple centers of characterization in which certain hereditary traits become fixed, only to mingle with those from some other area, and again to become stabilized in a new type after mixture, and then to repeat the cycle. At best, all the physical measurements of all the people in areas of true inbreeding throughout the world give us only the distribution of contemporary areas of characterization; they will not identify for us a few primary races from which all subsequent races have been derived by straight descent or by intermixture. We must accept human history for what it is, and try to think not in terms of a few primary races but in terms of an indefinite number of areas of characterization. As we have seen, most such areas have come about through recombinations of traits drawn from some mingling of former stabilized types. "Man," says the biologist Julian Huxley, "is unique among species of animals in the degree to which crossing between already differentiated groups and types has taken place. Accordingly, multiple ancestry is at least as important as common ancestry in considering the nature and origins of any group." [1]

Though multiple ancestry played a role of great importance in the history of old and stable racial types, it is even more apparent in modern Europe and America, where pressure of population in old communities has, owing to better transportation facilities and sometimes to political or religious conditions, resulted in an unparalleled mobility of populations. But the essential process is not new; it has been going on for centuries. Before we talk glibly about the common ancestry of Germans or Frenchmen or Old Americans, we must recognize the omnipresence of this multiple ancestry brought about by centuries of migration.

Voltaire once read a book which began: "The Franks from whom we Frenchmen are descended." "Hello, my friend," he wrote, "who told you so?" The Franks, one minor detachment of the Teutonic "barbarians" who overran Gaul in the sixth century A.D., contributed their quota to the multiple ancestry of France, as well as of Germany, but, though they gave France their name, they were only one sub-group of the Teutonic peoples who, although at the time they seemed to "destroy civilization," were absorbed into its population. The Franks are one minor incident in the long history of the movements of peoples which have affected the ancestry of France. In Old Stone Age times the land was occupied by a people whose drift had been across southern Asia, northern Africa, into Spain, and finally into France. In New Stone Age times several branches of the Mediterranean race and early Alpines came from the east, and by the seventh century B.C. Celtic invasions disturbed the earlier settlers. By the first century B.C. it was the Belgae and the Cimbri from Denmark who were the spearheads of bar-

---

[1] Huxley, Julian, and Haddon, A. C., *We Europeans,* New York, Pelican Books, 1939, p. 95.

barian invasion, and though this was checked for a long interval by the expansion of the Roman Empire, by the fifth century A.D. the Vandals had overrun Gaul and the Visigoths established a powerful kingdom in the south of France. It was in this fifth century, which saw the "fall" of Rome, that the Franks overran much of France, and the Huns swept into Gaul under Attila.

Out of all this succession of different peoples from different areas of characterization certain local types have developed in different regions of modern France. It is even possible that the early Paleolithic inhabitants of the country have left their mark in the bodily form found in southern provinces such as Dordogne and the cantons of the Pyrenees. The Mediterranean coast is characterized by short, dark, narrow-headed peoples—the Mediterranean sub-race. The mountains of Savoy and of Brittany and a great central belt of France are predominantly Alpine, and in some parts of south-central France the broad-headedness is extreme. In Normandy to the north, especially near the mouth of the Seine, there is a certain concentration of blond, narrow-headed people (Nordic). None of these types is peculiar to France alone, and in no region is any one of these types exclusive. The only groups who deserve the name of a stable race are inbred, long-settled peasants in remote valleys of the Rhone.

The composite racial history of France is not exceptional in Europe. It is from certain points of view less extreme than that of Germany, for in eastern Germany we have to take account of the Slavs, whose area of characterization seems to have been somewhere east of Poland. In the first few centuries of our era the Slavs occupied the whole of the present eastern Germany, and though a backward wash of German colonists later established the German language in this region, the population remained predominantly Slavic in physical type. "Eastern Germany is in many places more Slavic than Russia."

Nor is Europe exceptional in its history of migrations and racial mixtures. The story in Asia and Africa is the same, and if in post-Columbian America and in European colonies it seems to us to have become extreme, this is at least partly because we see with our own eyes, instead of having to be told by history, the mixture of racial types. But fundamentally it is still the same old story. If a motion picture film could condense into a half-hour's spectacle the hither-and-thither journeyings of mankind in the Old World, Americans would recognize in the mixture of peoples in the nations of Europe the very thing we have seen happening in Pennsylvania or in Minnesota. Just as the Pennsylvania Dutch (Germans) or the Minnesota Swedes are today gradually losing their separatism and intermarrying with once-alien groups, so the Celts, the Latins, the Slavs, and the Nordics have mingled. Just as in America there are still concentrations of blonds or of big noses in certain places, so in Europe there are certain concentrations of types. But in America the process is so obvious that we recognize how absurd it would be to measure all the cephalic indices of California and compare them, as a unit, with the cephalic indices of Ohio, or to compare the pigmentation in Illinois with that in Pennsylvania. We recognize that such counting could have no biological meaning. But the German "race" and the French "race" rest on the same absurd foundation, and are just as meaningless biologically.

In Europe, just as in America, the "blood" of peoples occupying the same territory mixes, and their offspring inherit from both sides. This process has not in the past caused civilization to stop short in its tracks. It is useless to frame arguments about either its good or its bad effects, for since it is universal in human history, neither human advancement nor human disaster can be chalked up to this cause. Obviously, because of historic conditions, which had nothing specifically to do with the "mixture of blood," the consequences of migration and conquest have been sometimes "good," sometimes "bad," according to the point of view of the period at which account is taken. All the rest is special pleading.

Nothing illustrates this special pleading more clearly than the famous attempts to explain the fall of Rome. The Romans themselves attributed it to the inroads of barbarians who overran and swamped the great Empire which had so noble a history. They did not analyze their own weaknesses and mistakes of the two centuries that had gone before the fall; the catastrophe was due to the barbarians. This view served the Renaissance, too. Deeply committed to classical views, the Renaissance was able to add that the destruction of classical civilization by the Vandals had thrust Europe into eight centuries of the Dark Ages. *Vandalism* became a vernacular word for wanton destruction of everything fine and precious. Europeans of a later date, proud of their descent from these Teutonic hordes, offered a different interpretation. The Teutons had saved Europe from "the everlasting bestial"; they were young human gods who cleared the world of an effete race. But, these spokesmen of Teutonic racism pointed out, the fall of Rome contains a lesson for us today: Rome fell because she mingled her "blood" with that of the barbarians. Had she passed laws forbidding mixture, she would have prevented her own destruction. Thus the fall of Rome came to be for Teutonic racists a moral tale that proved the necessity of racial hygiene.

History tells the tale otherwise. Rome in the fourth and fifth centuries, passing laws of racial hygiene to stop the march of history, would have been like King Canute commanding the tides to stop short. The Emperors could not by such acts have legislated away the declining vigor of the Roman administration of the world and the loss of leadership she had suffered. Internal developments in the Roman Empire had weakened it, and the Teutonic hordes took advantage of this weakness; a few centuries earlier they had been powerless against its strength. The decline of the Roman Empire is a long and complex story of lack of vision and of internal violence. At last she was no longer mistress of the world. While she was vigorous, she Romanized whole areas of alien peoples; intermixture accompanied her great period as well as her decline. Racist explanations of the fall of Rome are a travesty of the facts.

The exaggerated claims that are made for programs of racial hygiene are, therefore, not upheld by historical evidence. Nevertheless, patriots in most of the Western nations have warned their fellow-citizens of the evils of racial intermixture with some lesser breed. In America we are told that the Nordics must save themselves pure from contamination with peoples of Southern Europe. In Germany racial purity is not lost by marriage with a Japanese but defilement comes from marriage with a Jew. The English in India regard intermixture as betrayal of white supremacy. The evils of these prohibited mixtures in Germany and in India are unquestioned; they are apparent to any observer. Those who have themselves made mixed marriages and the children of such unions are the first to testify to the unsatisfactory situation in which they find themselves.

Modern instances of the evils of racial mixture do not, however, prove that intermixture is a biological evil. In the first place, history has shown that such mixed races have flourished and progressed even in those extreme cases where intermixture has been across the color line. The Arabs are of Caucasian race, and have always taken wives freely from among the native peoples. In their dispersement over northern Africa a mixed race of Black and White grew up which created great kingdoms of wealth and splendor. In the western Sudan these kingdoms culminated in the sixteenth century in the great Empire of Bornu. Moslems have never attached importance to ancestry, and there was no adverse discrimination against the offspring of Arabs and the native women of their harems. On the contrary, intermixture produced great political leaders and men of wealth, and facilitated the spread of higher culture.

Even in some parts of the modern world mixture of races shows no evil effects. Students have always pointed this out for Hawaii, where the code of racial separatism has been conspicuously lacking. Intermixture in Hawaii does not have to be illicit; marriages between the most diverse races take place in the churches. There is no discrimination against the offspring of such crosses; they can hold eminent positions if they have ability. At the governor's receptions and university dances there is no color line. The cultural development of Hawaii has not suffered.[1]

When, therefore, we find in many parts of the world glaring evidence of the mediocrity of the half-caste, it is worth examining the social discrimination to which he is subjected. Where there is strong racist sentiment, the Eurasian or the Eurafrican is an outcast among both the kin of his father and the kin of his mother. His mother is scantily provided for, and when he is grown he must confine himself to inferior jobs allotted to his kind. The cards are stacked against him. Social discriminations of this kind prevail generally in the world today, and most objective observers say frankly that not many of the dominant "race" would, if they lived under similar conditions, make a much better showing. Some Whites, though born to poverty and brought up as

[1] Adams, Romanzo, "The Unorthodox Race Doctrine of Hawaii," in *Race and Culture Contacts,* ed. by E. B. Reuter, New York, 1934, p. 145 ff.

outcasts, would nevertheless rise to positions of eminence. But so also do some of the half-castes.

The social rather than biological explanation of the low condition of mixed bloods in most parts of the world is borne out by anthropometric studies. "Hybrid vigor" has been shown in studies of American Indian-White mixture, stature in the half-breeds being greater than that of either race contributing to the cross. Mixed bloods also show over and over again evidence of increased fertility. The descendants of the famous English-Tahitian cross on Pitcairn Island had during their early life on the island one of the highest rates of increase yet recorded. Nature apparently does not condemn the half-caste to physiological inferiority.

The rule for the breeding of good human stock is that both parents be of good physique and good mental ability. Since the best quarter of the world's population according to these standards includes individuals of all races, on the basis of any measurements yet devised, improvement of human stock is not a matter of racial separatism. "Good" ancestry has been given a racist meaning in the modern world and may include progenitors that are very inferior when reckoned by standards either of health or of mental ability. As is well known, individual offspring rise even above such a handicap. It is, however, a handicap which has to be reckoned with, whatever the social conditions. Half-castes, when they have healthy and capable ancestors, have never been shown to be similarly handicapped by Nature. "If," says Julian Huxley, "the alleged inferiority of half-castes really exists, it is much more likely to be the product of the unfavorable social atmosphere in which they grow up than due to any effect, which would be biologically very unusual, of their mixed heredity." [1]

---

[1] Huxley, J. S., *Eugenics and Society*. Galton Lecture, Eugenics Society, London, 1936.

The movements of peoples over the face of the earth, therefore, inevitably produce race mixture and have produced it since before history began. No one has been able to adduce evidence of its inherent evil. It has sometimes been a social advantage, sometimes a running sore threatening the health of the whole society. It can obviously be made a social evil, and, where it is so, sensible people will avoid contributing to it and grieve if their children make such alliances. We must live in the world as it is. But the evil of racial intermixture has no known basis in the immutable laws of Nature. The doctrines of racism have much to answer for, but the lot of the half-caste in the world today is one of the bitterest fruits they have produced.

WHAT THEY SAY

Thus from a mixture of all kinds began
That heterogeneous thing, an Englishman.

Daniel Defoe, *The True-Born Englishman.*

Every civilized group of which we have record has been a hybrid group, a fact which disposes effectually of the theory that hybrid peoples are inferior to pure-bred ones.

Ralph Linton, *The Study of Man.* New York, D. Appleton-Century, 1936, p. 34.

There is no necessity to postulate the existence of a specific and universal instinct of racial antipathy; while on the other hand there is strong positive evidence that such an instinct does not exist. An adequate explanation of racial antagonisms can be found in impulses and motives that are independent of race.

These impulses and motives, however, though not racial in their origins, may become racial, through being connected in the mind with the thought of another race. When this association takes place the feelings may be aroused by contact with any member of that race, and operate with all the force of an instinctive antipathy.

> J. H. Oldham, *Christianity and the Race Problem.* New York, George H. Doran Co., 1924, p. 43.

The racist says:

This accurately expresses the racial view held by National Socialists [i.e., the Third Reich in Germany]: that each race on this earth represents an idea in the mind of God. This is just what we do believe and therefore we call for a clear-cut differentiation between blood and blood, so that God's idea may not be blurred and caricatured in the half-breed.

> W. Gross, in *Racio-Political Foreign Correspondence,* published by the Bureau for Human Betterment and Eugenics. Berlin, April 1935.

But the biologist says:

The sociologist who is satisfied with human society as now constituted may reasonably decry race crossing. But let him do so on social grounds only. He will wait in vain, if he waits to see mixed races vanish from any biological unfitness.

> W. E. Castle, "Biological and Social Consequences of Race-Crossing." *American Journal of Physical Anthropology,* Vol. IX, p. 156.

And the Brazilian statesman says:

In South America our experience of centuries has taught us that there is no real understanding except the one that comes through the fusion of races.

> Dr. Oliviera Lima, quoted by Cedric Dover in *Half-Caste.* London, Secker & Warburg, 1937, p. 248.

V. WHAT IS HEREDITARY?

HEREDITY IS the transmission of traits from parents to off-spring. An "Old American's" heredity comes to him from his biological ancestors, as any other Anglo-Saxon's comes to him from his biological ancestors; their ancestors may have something in common but much that is diverse. They are not the same persons, and their heredity will therefore not be the same. For one to speak of his "Aryan," Anglo-Saxon, or Jewish heredity is biologically meaningless, for it lumps together as one's ancestors vast numbers of people who are in no sense one's forebears, and does not distinguish all those varied human types who are actually one's ancestors. If mankind were a series of mutually infertile species, such as those into which wild animals are divided, this lumping would not be a serious error; no family line of the red deer has ancestors who were elk; all of them were exclusively red deer. As we have seen, however, human beings do not fall biologically into species of this kind; differentiated human types cross and recross, and the only ancestry that accounts for the individual is his own. Heredity in this sense follows very precise biological laws, many of which are known, but racial heredity in Western civilization is a myth which sets up, in place of true heredity in family lines, an absurd picture of heredity from a race. *Race* is an abstraction even as it is defined by a geneticist; as it is defined statistically by a physical anthropologist it is even more of an abstraction. It is not the *race* which copulates and reproduces.

Heredity from parent to child is studied in the science of genetics. Though its foundation was laid in Darwin's *Origin of Species*, which was published in 1859, modern genetics is based on Mendel's studies of garden peas—work which was done shortly after the publication of the *Origin of Species* but remained unknown until 1900. The facts which Mendel observed contradicted in several ways the expectations of Darwinian evolutionists. These earlier evolutionists had expected to find that heredity operated to produce a uniform blend, as if the heritable traits of the mother and those of the father were respectively a trickle of ink and a trickle of water which mingled in their offspring to form a uniform watered ink. But this is an oversimplification. The role of bisexual reproduction proves, as the result of Mendelian observation, to be much more complex than this. Inheritance is passed along to the offspring as a long series of characteristics contributed by the father and the mother, and these have to be conceived not as ink and water mingling but as a pile of beads sorted out anew for every individual. For many traits these sortings follow certain statistical rules. Mendel in his studies of garden peas followed out the process in detail.

Mendel riveted his attention upon the history of tallness or dwarfness, yellowness or greenness, in generations of peas, that is, upon a single pair of alternative characters at a time. He crossed a tall pea with a dwarf pea and got all tall peas. He then allowed this generation of peas to cross-fertilize itself and the picture changed: though three-quarters were tall, one-quarter of all the resultant pea plants were dwarf and bred true to dwarfness as if their ancestors had never been crossed with a tall variety. Long series of experiments showed that tallness and dwarfness—like yellowness and greenness, smoothness and wrinkledness—sorted themselves out in offspring but retained their identity; in biological terms each is an *allelomorphic pair* and represents alternative characteristics of a single trait. For most traits one of these alternatives is *dominant* over the other; that is, the non-dominant, or *recessive,* trait will not be visible in the offspring even though it can be transmitted to the next generation. The original male parent peas had a double dose of the dominant factor (or gene) for tallness (TT) and the original female pea a double dose of the recessive trait for dwarfness (dd). Since tallness was dominant, the first generation (F^1) were all tall, having, each of them, a single dose of tallness and a single dose of dwarfness (Td), of which the dwarfness did not show. But dwarfness was not lost. The next inbred generation (F^2) inherited Td from *both* parents, and, just as when you make all possible combinations of two long matches and two short matches, the unit characteristics in this generation were in the proportions of: TT, Td, dT, dd.

DIAGRAM I

Female Parent, F^1

		TALL		dwarf	
Male Parent, F^1	TALL	F^2: TALL	TALL	F^2: dwarf	TALL
	dwarf	F^2: TALL	dwarf	F^2: dwarf	dwarf

Since T was dominant, the first three groups all had the same appearance, that of TT. That was why Mendel's peas in the F^2 generation were one-quarter dwarf and three-quarters tall.

The importance of this law of inheritance is that it laid the basis for understanding the role of sexual reproduction in giving rise to new combinations of traits. Mendel went on to see what happened when parents differed, not in one allelomorphic pair but in two. He bred tall (T) yellow (Y) peas with dwarf (d) green (g) peas, yellow being dominant over green, as tallness is over dwarfness. The problem was to find out whether dwarfness always stayed with greenness and tallness with yellowness. But he found that in F^2 the numerical distribution in the offspring was independent of the original "type" the parent generation represented; the unit characteristics could, again, be sorted out like different matches or different beads. Since two allelomorphic pairs are involved, the distribution in the F^2 generation is not in multiples of four as when one allelomorphic pair is in question, but in multiples of sixteen.

Every possible combination occurred in the second generation: nine TALL YELLOW; three TALL green; three dwarf YELLOW, and one dwarf green. Though the original parents were one of them TALL YELLOW and one of them dwarf green, in F^2, six out of sixteen offspring had combinations of traits not represented in the original parents, i.e., three TALL green, and three dwarf YELLOW.

This biological principle which underlies new combinations of traits is known as the *independent segregation* of unit characteristics; and though many facts in human inheritance are still obscure, it is certain that this principle is operative in human inheritance of allelomorphic pairs. Long-headedness and blondness have been singled out as Nordic characteristics and broad-headedness and swarthiness as Alpine characteristics, but the fact that blondness splits off from long-headedness and broad-headedness from swarthiness is no longer a mystery. The map of physical forms in Europe, for instance, becomes only what one would expect

DIAGRAM II

Female Parent, F^1

Male Parent, F^1	TALL YELLOW	TALL green	dwarf YELLOW	dwarf green
TALL YELLOW	F^2 { TALL YELLOW, TALL YELLOW	F^2 { TALL green, TALL YELLOW	F^2 { dwarf YELLOW, TALL YELLOW	F^2 { dwarf green, TALL YELLOW
TALL green	F^2 { TALL YELLOW, TALL green	F^2 { TALL green, TALL green	F^2 { dwarf YELLOW, TALL green	F^2 { dwarf green, TALL green
dwarf YELLOW	F^2 { TALL YELLOW, dwarf YELLOW	F^2 { TALL green, dwarf YELLOW	F^2 { dwarf YELLOW, dwarf YELLOW	F^2 { dwarf green, dwarf YELLOW
dwarf green	F^2 { TALL YELLOW, dwarf green	F^2 { TALL green, dwarf green	F^2 { dwarf YELLOW, dwarf green	F^2 { dwarf green, dwarf green

after the mingling of all the diverse types that have gone into its ancestry. The more unit characters in which parent types differ, the more recombinations are possible in the second and later generations. If we could isolate ten unit characters in human beings, and the parents should differ in all ten, there are 1022 combinations possible ($2^{10} = 1024$, minus the parental pair, i.e., 1022). The human reproductive cells are thus able to play countless variations upon the original inheritance, and in all regions of the world they have done so.

The question of pure races thus takes on a different aspect in view of modern genetics. Physical anthropologists still often speak as if the question were one of identifying the traits that belong to original human types, i.e., of identifying a Nordic type in which narrow-headedness and blondness are bracketed. Then one student, discussing a type which is narrow-headed and swarthy, will deny its relationship to the Nordics on the basis of its pigmentation, and another will "prove" the relationship on the basis of its cephalic index. The dispute waxes bitter. But according to genetic principles both traits are relevant; inheritance by its very nature constantly produces types which are not duplicates of any ancestral form. The particular series of traits any one student may identify as a basic "type" is a convenience for arranging his data rather than genetically significant.

The laws of genetics are also important for a knowledge of human races because they lay the basis for the only scientific means of identifying pure race as over against mixed race. Mendelian principles make necessary an entirely different method in the study of racial crossing. As we have seen, when the father and mother are of different physical types, the distribution of traits in the offspring makes these offspring unlike each other, whereas if the two parents are of the same type their offspring will be alike. No human group has been observed where this latter condition occurs, i.e., where the brothers and sisters in a family present no significant differences one from the other. Hence all the human material we have indicates that, even in segregated communities, there is some multiple ancestry and some of the children incline toward one ancestral strain and some toward another. Racial purity, in the sense that all individuals have all the same traits, is not recorded though it is possible that it existed before contact with Whites among some small groups of subarctic Eskimos who had been isolated for centuries. Racial purity in any human group can only mean that each fraternity (brothers and sisters born of one father and mother) duplicates every other fraternity in inherited traits; that is, that though, according to genetic principles, there will be some recombinations of traits within each fraternity, inbreeding has continued down the generations till all these fraternities resemble each other because they share the same inheritance. Among the mountain Whites in isolated Tennessee valleys; among the Bastaards of South Africa, a community whose ancestors were early European male colonists and Hottentot women; in the Malay Archipelago island of Kisar, a community descended from Dutch fathers and Malay mothers, all the fraternities in each group are genetically similar. The brothers and sisters in South Africa and in Kisar differ more within one fraternity than the mountain Whites, since their component strains are more diverse, but they have, by inbreeding, attained a high degree of racial homogeneity. If a physical anthropologist takes the measurements of one fraternity in these communities, he has closely approximated the measurements of all the fraternities, and one fraternity can stand as a very fair sample of all of them.

In any investigation of race this index is the one which

reveals to us the degree to which a homogeneous race has been attained. It is not attained in urban centers of Europe, where many family lines having no correspondence one with the other are universally found, and where measurements of one fraternity cannot possibly stand as representative of other fraternities. But a homogeneous race, measured in this way, is the only "pure race" which has meaning within the human species. It is ironic that it is those very European nations in which anthropometric investigation shows no pure race which base their claims to superiority on allegations of their "pure" blood.

Genetics, in recent years, has made another essential contribution to the understanding of heredity. It has shown that new traits arise by mutation. Sometimes a fruit fly or a calf is born with characteristics that are not due to its pooled heredity and it passes on this new characteristic to its offspring and their descendants. Herefords have been for a long time the most popular ranch cattle in the United States and Canada. When in 1889 a hornless calf was born on a Kansas farm, stock breeders recognized the advantage of ranch cattle without horns. From this Kansas calf have been bred all the present "polled" Herefords. The fact of mutations is today undeniable, and it is known that the likelihood of such occurrences is greatly increased by certain environmental conditions. For instance, it is increased under the influence of radiation at high altitudes, and, in the laboratory, by X-rays.

The older evolutionists assumed a quite different theory of the way in which new traits developed. About the time of the birth of Darwin, Lamarck argued that new traits were due to the inheritance of acquired characteristics. Giraffes grew longer necks as they reached out for higher and higher leaves, and each new generation, by hereditary transmission of this acquired trait, became longer-necked. Or fish in caves lost their eyesight through disuse and transmitted blindness to their descendants. In the human race, therefore, acquirements of parents were believed to be transmitted to their children.

Modern genetics has performed experiment after experiment, all of which show that this view was mistaken, though it was not challenged by Darwin and his contemporaries. Inheritance of acquired characteristics does not occur. New traits are due to mutations, which occur even in the most closely bred lines. These mutations are haphazard and few of them could give to their possessor any possible advantage. The characteristic features of different races arose thus through mutation—blue eyes, for instance—and became characteristic of large populations by inbreeding in those "areas of characterization" where groups of the human race settled down in the early history of mankind. But the idea that the *achievements* of forefathers are passed on to their descendants by heredity is completely discredited. Heredity takes no notice of the glories of civilization, whether they are in science or in technology or in art; these can be perpetuated in any group, not by Nature, but by nurture.

WHAT THEY SAY

The biologists say:

With full responsibility for my words as a professional biologist, I do not hesitate to say that all existing and genuine knowledge about the way in which the physical characteristics of human communities are related to their cultural capabilities can be written on the back of a postage stamp.

Lancelot Hogben, "Preface on Prejudices" in Cedric Dover, *Half-Caste*. London, Secker & Warburg, 1937, p. 9.

In regard to really important characteristics, the natural differences between the races pale into insignificance beside the natural differences between individuals—so much so that an impartial science of genetic improvement could not afford to take the former into account at all in its procedure.

H. J. Muller, *Out of the Night; A Biologist's View of the Future.* New York, Vanguard Press, 1935, p. 120.

When it is remembered that we are still uncertain whether hereditary differences have any part at all in causing the class differences in intelligence, while it cannot be denied that the environment has some hand in this, the priority of environmental over genetical methods of raising the general level of intelligence becomes obvious.

C. H. Waddington, *An Introduction to Modern Genetics.* New York, Macmillan Co., 1939, p. 358.

VI. WHO IS SUPERIOR?

THE SCIENTIFIC STUDY of race tells us many important facts which have nothing to do with the question of the superiority or inferiority of given races. It tells us unrecorded and forgotten facts of early history and of the movement of peoples; it tells us what combinations of traits occur upon the mixture of two racial types; it distinguishes between a group of people who constitute a nation and a group of people who constitute a biological type (race). This scientific study of race has been an integral part of anthropology from its earliest beginnings because it provided a record, written in the bones and other bodily characteristics of men, of the history of mankind; and in this study anthropologists have found overwhelmingly that race did not correlate with superiority or inferiority. From the great pioneer anthropologist Theodor Waitz, who examined the question in 1859, to the most recent studies of Franz Boas, they have reiterated that on this point the study of race gives only negative evidence.

Of all human questions, however, that of superiority and inferiority lies closest to the heart of man. He has always, like the simplest savages, called his own immediate concerns not simply dearest to him, but the most important in the universe; in a word, "superior." Whatever information comes to hand, he scans it for proofs of his belief. It was inevitable, therefore, that new facts about race should have been studied over and over again from this point of view. In this there was nothing that was peculiar to race; religions have been similarly classified and absolute judgments pronounced; so have class differences and sex differences, and differences between one grand duchy and a neighboring one, and between one nation and another, even when they both have the same racial composition. With the growth of knowledge about race after the middle of the nineteenth century, students attempted to find a scientific basis on which to judge the innate superiority or inferiority of one racial group to another. Work was carried on in three fields: physiological, psychological, and historical.

Physiological

The early evolutionists believed that man's physical evolution had proceeded in a straight line from his pre-human progenitors up to the White race. They considered the evolutionary process a ladder, each rung of which had marked some advance upon the ape. Thus the apes have broad flat noses, as have also the Bushmen, Negroes, and Australians; Europeans have narrow prominent noses. More prominent configuration of the nose and lessened limb length were therefore end results of evolution and were characteristic of the White race.

Investigations on the anatomical form of apes and human beings have shown, during the last fifty years, that the evolutionists' belief in a unilinear development of human anatomy was mistaken. Both in anthropoids and in human races, special developments have occurred locally which cannot be arranged in a unilinear series. The most obvious differences between apes and men is that between the hairy coat of the anthropoids and the human skin. Of all human races the Mongoloids are the freest of body hair; the Whites, along with the Australian aborigines and some local tribes belonging to other races, are the hairiest. The anthropoids have thin lips, and the most contrastingly "human" development is the full lips of the Negro; Whites have much more "primitive" lips. Neither by the test of hairiness nor by the test of lips would the Whites belong to that branch of the human race anatomically farthest removed from the ancestral type. No race has a monopoly of evolutionary end products, and no arguments for superiority can be based on single traits selected just because they favor the White race.

The most important contention of the early evolutionists was that superiority was manifest in the increasing size of the brain cavity. Apes have receding foreheads and small brains; men have prominent foreheads and large brains. Therefore the average brain size in any race would indicate its place on the evolutionary ladder. The average weight of the brain in proportion to total bodily weight is smaller among Negroes than among Mongoloids and somewhat smaller among Mongoloids than among Whites. These differences are average differences, but the overlapping is so great that almost any individual human brain might belong to any of these three great races. Nor is the absolute difference great; human brain sizes, except for the pygmies, fall within a very small range as compared to the gap between man and the anthropoid apes. Boule [1] gives the maximum size for the latter as 621 cubic centimeters; whereas for Negroes he gives 1477 c.c. and for Parisians 1550 c.c. Pearson's series of European males, on the other hand, aver-

---

[1] Boule, Marcellin, *Fossil Man· Elements of Human Paleoethnology*. Translated from the French by Jessie E. and James Ritchie. Edinburgh, 1923, p. 229.

ages 1490 c.c.—almost the average Boule gives for Negroes—whereas Pearson finds that Negro males average 1350 c.c.[1] Figures for the human species therefore cluster together and are far removed from those for the ancestral types. The only human brain sizes that are to any marked degree intermediate are those of pygmy races and tribes of very slight body build, and such brain sizes are just one measurement among many which are smaller because a smaller individual is being measured. We are not justified in leaping without more proof to the conclusion that this slighter build places them at a congenital *mental* disadvantage.

In all races where there is comparable body build, brain sizes in one racial group overlap those of the others except for the most extreme cases, and individuals whose race is not known cannot be assigned to one race or another on the basis of this measurement. The difference between individuals in brain size is very great; the difference between racial averages very small. Except for the pygmy and semi-pygmy groups, the quarter of the world's population having the largest brains would include individuals from all races. It would be more realistic, if we were really convinced of the importance of this criterion, to favor all large-brained individuals of whatever race.

But even this claim to *individual* superiority based on brain size is an error. Very eminent Europeans have had brains that were unusually small. The real point is how the brain functions. So far as functioning has an organic basis, it seems to depend not on gross size but on the extent of the brain's surface area, which increases as the brain has more convolutions. Anatomists have studied cross sections of the brain under the microscope, but no anatomist with the finest microscope can tell to what race that brain belonged.

Organic differences in the brain can never by themselves

<hr>

[1] Pearson in *Biometrika*, Vol. 8, 1912, pp. 292–337.

answer the question of superiority and inferiority. In the absence of significant differences which set the races of comparable body build apart from one another *as races,* the real problem in this matter, as in the study of any other human organ, is the relation between structure and function. Even in our own personal lives each of us knows the difference in functioning that may go along with one fixed identical organ. So long as no disease invades our lungs or our hearts, we each of us have the same lungs, the same heart, from the end of adolescence to senility. But the functioning of these organs varies greatly. When we climb mountains, our hearts pound and our breath comes short; when we compose ourselves for sleep, our heart-beats are slight and our breath long and regular. When we spend a summer at a high altitude or when we winter in the tropics, temporary changes take place. The heart structure or the lung structure has not changed; these organs merely have a considerable margin of safety so that they live within their means whether they function in one way or another. This circumstance, which we all have good reason to know in our own lives, is basic also when we compare groups of people. There too we find evidences of this same margin of safety. Races with low basal metabolism function in many regions alongside races with high basal metabolism, and this physiological difference does not prevent their adjustment. The eyesight of different peoples may test the same, yet some primitive peoples seem to white explorers to see as if they were using binoculars or microscopes; they have trained their eyes to serve in certain situations with such attention to minutiae that the result seems miraculous. On the other hand, primitive people find our ability to discriminate letters on a page equally miraculous; the difference is not in the organ but in the experiences in which the organ has habitually functioned.

The brain is not a case apart. People with brains of similar structure may use them very differently, and this is also due to the various experiences in which their minds have habitually functioned. We should be guilty of the ultimate crudity if we confused hereditary structure with learned functioning. There are of course organic limits, just as there are bad hearts and astigmatic eyes, but individuals with organically inferior brains are born in all races; no race as a whole is condemned to feeblemindedness.

In all this discussion of brain size I have excepted the pygmy and semi-pygmy races. Whether these races could function in modern civilization is a purely academic question. It is not a live issue, for they are slated for destruction on social grounds. They have been pushed back into unwanted mountain fastnesses and deserts from regions which have been their hereditary homes. No one, I think, can look at the famous group of the little Bushman family by Malvina Hoffman without wanting to set the clock back and let them live out their lives in peace no matter what their brain size is. They were sufficiently gifted, at all events, to cover the rocks of their desert country with spirited paintings of animal hunts that excite the admiration of European painters today. Their old tribal ways of life were kindly and inoffensive. But to the early white farmer and cattleman their cardinal sin was that they refused to submit; to the last they resisted the encroachments of the stranger. Therefore they were killed on sight, as one contemporary put it, "by the powerful hand of the Ruler of heaven and earth," and it was only the occasional white outsider in those days who wrote that he was revolted by the wanton killing of these helpless men and women, and shocked at the administrator, otherwise so sensible a gentleman, who regarded it as a routine part of his daily work and ordained by Heaven. It was only an occasional traveler who marveled at "the beautiful symmetrical form of our Bushman guide, who walked and sometimes ran before us with a gait the most free and easy I have ever beheld. His well-proportioned, although small and delicate figure, his upright and manly port, his firm, bold steps, and the consciousness of liberty which beamed in his countenance afforded us indescribable pleasure." [1] The Bushmen might not have been able to adjust themselves to machine civilization, but in spite of their cranial capacity they were not a reproach to the human race.

Psychological

Psychological tests of racial superiority are an attempt to apply less crude, more relevant standards than the mere gross size of the brain. They test some of the end results of the brain's functioning, and it is this question of what the brain can do which is crucial. There have been, therefore, a long series of psychological investigations during the last twenty-five years which have rated intelligence quotients of different racial and national groups as shown in their achievements in various kinds of individual and group tests.

Most intelligence testing has been done in America. During the First World War tests were given to the American Expeditionary Forces, and the enormous number of individuals from all sections of the country made this test population an ideal sampling compared to all earlier attempts. The scores on these tests were arranged by crude racial and national groupings—Negroes, Jews, persons of British or of Italian ancestry—and an average "mental age" for each group was derived. The differences were great. Whereas the average mental age of the White race in the army was 13.1 years, that of the Negroes was 10.4, and the

---

[1] Burchell, quoted in W. J. Sollas, *Ancient Hunters*, London, 1911, p. 272

overlap was only 12 per cent.[1] Among the various immigrant white nationalities, the Poles were at the bottom of the list; the Italians were on about the same level as the Poles.

The results of these army scores posed a problem on which the intelligence testers have been working ever since. The first reaction to the results was that here at last was an answer to the question of whether intelligence was transmitted by inheritance. Terman, one of the early investigators, had described the Binet test as giving a measure of innate intelligence scarcely influenced by education and experience. Brigham, who interpreted the army tests on immigrants from different parts of Europe, concluded that, since the scores of individuals of Northern European ancestry were higher than those of Southern European ancestry, Nordics had more innate intelligence than Alpines and Mediterraneans. The low scores of Negroes were held to measure directly their congenital inferiority to the Whites.

Work during the last decade, however, has led racial psychologists to doubt this conclusion. The intelligence tests were of several different kinds. Some were highly verbal, including vocabulary as one item of the test. It was obvious that those who spoke English at home and used it easily scored higher than those who spontaneously expressed themselves in another language. Many of the words in the vocabulary and some of those in the directions given the person taking the test were not used commonly in the vernacular and could be known to children from many homes only from book knowledge. Negroes and recent immigrants or children of foreign-born parentage were at a disadvantage. Such a language handicap was obviously not congenital, and this fact had to be taken into account before the value of

---

[1] Yerkes, R. M., "Psychological Examining in the United States Army," *Memoir of the National Academy of Sciences,* Washington, Vol. 15, vi, 1921, p. 790.

the tests as measures of innate ability could be considered.

The testers also stressed another difficulty, not only in the army tests but in all subsequent testing. The results are comparable for two groups only when both are interested in doing as well as they can. The differences in this particular are only too apparent to the tester, and they influence the results. Garth even suggests, instancing the high scores of the Japanese and Chinese tested in America—intelligence quotients of 99 as against the Whites' 100—that perhaps the reason the Negroes, Mexicans, and Indians did so poorly in comparison was that they could not "take the white man's seriousness seriously." [1] The Stanford-Binet test is indeed far from resembling anything which is to them traditionally important.

There are even more specific differences among different groups in this matter of doing as well as they can. Good manners differ in different cultures in ways which influence the tests. Among many peoples, and especially among American Indian tribes, a person is trained never to answer a question or state a fact except when he is absolutely and unassailably sure of himself. Any minor uncertainty, which an American school child typically takes very lightly, will render him dumb. His great humiliation comes, not like our children's, from being slow or backward in answering, but from having ventured at all unless he was on completely firm ground. He will not retell the little test story at all unless he can cover each detail; he will not interpret the picture if there is a "Western Union" envelope in it which he never saw before. Klineberg [2] remarks on the difficulties caused by the Dakota Indians' good manners, which taboo giving any answer in the presence of someone who does

---

[1] Garth, Thomas Russell, *Race Psychology, a Study of Racial Mental Differences,* New York, 1931, p. 183.

[2] Klineberg, Otto, *Race Differences,* New York, 1935, p. 155.

not know the answer. Tests made among children with such rules of politeness are not really comparable with tests made in another culture where there is a taboo against presuming to answer in the presence of someone who *does* know the answer, and with tests made in our culture, where most children will try to give an answer under any circumstances. In societies where great deference is accorded to chiefs or high castes any group test situation is hopelessly distorted. In all these cases the rules of etiquette influence the scores.

There are endless difficulties of all kinds. In the test of matching colors the Balinese children spent all their time putting harmonious colors together "for a pretty belt." The Balinese are very sophisticated about color and they could not accept the idea of wasting time putting the *same* colors together when they might be showing their taste in color arrangement. The commonest difficulty in the color tests in other societies is that the categories of colors differ so widely. The spectrum is a color continuum with no sharp breaks anywhere; the English language draws a line at one point and we see "yellow" on one side of that line and "green" on the other. Another language decrees a dividing line at another point, somewhere, let us say, between light green and dark green, and it calls the light green *and certain yellows* both "young leaves color," and the dark greens *and certain blues* both "shaded water color." Their grouping of colors is as reasonable as ours but their test performances cannot be rated on the same scale as ours. Certain other cultural peculiarities are not so easy to correct as the color categories. In word tests, like those of "opposites," the Samoans attained very high scores. They are accustomed in their culture to verbal play, to puns, to epigrams. In other test situations, their performances often failed miserably according to our standards, just as the Balinese failed in matching colors.

Even granting the doubts that were raised about the tests themselves and the growing belief among testers that the results gave an indication of scholastic achievement rather than of innate intelligence, the chief doubt which gained ground was whether the results indicated *racial* differences or were only so presented that they seemed to do so. The scores whether for Whites or Negroes were obviously not the same from different parts of the country. It was worth investigating whether the differences were sectional. The testers therefore tabulated the Whites of Southern states as against the Negroes of Northern states and the results were startling—arranged by median scores Southern Whites fell below Northern Negroes.

WHITES [1]

Mississippi	41.25
Kentucky	41.50
Arkansas	41.55

NEGROES

New York	45.02
Illinois	47.35
Ohio	49.50

Such a break-down of the results showed a fundamental fallacy in the original interpretation. The Negroes of the United States are massed in the South; their I.Q. (intelligence quotient) was significant not only in so far as they were *Negroes,* but as *Southerners.* Obviously even the dominant White race did badly in the tests if they had been reared in certain Southern states, where per capita expenditures for education are low and the low standard of living is revealed in every survey and to every casual visitor. The

[1] Klineberg, *op. cit.,* p. 182.

testers felt that there was reasonable doubt concerning conclusions of inherent racial differences, and they gave further
tests. They tested Negro and White boys in Nashville, then
in Chicago, and then in New York City. The Negro scores
were farthest below the White in Nashville, somewhat below in Chicago, and equaled the White score in New York
City. They tried Los Angeles, where Negroes are few in
number and are educated in the same classrooms with
Whites; their average I.Q. was 104.7 (as over against an
average I.Q. for the Southern Negro of about 75) [1] and this
was "slightly above that of the white children with whom
they were compared." The results of the tests varied with
educational opportunity.

Some testers still believed that these results cast no fundamental doubt on the original interpretation because only
superior Negroes had gone North or West. This explanation
is called "selective migration." The testers therefore examined school records in Southern cities to find evidence that
the brightest boys went North. The average of all emigrants
to the North was almost exactly the average for the whole
Negro school population in those cities.[2] Then they tested
Negro school children in New York schools; if the high
average they attained was due to the fact that only the cream
of the Southern Negro population came North, the length
of time they had been in New York would have no influence on their scores. But the lowest I.Q.'s were those of the
newest arrivals, and length of residence strongly affected
the scores. There was still a further question to be answered: could it be that the newer arrivals from the South
were inferior to the earlier? Tests were given and the results showed that it was the other way around; in the groups
sampled the later migrants made the better scores. All that

---

[1] Garth, *op. cit.*, p. 219.
[2] Klineberg, *op. cit.*, pp. 185–86.

was left, therefore, was the correlation between test scores and social and educational advantages. The environmental advantages of the Negro in the United States never equal those of the Whites of the same economic level, but wherever they became more similar the "inferiority" of the Negro tended to disappear.

Intelligence testers therefore have swung to an interpretation of their data radically different from that of the 1920's. As Thorndike put it as far back as 1914: "The facts [i.e., data on I.Q.'s of different races and nationalities] are measurements of differences between groups which are distinct to an unknown degree in traits which are influenced by training to an unknown degree." [1] Garth, whose life was largely given to racial testing and whose book is a standard reference on the subject, says that, though his work began with "a silent conviction that he would find clear-cut racial differences in mental processes," he came, from a consideration of all psychological tests, to the conclusion that "it is useless to speak of the worthlessness of so-called 'inferior peoples' when their worth has never been established by a fair test." [2] Klineberg, whose *Racial Differences* contains a clear summary of mental testing, concludes: "Intelligence tests may therefore not be used as measures of group differences in native ability, though they may be used profitably as measures of accomplishment. When comparisons are made within the same race or group, it can be demonstrated that there are very marked differences depending upon variations in background. These differences may be satisfactorily explained, therefore, without recourse to the hypothesis of innate racial differences in mental ability." [3] Even

---

[1] Thorndike, E. L., *Educational Psychology*, Vol. III, New York, 1921, p. 207.

[2] Garth, *op. cit.*, pp. vii and 101.

[3] Klineberg, *op. cit.*, p. 189.

Brigham, whose interpretation of the army tests in 1921 was that they showed racial superiority of the Nordic over the Alpine and Mediterranean, has reversed his conclusion. In 1930 he wrote: "Comparative studies of various national and racial groups may not be made with existing tests. . . . In particular one of the most pretentious of these comparative racial studies—the writer's own—was without foundation." [1]

The intelligence testers at the present time, therefore, regard their data as indicating achievement and primarily scholastic achievement. For this both innate aptitude and specific training are necessary; in other words, both heredity and environment play their parts. The problem is whether the hereditary factor is a *racial constant*. The results of racial tests are believed today to show that hereditary aptitude is not distributed by races and that when environmental conditions for different groups become similar, average achievement also becomes similar. Individual differences will still remain in all races, but the results indicate that any program which proposes to increase human achievement will attain its ends by providing adequate and continued opportunity for any individual without regard to race or color. As the biologist H. J. Muller puts it: "In . . . really important characteristics the natural differences between the races pale into insignificance beside the natural differences between individuals—so much so that an impartial science of genetic improvement could not afford to take the former into account at all in its procedure." [2]

The whole procedure in the racial psychological tests has been ill adapted to its original goal, even if the tests themselves had been unassailable. The goal was to discover the

---

[1] Brigham, C. C., "Intelligence Tests of Immigrant Groups," *Psychological Review,* Vol. XXXVII, Princeton, 1930, p. 165.

[2] Muller, H. J., *Out of the Night; A Biologist's View of the Future,* New York, 1936, p. 120.

relative capacity of races. The animal breeder has the same sort of problem; he wants to find good breeds which are more worth encouraging than others. He does not decide on good performance by averaging together all bulls of one breed regardless of the conditions under which they have lived. He knows that if his best specimen is sent to an unfamiliar range and given no care it will do nothing but sulk. This does not make him lose faith in the breed. He knows that his recommendations are not invalidated even though bad herding conditions will ruin his animals. He would not understand the method of the old psychological tester who presented averages of racial groups no matter under what conditions they lived. One good performance of his breed would outweigh for him a whole series where it had done badly; his one fine bull would make him alert to duplicate the success, since obviously the breed was capable under certain conditions of such performance.

So, too, in the psychological tests, if we are as much in earnest about human capabilities as the farmer is about the cattle he breeds, we will give more weight to isolated achievements than to averages. Individual instances are not only more interesting than averages: they are in this case more pertinent. In the Pintner Non-Language Test, a full-blood Indian girl of twelve from the United States Indian School at Santa Fé rated an I.Q. of 145, which is 45 points above the White average and more than 70 points above the Indian average. In the National Intelligence Test, a Mexican boy in the public schools of San Antonio obtained the same I.Q. of 145, outdistancing the White average by just as much as the Indian girl and outdistancing the average Mexican in the United States by 67 points.[1] A nine-year-old girl of apparently pure Negro stock in Chicago had a Binet I.Q. of

[1] Garth, *op. cit.*, p. 217.

approximately 200.[1] If these stocks can produce individuals who do as well as this in meeting the requirements of the test even under the conditions the Indian and the Mexican and the Negro have to meet in America, the *stocks* are not at fault. In all stocks individuals differ in ability, and civilization will always be the poorer if we close the gates of opportunity to those of superior ability whatever their blood may be.

Historical

Claims of racial superiority have also been based on history. It has been said that the rise and fall of civilizations are due to race, that in accounting for progress or deterioration one has only to examine the racial composition of the people. Eminent historians have many times protested against this misrepresentation of history. We need only to remember how many factors operated to bring about the change, for instance, from the twelfth to the thirteenth century or from the eighteenth to the nineteenth; change in the racial composition of any country, on the contrary, was negligible. Nevertheless German racist policy today is principally based on this pseudo-historical claim; Germany's enforcement of racial hygiene and its drastic penalties against mixing blood of Aryans and non-Aryans are put forward as measures dictated by history. Politicians and educators in the Third Reich reiterate constantly that pure race is the secret of great civilizations. The answer to this is that no people of high civilization have been racially pure; it is just as true to say that their rise was due to intermixture. The mingling of ethnic types began before the dawn of history and has always accompanied civilization both in periods of great

---

[1] Witty, R. A., and Jenkins, M. D., "The Case of 'B,' a Gifted Negro Girl," *Journal of Social Psychology*, 1935, vol. 6, p. 117.

achievement and in periods of retrogression. A constant factor cannot be the cause either of one or of the other.

A variant of this racist argument from history is that the Caucasian race has been responsible for all progress wherever it has appeared, whether in India, China, Mesopotamia, or Egypt, and that this is not due to exchange of knowledge and the stimulus of mutual intercourse, but to the inevitable operation of hereditary superiority in the Caucasian. More commonly the claim is made for the Nordic subdivision of the White race. Thus Greece and Rome, though they were predominantly non-Nordic, owed their greatness to individuals who, it is maintained, were Nordic.

We have already examined this special pleading. It is not history, and historians have over and over again disavowed it. Modern civilization has been built upon the inventions of a great array of different ethnic groups, and many of the greatest of these inventions were made when the people of Europe were still backward barbarians and the Nordics were still unheard of in the great centers of population. The whole argument ignores historic processes and substitutes for them an unashamed racial megalomania.

This argument is, besides, a contradiction of the "pure" races argument, though the racists commonly put them forward together. If advances in civilization are due to the presence of a handful of Caucasians or Nordics who have leavened the whole loaf, this means inevitably a mixed race, which in this case is adduced by racists as the cause not of decline, but of rise, of civilizations. This difficulty they meet by a travesty of fact. It is said that the reason this leavening had such good effects is that a race manifests in all its history the same innate mental and emotional characteristics. Thus the Teutons (read *Nordics*) have always been loyal to their chosen leaders, they have always been adventurous, they have always been conquerors. Whatever the period of past history, whatever the future may bring, these qualities are innate in the breed *and in no other*.

History has itself answered this argument on a grand scale. From two points of view history refutes this argument. In the first place, the racist who claims for the whole White race innate powers to progress in civilization does not attempt to prove conspicuous achievement for the whole White race. He is always speaking of the sample of the White race or the Nordic race with which he identifies himself. The peasants of Central and Southern Europe are as much a part of the White race as the aristocracy or the urban population, but their ways of procuring a livelihood, their narrow horizons in intellectual and social matters, are to the objective student less "civilized" than those of many Negro and Mongoloid "primitives." The Scotch-English of purest White race who settled in the Tennessee and Kentucky highlands did not by the fact of their race become leaders of civilization; their endless and bloody family feuds, their illiterateness, their preservation of old ballads make them picturesque and appealing to those who know them, but their racial descent did not cause them to advance civilization.

When the claim is made for the Nordic sub-race, the position is equally untenable. A German racist in describing Nordics speaks not of Nordics in Scandinavia, England, France, and America, but of *German* Nordics; a Frenchman speaks of *French* Nordics—or he discounts the claims of Nordic supremacy and says the same things about Gallo-Romans (read *Celts; Alpines; Mediterraneans*). The lesson of history is that under favorable conditions there have been adventurers and conquerors in every race and sub-race; any list of virtues that can be drawn up has had exponents in every race in some period of its history and in some social situations.

History refutes this argument of an inalienable racial soul

in still another way. The racial composition of Europe changes slowly, far too slowly to account by itself for the rapid changes in social behavior which history records. The England of Elizabeth and of Shakespeare changed in one man's lifetime to the England of Cromwell. The England of the Restoration, which is portrayed so vividly in Pepys' *Diary,* gave way, again, in another lifetime, to the England of the eighteenth century. We can trace the causes in political and social conditions, but not in any change of racial composition. It has been the same in Spain, in France, in Germany, and in Italy. Whatever lists of striking achievements or mental and emotional characteristics can be drawn up, no one set of these is automatically perpetuated over time by the "blood" of any people. They change rapidly with a social change from political and economic security to insecurity; they change, we often say, begging the question, with "the atmosphere of the times." But rapid changes in Europe cannot be traced to changes in racial composition.

This is just as true of the non-European world. Racially Japan has been for centuries much more stable than Europe. After centuries of Oriental civilization she has since 1868 adopted Occidental standards with fervor, and has become a great military power after the Western pattern. This right-about-face is in no way due to a change in the racial composition of Japan, though it can be accounted for in detail, as Sydney L. Gulick showed as early as 1903 in his *Evolution of the Japanese,* by taking account of social changes. As he says, if the racists believe that both these periods in Japanese history are due to an unalterable psychic constitution inherent in the race, it is incumbent on them to state what these inalienable characteristics are that overspan these periods. The racists were too precipitate. Le Bon said, in proving the permanent biological character of the Japanese: "A Japanese may easily take a university degree or become a lawyer; the sort of varnish he thus acquires is, however, quite superficial and has no influence on his mental constitution. What no education can give him, because they are created by heredity alone, are the forms of thought, the logic, and above all the character of Western Man." [1] At the present day the usual complaint is that Japan has too successfully taken over the character of the Western Powers. She has not in Le Bon's phrase "shown a mental constitution as unvarying as her anatomical characteristics." To get around this difficulty, Japan's "mental constitution" itself was a decade or so ago often described as fickle and given to a series of fads. This description is not common now that the Japanese are so well launched on their modern career; it is still more strikingly inapplicable to the fifteen hundred years of the old military social order that ended in the middle of the last century. In those centuries the permanence and fixity of Japanese life were greatly in excess of anything of which we have record in Europe. What was called innate fickleness at the turn of this century was evidently a temporary manifestation which accompanied rapid social readjustment. Another favorite description of the innate behavior of the Japanese was that it was ceremonious and at the opposite pole from the purposefully ordered conduct of Occidentals. Sir Edwin Arnold said the Japanese of 1890 had "the nature rather of birds and butterflies than of ordinary human beings"—by which of course he meant Europeans. Now we talk about the Japanese as subordinating themselves to their purposes more abjectly than the superior Europeans. At least the purposes of modern Japan are those the Western World also pursues, and we are therefore able to recognize them.

Historically the right-about-face of Japanese culture from its slow-moving ceremonious ways of life, its high apprecia-

---

[1] Le Bon, Gustave, *The Psychology of Peoples,* London, 1898, p. 37.

tion of aesthetic values, its feudal organization and military caste system—from these to its modern bustle, its dedication to commerce and imperialistic wars—was dramatically explicit and man-made. Japan recognized that the Western foreigners could not always be kept at arm's length by continued policies of exclusion, and she decided on a different course. She determined to learn from them all they had to teach and thus to put herself in a position of equality. Therefore, in 1868 the Emperor in the first year of this new "enlightened" policy—as it is called in Japan—stated in his edict: "The old uncivilized way shall be replaced. . . . The best knowledge shall be sought throughout the world, so as to promote the Imperial welfare." This social change has been carried out with enthusiasm, and can be seen reflected in the manifold developments in Japan up to the present time. These developments have proceeded at an extremely rapid pace in spite of the "Oriental mentality" which had formerly characterized Japan. Yet Japan's race is still Mongoloid as it has always been. She belies Le Bon's pronouncement: "Cross-breeding is the only infallible means at our disposal of transforming in a fundamental manner the character of a people, heredity being the only force powerful enough to contend with heredity."[1]

Swift and radical changes in mental and emotional behavior without an accompanying change of race occur constantly in native cultures when they come into conflict with white civilization. The American Indian of the Great Plains was a proud and undaunted warrior. His resourcefulness and courage, his eloquence, his generosity won the admiration of explorers and traders in the early days. With the expansion of white settlement, the buffalo, his mainstay of life, was slaughtered, and he could no longer procure food. His land was taken from him. The white men, unless at

---

[1] *Ibid.*, p. 83.

the moment they were using him as an ally in war, found it to their advantage to make his feats of bravery offenses punishable by bloody reprisals. His culture collapsed about him like a house of cards. Within a generation his independence and vigorous assertiveness were lost. His "racial soul" availed him nothing. Under the changed conditions he became the lackluster drunkard and beggar the full-bloods are all too often today on our reservations. There were of course honorable exceptions, but these exceptions were also cases of equally radical changes in psychic constitution. The old behavior pattern did not live on either in the morally and psychically broken Indians nor in those who were able under even the most difficult circumstances to adjust themselves to modern conditions.

The most drastic change of this sort is, however, that which took place in a generation or two among the Negroes brought to America as slaves. Most of them had been transported from Nigerian kingdoms with prized cultural achievements. Their elaborate and ceremonious political organization, the pomp of their courts, the activity of their far-flung economic life with its great market centers and tribute collected over great areas, their legal systems with formal trial of the accused, with witnesses and with prosecutors—all these excite the admiration of any student. Belatedly we admire today the incisive folk tales of Nigeria, their rhythmic dances, their wood carving that has excited the respect of modern European artists. But these are today collected in Africa. In America all this achievement was stripped from imported slaves as if they had never had part in it. Their patterns of political, economic, and artistic behavior were forgotten—even the languages they had spoken in Africa. Like the poor whites of the South, they gathered together instead for fervent Christian revivalist camp meetings; they sang the hymns the poor whites sang, and if they sang them better and invented countless variations of great poignancy, nevertheless the old forms which they had achieved in Africa were forgotten. Conditions of slavery in America were so drastic that this loss is not to be wondered at. The slaves on any one plantation had come from tribes speaking mutually unintelligible languages, and with mutually unfamiliar arts of life; they had been herded together like cattle in slave ships and sold at the block in a strange and frightening world. They were worked hard on the plantations. It is no wonder that their owners remarked upon their lack of any cultural achievements; the mistake they made was to interpret the degradation of the slave trade as if it were an innate and all-time characteristic of the African Negro. The Negro race has proud cultural achievements, but for very good reasons they were not spread before our eyes in America.

Radical and rapid changes in mental and emotional behavior, whether we consider them to be in the direction of progress or of deterioration, give the lie to the racists' contention that these patterns are eternal and are biologically perpetuated. They are reversed with reversals in social conditions and demands.

One further contention of superiority is put forward by the racists. It is simple in the extreme. "The Whites are today the most 'civilized'; therefore their 'blood' is superior." This is a non-sequitur of the kind we examined a moment ago, for higher civilization is not a characteristic of *all* Whites but only of certain areas of white civilization. To understand the development of elaborate forms of civilization, we have to turn to historical, not to biological, facts. History cannot be explained so simply. There is no law of the rate of cultural progress—let alone a biological law. The history of all civilizations, whether they are Caucasian or Malay or Mongol, shows periods of great vigor, and also periods of stability and even ossification. Since this is a general phenomenon, it is not necessary to invoke a special innate superiority of the White race to account for the present epoch of great Caucasian vigor. The particular direction white civilization has taken in the past centuries—successful control of the material world—has given it predominance in our times, but we do not know what the future will be. Our civilization has invented many things which white intelligence has not shown the ability to handle for our own obvious interests. Surely this too is a test of intelligence, and one in which Western civilization has not distinguished itself. We may possibly go down in history as a prime example of a great civilization which for want of a little intelligence destroyed itself at great social cost. Claims of innate Caucasian intelligence are only self-congratulation at a moment in history when it is dangerous to be misled by flattering phrases. Nothing biological guarantees to any human group the perpetuation of its triumphs.

There is one final argument for racial superiority which is advanced after all those we have just reviewed are rejected. This argument is that the best Caucasians, however few, are better than any other men; and since they are the leaders and the inventors, the higher destiny of the Caucasian is assured. To support this position Professor Hankins adduces only evidence from brain size and weight and the earlier racial interpretations of the intelligence tests,[1] and for both of these we have already examined the evidence as it is assayed by scientists today. However, the "great man" theory still arises in racial discussion. As Professor Hankins puts it: "The frequency of superior individuals born within

---

[1] Hankins, Frank H., *The Racial Basis of Civilization*, New York, 1926, pp. 308–19; 364–66.

the group is of the greatest significance for the role of that group in cultural evolution." [1]

The "great man" theory of history had a spectacular development in the hands of Carlyle and is now generally held to be either inadequate or naïve. Sociologists do not say today as one did in 1921: "In the long run supremacy will pass in every community, nation, or race to the more intelligent, the more capable, the more ethical." It is a pious wish, and true of some societies. But it depends upon what that society rewards with prestige. Great nations are directed at the present moment by individuals who have none of the qualifications mentioned by the optimistic sociologist of twenty years ago. Even if we grant the sense in which these leaders are indeed "superior individuals"—for at least they maintain themselves in power—we cannot therefore say that they have administered civilization to advantage. In our generation nations and communities have been ravaged by superior force of arms, and cultural progress has been compromised by these same "superior individuals." Race, moreover, has no specific bearing on whether or not a leader will arise who can take the helm and prevent cultural catastrophe. No racial measurements will guarantee that Germany will have an intelligent leader and China an unintelligent one. The course of history is much too complex. We cannot trust our hopes for civilization to the "great man" theory in racial biology.

Why Cultures Differ

Race, therefore, cannot account for all human differences. Nevertheless, the differences between a Frenchman and a German, a Chinese and a European, remain and are apparent to everyone. If race does not explain them, what does?

[1] *Ibid.*, p. 305.

Until we have some clear understanding of the processes which produce such different people, we may still in a pinch fall back on the racial explanation.

The human animal has, in comparison with all other animals, the widest range of potentialities. What he will become depends upon what potentialities his environment calls forth. His inherited traits are not specific, as a bird's are, for building a mud nest or a twig nest; they are extremely plastic. "Instinct" in man can be studied only in the protean forms it has taken as a result of the way a person was brought up as a child and the opportunities he has had as an adult to act in one way and not in another. His inherited tendencies are still present, but they do not operate as they do in birds or ants to lay down inexorably his whole way of life. It is on this fundamental fact that human achievements have all been built, for man's plasticity has proved to be even in the matter of self-defense a greater asset than strength to the lion or size to the elephant. It created the essential situation in which intelligence could be developed.

This plasticity, therefore, should be man's proudest boast. It follows that man reacts to his environment more completely and more quickly than any other creature. In an undeveloped country where he must meet conditions single-handed, he is a pioneer, self-reliant and courageous. In an industrial city he performs one operation, continuously repeated, for eight hours a day (if he can find work, that is). In America his own father may have been the pioneer and he and his brothers, in spite of their inheritance, the machine operators. The machine operator's son may perhaps get an education and become an academic notable, spending his life in the library and the classroom and turning out books on philosophy or sociology. Inherited traits have passed directly from father to son down the generations, but the different traits that were developed in each individual of the family line were due to the environment in which he found himself.

The influence of environment on any one individual, however, is limited by his life-span. "Three-score years and ten" is a short time, and civilizations have sometimes had hundreds of years in which special influences were brought to bear consistently on generation after generation. Whether they have had centuries in which to foster particular ways of living, or only two generations, societies have always been overwhelmingly effective in molding human material in different ways. Man is a highly gregarious animal and he·always wants the approval of his fellows. First, of course, he has to get the means of keeping alive, but after that he will try to get approval in forms which his society recognizes. His society may recognize conquest and he will engage in conquest; it may recognize wealth and he will measure success by dollars and cents; it may recognize caste and he will behave in all things according to the position to which he was born. There are always of course recalcitrant individuals who may perhaps persist in becoming artists when society regards artists as feeble-minded, or tyrants when society will not tolerate tyrants. These recalcitrants are always most numerous in times of upheaval; eventually the great majority in any continuing civilization take the mold which is set by cultural institutions.

Social anthropology is the study of such cultural institutions. Every little tribe awards special approval—some to this achievement, some to that—and the tribal institutions allow men to pursue the favored goal. If this goal is deeds of daring, the individual character fostered in that tribe is hardy and scornful of pain; if the goal is to raise a good crop in one's garden, man is industrious and patient of routine. There is incredible variety in these goals, and most societies honor several different kinds of achievement, usually compatible one with another; whatever the goals are and the social institutions which allow people to pursue them, human behavior is modified in conformity to them.

The social institutions of any one tribe are not inevitable expressions of racial genius, for other tribes of the same race have radically different ones. The rugged individualism of American Indian tribes of the Western plains is a dramatic contrast to the mildness and sobriety of some Pueblo Indians, and both kinds of character are responses to the different ways of arranging social life and the different opportunities for the individual provided by the two cultures. Both groups are racially American Indians. The contrast between the high civilization which Cortez found in Mexico and the culture of tiny wandering groups of root-diggers and seed-gatherers in the great basin between the Sierras of California and Colorado was, again, not based on race. American Indians were responsible for the one as well as for the other. In Mexico social behavior responded to the more complex conditions which had grown up historically in that country.

The social environment in our own cultural background, as well as in the primitive world, has been favorable now to one kind of achievement, now to another. For a brief moment of time in the Age of Pericles, Athens accorded great liberty to the free-born Athenian; it honored intellectual examination of all questions and the creation of art forms both in sculpture and in the drama. We have wondered ever since at the achievements a tiny city—smaller than Denver today—made in only two generations. The moment passed; social conditions changed. No "racial" superiority availed to carry the torch down the generations once Athens had become involved in defending her empire and her wealth. In what we might almost call a fortunate accident men had shown what they might achieve under favorable conditions.

Conditions since the days of Athens have been favorable, now in one place and now in another, for certain achievements. The Renaissance in Italy was favorable for the development of art, and no one who has read the *Autobiography* of Benvenuto Cellini will wonder at the great efflorescence of art in those days. Cellini may have exaggerated the court paid to him as an artist by princes, but we know that the picture is essentially true to the times. Many kinds of intellectual activity, however, were definitely discouraged, as we know from the notebooks and life of Leonardo da Vinci. What opposition intellectual achievement of the wrong sort could arouse in high quarters, if it was pursued, has been made famous in the story of the trial of Galileo by the Inquisition.

In modern times there have also been now and again periods of great freedom and well-being, directed, however, not so much toward the intellectual life the Greeks rated so highly or the artistic creation the Florentines honored, as toward the conquest of the material world and the acquisition of wealth. In these fields we have achieved the great and characteristic successes of modern times, and the personality type which can best succeed in this endeavor has become increasingly prevalent, with various modifications, in nation after nation. The attainments that are honored and the opportunities of reaching goals differ in the various nations and still more in different classes in each nation, and these differences we sum up in catch-phrases of "what the Irish are like" or "what the Italians are like," "what peasants are like" or "what bankers are like." All these characterizations are crude sketches of these groups as they are shaped by immediate conditions and have no valid pretensions as descriptions of innate characteristics which would persist under different conditions.

The racists have claimed superiority for this race or for

that. But superiority has never been perpetuated in any community by mere germ plasm. Wherever we look in the past history of Western civilization, we find that favored groups have achieved brief, brilliant success when they were assured economic sufficiency and freedom and opportunity in certain directions. When these favorable conditions no longer existed, the torch soon fell from their hands. In the past the social conditions which have favored achievement, now here, now there, have been limited to a certain class, like the free-born citizens of Athens, usually reckoned as one-seventh of the population, or the court and its satellites in England under Elizabeth. With growing literacy and extension of voting privileges and the spread of common ideas up and down the whole scale of the population in modern nations, this selective restriction of social opportunities no longer works so satisfactorily as it did in earlier times. In America we have systematically destroyed the serf mentality which looked upon overlords as a world apart and regarded the poverty and dependence of underlings as part of the ways of God. In Europe, Asia, and Africa, people are demanding greater opportunities more equitably distributed. Those in power are faced with two alternatives: they must keep down the rank and file by the use of naked force, or they must see to it that the major goods of life are available to a much greater proportion of the population than in earlier European history. We are far from having made economic sufficiency general in America, and essential liberties—opportunity to work, freedom of opinion on moot points, and equality of civil liberties—are far from won. They are, however, not unattainable if we will bend our efforts to achieve them, and we have a much clearer idea than we had a decade ago of the measures that would have to be taken. If we are serious in our hopes for the human race, we will devote ourselves to providing those social conditions under which they can be realized and we shall not blindly trust the racists' flattery that the highest attainments will always be ours however we muddle through in our social life.

WHAT THEY SAY

Of all vulgar modes of escaping from the consideration of the effect of social and moral influences on the human mind, the most vulgar is that of attributing the diversities of conduct and character to inherent natural differences.

> John Stuart Mill, *Principles of Political Economy*. New York, Colonial Press, Vol. I, 1899, p. 390.

"Race" is the cheap explanation tyros offer for any collective trait that they are too stupid or too lazy to trace to its origin in the physical environment, the social environment, or historical conditions.

> E. A. Ross, *Social Psychology*. New York, Macmillan Co., 1915, p. 3.

Heredity may explain a part of the pronounced mental similarities between parents and children; but this explanation cannot be transferred to explain on hereditary grounds the similarity of behavior of entire nations in which the most varied lines occur. These assume their characteristic forms under the pressure of society.

> Franz Boas, *Aryans and Non-Aryans*. New York, Information and Service Associates, 1934, p. 11.

[Cultural differences exist and have been emphasized in this volume] but they are only passing products of the milieu. Having come about as the result of external circumstances, they disappear in the same way.

> Jean Finot, *Race Prejudice*. Translated by Florence Wade-Evans. London, Archibald Constable & Co., Ltd., 1906, p. 317.

We have seen in detail that every characteristically Japanese moral trait is due to the nature of her past social order, and is changing with that order. Racial moral traits, therefore, are not due to inherent nature, to essential character, to brain structure, nor are they transmitted from father to son by the mere fact of physical generation. On the contrary, the distinguishing ethical characteristics of races . . . are determined by the dominant social order, and vary with it.

> Sydney L. Gulick, *The Evolution of the Japanese*. New York, F. H. Revell, 1903, p. 285.

Men indeed differ in learning but are equal in the capacity for learning; there is no race which under the guidance of reason cannot attain to virtue. Cicero, first century B.C.

If we were to select the most intelligent, imaginative, energetic and emotionally stable third of mankind, all races would be represented.

> Franz Boas, *Anthropology and Modern Life*. Revised Edition. New York, W. W. Norton & Co., 1932, p. 79.

PART TWO. *Racism*

VII. A NATURAL HISTORY OF RACISM

RACE IS A SUBJECT which can be investigated by genealogical charts, by anthropomorphic measurements, by studies of the same zoological group under different conditions, and by reviews of world history. It can be investigated from the point of view of anthropometrists, genealogical experts, geneticists, and historians. In other words, it is a scientific field of inquiry and its special problem is that of genetic relationships of human groups. It ranks as an important field in any study of human civilizations and concerns itself with important facts about the history of the world. It tells us, for instance, from the skulls and bones of living races, about migrations of prehistoric peoples over two continents. It is the evidence upon which we base our knowledge of many facts of history. It tells us, as we have seen, that the Manchu rulers of China were by blood a rude Paleoasiatic tribe—a racial family with members who remained primitive herdsmen—and that the strain of the Hamites, so prominent in dynastic Egypt, is also represented by modern primitive tribes like the Galla and Somali.

Race is not "the modern superstition" as some amateur

egalitarians have said. It is a fact. The study of it has already told culture-historians much, and further investigations, for which as yet science has not the necessary basic knowledge or tests, may even show that some ethnic groups have identifiable emotional or intellectual peculiarities which are biological and not merely learned behavior. For example, certain ethnic groups show different *averages* in measurements of some hereditary glandular condition or metabolic peculiarity although each group contains many individuals who fall within a range common to all groups. History, however, has already shown, in instance after instance, that any such specializations, if they occur, leave such groups within a "margin of safety" sufficient so that any race, when opportunity has offered, has adjusted itself to the most contrasting cultures and participated in them.

Race, then, is not the modern superstition. But racism is. Racism is the dogma that one ethnic group is condemned by Nature to hereditary inferiority and another group is destined to hereditary superiority. It is the dogma that the hope of civilization depends upon eliminating some races and keeping others pure. It is the dogma that one race has carried progress with it throughout human history and can alone ensure future progress. It is a dogma rampant in the world today and which a few years ago was made into a principal basis of German polity.

Racism is not, like race, a subject the content of which can be scientifically investigated. It is, like a religion, a belief which can be studied only historically. Like any belief which goes beyond scientific knowledge, it can be judged only by its fruits and by its votaries and its ulterior purposes. Of course, when it makes use of facts, racist interpretation can be checked against those facts, and the interpretation can be shown to be justified or unjustified on the basis of history and of scientific knowledge such as we have reviewed in previous chapters. But the literature of racism is extraordinarily inept and contradictory in its use of facts. Any scientist can disprove all its facts and still leave the *belief* untouched. Racism, therefore, like any dogma that cannot be scientifically demonstrated, must be studied historically. We must investigate the conditions under which it arises and the uses to which it has been put.

Racism is essentially a pretentious way of saying that "I" belong to the Best People. For such a conviction it is the most gratifying formula that has ever been discovered, for neither my own unworthiness nor the accusations of others can ever dislodge me from my position—a position which was determined in the womb of my mother at conception. It avoids all embarrassing questions about my conduct of life and nullifies all embarrassing claims by "inferior" groups about their own achievements and ethical standards.

It has also the advantage of great simplicity. It avoids any of the actual complexities of human nature and of human history and sets up a five-word proposition which the most uneducated can remember and glory in: "I belong to the Elect." For political purposes the racist formula has no rival.

This formula in its modern guise would have been impossible before the days of Darwin and of anthropomorphic measurements. It appeals to evolution and to anthropometry. It claims that the Elect to whom I racially belong are *biologically* destined to lead human destiny and that in destroying others they achieve the survival of the fittest. These Elect, moreover, can be identified by measurements of the body. These refinements could not have arisen in the world before the nineteenth century. Nevertheless the natural history of racism did not begin with this elaborated dogma.

Prehistory of Racism

The formula "I belong to the Elect" has a far longer history than has modern racism. These are fighting words among the simplest naked savages. Among them this formula is an integral part of their whole life experience, which is, from our point of view, incredibly limited. They may place the Creation of Man in the days of their father's great-grand-father; they may bound the world by a sea ten miles to the west and a range of hills twenty miles to the east. Whatever was outside of this tiny territory, before the restless white people came, was as alien to them as the surface of Mars; they did not dream of man's long history on the earth. Their own little group, in this tiny corner of the world, lived and worked together, and in most tribes what benefited one bene-fited all; and their name in their own language for this tiny tribe was grandiloquently "The Human Beings," "Men." The designation applied only to their tiny group. Other peoples, the not-human, were fair game; they might be hunted like animals. They were not people with whom my own tribe had common cause, God did not create them of the same clay, or they did not spring out of the same water jar, or they did not come up through the same hole in the ground. But my own little group was under the special provi-dence of God; he gave it the middle place in the "world" and he foretold that if ever it was wiped out, the world would perish. To my tribe alone he gave the ceremonies which pre-serve the world.

Such a world-view in a small primitive tribe is not incon-sistent with its experience. The tribe asks nothing from any other group; it supports itself adequately in isolation, and anything it can take from other people is clear gain. Even where primitive tribes include many thousands of people and occupy large territories, the picture usually does not differ essentially; the "in-group"—the tribal unit within which benefits are shared and activities carried out in common and where I behave with a certain ethical restraint toward my neighbors—this in-group knows its own worth and claims unique importance.

Such a primitive in-group is not a race, not even a small local sub-race or breed. The smallest racial unit is usually split up into many mutually death-dealing in-groups. Their antagonism is not racial but cultural. They do not keep their "blood" separate; each tribe may have made a practice of raiding for women in the other group, and their ancestry therefore may be traceable to the despised group almost in the same proportion as to their own vaunted one. Or recurrent peacemaking between them may be signalized by intermarriage, or marriages may be consummated for economic and social advantages. These practices occur whether neighboring tribes are of one breed, or whether they belonged at some period to two which can be distinguished by different anthropomorphic measurements. The duty to keep the "blood" unmixed is a refinement based on so-called science.

This primitive in-group, dealing death to outsiders and furnishing mutual support to insiders, yet often taking wives from its enemies, easily became, even in many primitive regions of the world, an overlord tribe taking tribute or consolidating a larger empire. Even the conquests of Alexander the Great were fundamentally like those among many primitive African tribes. Aristotle was Alexander's mentor and he wrote out in his *Politics* (Chapter VII) the reasons why the fair-skinned barbarians and the Asiatic peoples could never rise to the level of the Greeks. His argument was the same as that of a Zulu of South Africa talking about the Bathonga: Was it not obvious that the foreigners' cultural attainments were inferior? Because he was not making a racist argument there was no reason why he should consider the attainments of Hellenized Asiatics; they were not pertinent to his argument because their attainments were high. Nor did he argue that Greek blood must be kept pure. His pupil Alexander, in the course of his conquests, advocated intermarriage, and ten thousand of his soldiers took wives from the natives of India. Alexander himself married two Persian princesses.

Aristotle's attitude was characteristic of Europe in ancient times, and the Roman Empire therefore did not have to free itself of racist doctrines in the building of its great cosmopolitan state. As Roman objectives became clearer and imperial edicts embodied these in law, the privileges of the capital city were more and more extended to the provinces. The Roman Empire was in many ways a new invention in human history, extending old in-group advantages over a great part of its enormous territory. Restrictions on trade and intercourse, which had earlier crippled each little separate district, were removed and large customs districts established, on the borders of which duties were levied for revenue only; and Rome reaped both prestige and profit from the rapid and progressive Latinization of its empire. An essential part of its administration was its consistent use of provincials in high office, where they were advanced according to ability. Provincials rose to high rank as soldiers, statesmen, and men of letters. The Roman legions were increasingly recruited from the provinces. From the first the highly prized prerogatives of Roman citizenship were extended to responsible persons of alien races. Paul's famous boast, made in the early years of the Empire, has brought this home to all readers of the New Testament: "But I am free [Roman] born"—that is, his father or his grandfather, Jews of the distant city of Tarsus, had been awarded Roman citizenship for their services or had bought it, like Paul's guard, "with a great price." Eventually the Roman franchise was extended to all inhabitants of the Empire who had not been born in slavery.

This lack of discrimination against aliens was not the result of specific ethical teaching, but of social forces which Roman administrative genius was able to use to its profit. It was a tolerance which was compatible with imperialism as it was practiced until very recent times. The principal objective of early imperialism was to secure tribute and to bind the subjugated areas to the capital, not, as in later forms, to exploit a new labor market in working mines or plantations. Therefore it was economical to honor the most able of the conquered peoples and depute authority to them. In regard to the folkways and cultural life of the provinces, Roman policy was one of *laissez faire*.

This attitude of the Roman Empire toward outsiders was historically an important step in widening the circle within which certain in-group prerogatives could be shared. An imperial peace was imposed over great areas of the world, and a civil administration that looked to a common authority. Such social innovations had their repercussions in lessening the grandiose claims of each little local group, and in breaking down the earlier barriers.

The Christian religion arose and spread in the same world that gave rise to the Roman Empire. Jesus taught the brotherhood of man. In Palestine in his day the alien was the hated Samaritan, and when the Samaritan woman said to him: "How is it that thou, being a Jew, askest drink of me which am a woman of Samaria? For the Jews have no dealings with the Samaritans" (John 4:9), he preached his gospel to her and her townsfolk and "many of them believed." His disciples were horrified, but at the end of his ministry they too believed that they were "to go into all the world and preach the gospel," and Paul, the most effective of these followers, taught that "there is neither Jew nor Greek, there is neither bond nor free, there is neither male nor female, but all are one in Christ Jesus" (Galatians 3:28).

Such a program and such a teaching were congruent with secular attitudes of the first-century Roman Empire as they had not been, for instance, in the times of Zoroaster, some thousand years earlier in Persia. Zoroaster had established a national cult that did not look beyond Persia; it was non-proselyting, like a primitive religion. Confucius, too, in China in the era of rival overlords, left among his followers no idea of extending his teachings among all races of the world. The program of Christianity, in its early growth, had behind it the secular idea of a larger community of all peoples such as the Roman Empire had been able to create.

The Hebrew law and the prophets also contributed to the foundations of Jesus's teaching. The ancient Mosaic Law lays down gracious rules: "The stranger that dwelleth with you shall be unto you as one born among you, and thou shalt love him as thyself; for ye were strangers in the land of Egypt: I am the Lord your God" (Leviticus 19:34). "One ordinance shall be both for you of the congregation and also for the stranger that so joineth with you, an ordinance forever in your generations: as ye are, so shall the stranger be before the Lord" (Numbers 15:15).

After the Assyrian captivity, however, an opposition party arose which advocated separatism. The prophet Ezra preached the abomination of mixing the seed of Israel with the seed of the Ammonite and the Moabite, and all wives and children of foreigners were deported and all future mixed marriages brought under a strong ban. Fanatical racism therefore occurred in Israel long before the days of modern racism, but no trace of it is to be found in the words of Christ. His teachings of a great community of peoples without regard to race agreed with the older Hebraic law, and were given a solid basis, also, by the achievements of the Roman Empire.

The Church of Rome, after Christianity became the state

religion, inherited both from imperial tradition and from the teachings of Christ and his followers this belief in the brotherhood of man without regard to race, and acted upon it in its long overlordship of many diverse nations and peoples in the Middle Ages. Even today, in a world given over to racism, the Papacy follows its long and honorable precedent and opposes race prejudice in its pronouncements.

The social order in Europe changed radically in the thirteenth century. That century marks the decay of feudalism and the beginning of the decline of the secular power of the Papacy. In long-range perspective, when that century ended it carried with it the great institutions of medieval times and was succeeded by those which led up to the modern age.

Feudalism in the early Middle Ages had bound together for certain mutual advantages all the ranks of society from the highest to the lowest and placed upon all of them mutual obligations of loyalty, protection, and service. This condition was gradually altered; with the collapse of feudalism serfs were no longer "tied to the land," and were therefore no longer the responsibility of their feudal lords. The security they had had was one which gave them pitifully little of this world's goods, but it offered at least a defense against utter destitution. Like their lord's horses they had been worth their stabling; they could look to their overlord for a roof and something to eat. Their new freedom was not much more than the freedom to starve, and strife between the classes became bitter and disastrous.

From the first beginnings of the modern age those who held power in their hands had opportunity for aggrandizement on a greater and greater scale. On the Continent local groups, when they were at least potentially equal, bled each other in a long series of mutual reprisals; when they conquered and could incorporate the new territory under their own authority, these larger units matched themselves again

with enemies of equal pretensions. The warrings camps therefore grew from small local grand duchies to unified nations.
Their one consistent policy has been to do to the other what
the other would do to them and to do it first. We are still in
this era of international anarchy, though the warring groups
have grown until they are in our century almost worldwide.
Wars have been, and still are, disastrous just in proportion
as the commercial and social interests of the warring camps
have become actually more interdependent. This modern
period from the thirteenth century to the present has been a
struggle between warring camps in a civilization which, even
as early as the period of the Roman Empire, had been administered as one, and as late as the Middle Ages had looked
to one Universal Church which exercised both secular and
religious authority. In the modern world the animosities and
punitive policies of each group have become not only life-and-
death threats to its neighbors, but suicidal to itself. In such a
world doctrines of the brotherhood of man have lost what
basis in experience they had had in earlier times.

The modern world, from its earliest days, therefore, has
been an uncongenial home for the doctrine that God had
made of one clay all the peoples of the earth. The warring
and competing groups into which this world had for the
time being resolved itself, whether they were nations or
classes, had little experience on which to base a belief in the
brotherhood of man; they needed instead a doctrine which
taught that in the struggle of rival interests which was the
rule of the day, their favored group was made of special clay.

Racism and European Expansion Overseas

An occurrence, unprecedented in history, contributed to
this separatism at the very beginning of modern times: the

discovery of the New World and the exploitation and settlement of hitherto unknown islands and continents that followed. All Europe was excited by the discovery of so populous a world inhabited by so many different races. The excitement often took romantic forms in the stay-at-homes safe in the capitals of Europe who read with delight fanciful tales of the noble red man like Saint Pierre's *Paul et Virginie* and Chateaubriand's *Les Natchez*. Chateaubriand, it is admitted today, had never himself lived among the Indians; he had therefore not been imbued with frontier attitudes toward the savage. For, however stay-at-homes glorified "natives," frontiersmen and plantation owners and slave traders knew their place. Europeans overseas were waging an implacable war of extermination and subjugation. There were differences in the attitudes that settlers of different nations took toward the alien natives, and the Spanish and Portuguese and Dutch did not share the horror of miscegenation the English had, nor did the French institute the iron-clad caste distinctions the English did. Frontiersmen of whatever nation, nevertheless, were out to gain their ends by whatever means, and none of them dealt with natives according to the cultural *laissez faire* of the Roman Empire.

In tropical countries Europeans wanted cheap labor and markets and slaves; in temperate countries they wanted the land to occupy as settlers. Wherever they went, Europeans were bent on extirpating the native religions. The natives were regarded as outside the pale of humanity, without religion, law, or morals. Bounties were placed on their heads, and they could be freely kidnaped or massacred. They had no redress but to strike back and so to bring upon themselves merciless reprisals. Even these presently became impossible, and the native remnants were herded onto reserves or became hopeless slaves in the mines or on the plantations.

Those natives were alone fortunate who lived in countries that could not readily be exploited by Europe's traders or settled by her colonists.

The dogma of racial superiority and inferiority, however, even under these drastic conditions, did not arise for more than three centuries. Natives were outside the pale of humanity, but this was regarded as a consequence of the fact that they were not Christians, not of the fact that they belonged to the darker races. Religious persecution was the old familiar idea of the Middle Ages which had always been invoked against heretics and against Jews; racism had not yet appeared on the horizon. Like the Moslem today, the early European settlers divided mankind into the conquering "believer" and the victim "unbeliever." Even the slave trade was originally justified on the grounds that the victims were lost souls and heathen. Of Prince Henry the Navigator it is said that "in pursuit of his crusading purpose he did not hesitate to sacrifice himself, and his zeal for religion led him to rejoice when a company of adventurers brought back cargoes of natives because of the salvation of those souls that before were lost." [1]

The "unbeliever" theory of native inferiority involved the Whites in many contradictions. In the early days the mere act of discovering a new part of the world was held to give that territory and its inhabitants to the European nation financing the expedition, but the duty of converting the natives to Christianity was a condition of this legal title. Missionaries, often devoted and courageous, therefore accompanied every ship, especially those from the Catholic countries; and for the native who professed the faith, the chasm that separated the white Christian from the colored heathen was theoretically bridged. This meant specifically that he

[1] Quoted in I. D. MacCrone, *Race Attitudes in South Africa*, London, 1937, p. 7.

could not be held in slavery, for the idea of a Christian slave was abhorrent in those times. Henry the Navigator's long crusade against the Moors was waged to free their Christian slaves—to wipe out such an insult to Christendom.

The activities of missionaries, therefore, hampered the activities of exploiters and slave traders; and particularly in those countries overseas which were dominated by the Protestant nations of Europe, the practice of freeing slaves who professed Christianity gradually died out. In South Africa the Dutch, in order to avoid any question of emancipation, ruled that children born in slavery were neither to be baptized nor to be given religious instruction. It was not till 1792 that the Church Council of Capetown went on record with the statement that neither the law of the land nor the law of the Church ruled that Christian Negroes had to be freed; it added that in Capetown many slaves were Christian. By the beginning of the nineteenth century in South Africa, therefore, the old theory of a division of the human race into believers and unbelievers no longer corresponded to the facts, and the same dilemma was arising in other parts of the world. Sometimes, as in South Africa, it arose in relation to slavery; and sometimes, as we read in old protests of Jesuit and Franciscan missionaries in the New World, in relation to massacres of Indian converts. The time was ripe for a new theory of superiority and inferiority, and people began to talk of natives as sub-human, as related to apes rather than to civilized man. After all, color was the most conspicuous difference, and it set off the opposing parties on the frontier as religion often no longer did. But the shift from one basis for the white man's superiority to the other was gradual and was not formulated. It was an inevitable response to social conditions and was practical rather than intellectualized. The situation on the frontier was a rough-and-ready one in which settlers and administrators acted according to the needs of the moment and did not generalize their difficulties into racist dogmas. They did not trouble themselves about cosmic justifications; it was quite enough for them that the natives were in the long run helpless before them.

In those overseas countries colonized by England the division into "believers" and "unbelievers" had, from the earliest times, a much less important place than it had in countries held by the nations of continental Europe. The English took from the first a highly secular attitude toward natives; in their administration the establishment of missions was not a regular part of claims to the territory, and if missions were established and natives converted, the difference between Christianized and non-Christianized natives was not official important. The English dealt with natives as with a low, though sometimes useful, caste. They practiced a rigid separatism. Whereas in the French, the Spanish, and the Portuguese colonies marriage with native women was common and a mixed population sprang up, in English colonies intermarriage was the great exception and there was strong feeling against it. In the colonization of that territory which is now the United States, therefore, the English frontiersman made a *racial* distinction; it was not phrased as such, however, because the fundamental conflict was a fight for land. The Englishman wanted the territories of the Indian, and he wanted them free of Indians. The early royal grants of land in the New World had made no mention of the natives already living there; they read as if no human being occupied the territories. The dearest wish of the settlers was to achieve this happy condition as soon as possible. They did not use the Indians in agricultural labor or in opening up the country as the Spanish did in Mexico; according to their scheme of things even that kind of contact with natives was too close.

Their one use of natives was as fighting allies against the French. In this they were singularly successful; their success in enlisting the Iroquois on their side against the French has often been declared decisive in preventing French expansion south of the St. Lawrence. When the wars were won, however, the aid they had rendered the English profited the Iroquois nothing. Again during the Revolution and especially during the War of 1812, Indian tribes fought alongside their white allies. But the gulf was not to be bridged by such alliances. Those who fought on the side of the colonists and those who fought on the side of the British were equally stripped of their lands and herded onto reservations. In comparison with India and Africa, North America was very sparsely populated; and the English therefore could attain their prime object of separatism in a more drastic way than in the former countries where it had to be secured by caste distinctions. In America it was achieved by extermination and segregation. The conflict with the Indians remained a conflict for land and a series of reprisals; it was not ideological—not thought of, that is, as a "holy war" against a "tide of color," nor were the Indians regarded as "the Mongol in our midst."

European expansion overseas, therefore, set the stage for racist dogmas and gave violent early expression to racial antipathies without propounding racism as a philosophy. Racism did not get its currency in modern thought until it was applied to conflicts within Europe—first to class conflicts and then to national. But it is possible to wonder whether the doctrine would have been proposed at all as explaining these latter conflicts—where, as we have seen, the dogma is so inept—if the basis for it had not been laid in the violent experience of racial prejudice on the frontier.

Racism and Class Conflicts

Racism was first formulated in conflicts between classes. It was directed by the aristocrats against the populace. The first statement of the doctrine in modern Europe was directed against the monarchy also, since in France in 1727 the nobles felt themselves as much imposed upon by the king and his ministers as they were exasperated by the growing demands of the people. The Count de Boulainvilliers was a Norman with an extravagant admiration for the feudal system (already giving way to modern nationalism) and for the aristocrats who had been the feudal lords. He devoted himself to proving the pretensions of his family to membership in this ancient nobility. The feudal taxes that had been levied by the Crown, the arrogant authority of Louis XIV, roused in Boulainvilliers the dream that the nobles of his day would assert themselves against the State—*L'Etat, c'est moi,* Louis XIV had said—and re-establish their old glory. The wish was not new. In England under different circumstances it had led to the Magna Charta. But Boulainvilliers' procedure was quite different. He invoked racism. The nobles were the blood of the *Germani,* the Teutonic barbarians who had overrun the Roman Empire and had been enthusiastically described by the disaffected Roman moralist Tacitus about A.D. 100. Tacitus, disgusted by what he considered the degeneracy of Rome—he wrote in the reign of Trajan—extolled the hardihood and fierceness of the barbarians and their "leadership principle": "Their generals control them by example rather than by authority. If they are daring and adventurous and conspicuous in action, they procure obedience from the admiration that they inspire." This aristocratic freedom of the Teutonic tribes of the first century was, according to Boulainvilliers' argument, the racial heritage of the "Frankish" nobles of the eighteenth century, and their blood demanded that they re-establish the aristocratic leadership that was theirs by blood. They must end the absolute monarchy which stemmed from the Roman idea of empire. The populace, on the other hand, was of different clay; they were by race the old conquered Gallo-Romans (read *Celts; Alpines; Mediterraneans*). They were racially destined to inferior status just as the nobles were to superior status.

The nobility, however, in spite of the Count's racist argument, did not prove to have been eternally destined to hold their ancient rank, and by the time of the French Revolution in 1791 the "two Frances" into which Boulainvilliers had divided the population had shifted their relative positions. By that time spokesmen of the populace could call the tune on the other side. The Abbé Sieyès, for example, accepted the claims of the nobles that they racially inherited the fruits of the Frankish conquest. "Very well, we, the Gallo-Roman plebs, will now conquer the nobility by expelling and abolishing them. Our rights will supersede theirs on exactly the principle they invoke." He was right; a less pretentious statement of the fundamental racist dogmas is that nothing succeeds like success.

Racism, however, had no mass triumph in the days of the French Revolution. The great classic racist pronouncement was published in 1853–1857: Count de Gobineau's *Essay on the Inequality of Human Races*. Like Boulainvilliers, he taught that the hope of the world was and had always been the fair-haired Teutons, whom, according to the current fashion, he now called Aryan (today, read *Nordic*). But it was not a nationalist gospel he proclaimed. Gobineau, like Boulainvilliers, was French and he was disgusted with political developments in France. He dedicated his two-volume essay to George V of Hanover, the blind German king who had just swept away the liberal constitution the people had compelled his father to grant, but Gobineau had no more faith in Germany's racial superiority than in that of France. Neither in France nor in Germany—nor in Scandinavia, when he visted Sweden—were there more than a handful of pure Aryans left. All European countries alike were swamped by the Gallo-Romans (today, read *Celt; Alpine; Mediterranean*). No European nation had enough racial aristocrats to base upon them any *national* claims to precedence. The Count de Gobineau wrote not as a modern nationalist, but, again like Boulainvilliers, as a conservative aristocrat. He was angered and disturbed by conditions which had just led up to the revolution of 1848. He had himself in that year been one of the founders of a *revue* to work for the establishment of a republic led by aristocrats. There was widespread unemployment and great distress. Action was necessary. The socialist leaders succeeded in getting the principle of "the right to work" accepted, and a sort of WPA was established under the government. These were called "national workshops," and they encountered the familiar trouble of our days; remunerative work could not be provided for all the unemployed and doles had to be substituted. Even these inadequate doles kept alive a horde of malcontents dangerous to the government, and the whole arrangement was suddenly revoked. What followed were the massacres of June—another struggle between the "haves" and the "have-nots" at the barricades in the streets of Paris.

It is the more necessary to root Gobineau's essay in its historical background because he was not a closet student nor an academician. He was a man of the world whose stakes were in public life. He was during his lifetime Cabinet Secretary, Minister to Persia, and his government's representative on missions to Brazil and many European capitals. He was a writer of novels, plays, and travel books. He was caught up in a world in which the unwashed mob were in despair and were demanding some means to live. It could not be denied them on the basis of Rousseau's Social Contract or even of Hobbes's idea of the State; it could be denied them, however, on the basis of hereditary inferiority, that is, on the basis of race. As he himself wrote, his object was to fight well against the growing demands of the underprivileged; he wanted to "do better than De Maistre and De Bonald against liberalism." [1]

Therefore, dedicating his volume to George V of Hanover, who had just had a similar conflict on his hands, he wrote: "Gradually I have become convinced that race overshadows all other problems in history, that it holds the key to them all, and that the inequality of people from whose fusion a people is formed is enough to explain the whole course of its destiny. I convinced myself at last that everything great, noble, and fruitful in the works of man on this earth, in science, art and civilization, derives from a single starting point; it belongs to one family alone, the different branches of which have reigned in all the civilized countries of the universe." These aristocrats, who had reigned in all countries, were now threatened by the degeneracy of democracy and by claims of equality. When he divided the races of the world into White, Yellow, and Black, his application of the matter was that the Alpines were of Yellow extraction and the Mediterraneans of Black extraction; his Whites were represented, therefore, in Europe only by the group which is today called Nordic. They were the only ones on whom the hope of civilization could be pinned. They alone had "reflective energy," "perseverance," "instinct for order," "love of liberty," "honor." The loss of their position in Europe meant the twilight of civilization.

This gospel of Gobineau's has been distorted by his twentieth-century followers into a gospel of nationalism,

---

[1] Letter to Probusch—Osten, June 10, 1856, quoted in Barzun, Jacques, *Race, A Study in Modern Superstition*, New York, 1937, p. 93, n. 5.

and Germany today reads "modern Germans" wherever
Gobineau wrote "Aryans"—this in spite of his insistence that
his Aryans were no more common in Germany than elsewhere. His argument has been misread also by modern crit-
ics, who all read nationalism into his racial doctrines. They
therefore point out absurdities and contradictions which
stem from their own misunderstanding rather than from
Gobineau's position. They make much of the fact that he
insists over and over again that no civilization has been the
work of a pure race, and nevertheless concludes that societies
perish only because they have lost their pure and uncon-
taminated blood. This would have been a contradiction had
he been writing a nationalist manifesto, but Gobineau was
defending the role of the aristocratic remnant endangered
by a bastard proletariat. His whole volume is an attempt to
prove that civilizations rise and fall along with the fortunes
of the conquering aristocracy, an aristocracy which is defined
by birth. When the aristocracy is lost in the surrounding mob,
the country is doomed.

Gobineau, therefore, accepts as the very basis of his racist
doctrines the fact that civilizations are all built on a mixture
of races. His Aryan race was a race of rulers, and "every
founder of a civilization would wish the backbone of his
society, his middle class, to consist of Yellow races." (Alpines,
numerically predominant in France, he had defined as of
Yellow extraction.) "It would be unjust," he says, "to say
that every mixture is bad and harmful"; in fact, "from the
point of view of beauty" the finest racial blend "is the offspring of the White and Black." (Gobineau had described
Mediterraneans as Black. A Frenchman could talk of miscegenation between Black and White; an Anglo-Saxon
would hesitate to do so.)

The fact that all nations are a composite of races means to
Gobineau that they are stratified into classes and that their

glory depends upon only one of these classes. He never preached the doctrine of pure race as the basis of any civilization; "Aryans had ceased to be pure as early as the birth of Christ." Nevertheless, his whole argument depended, consistently enough from his point of view, upon the fixity of racial type—in the individual, not in the nation. It was the "nobility of our species" (the Aryans) which was indestructible and which had been transferred intact down the ages by heredity; their racial type had not been affected by climate, country, or lapse of time. Upon this depended the unbridgeable chasm between the aristocrat and the populace, the importance in world history of the one and the negligibility of the other. He wrote to make the artistocratic "Aryan" remnant conscious of its "mission" in the high purposes of civilization and to convince the non-Aryans that their sole duty was to respect this "mission."

Only as individuals could Gobineau hope to identify his "Aryan" supermen, individuals here and there who still held in their hands, by racial destiny, the hope of the world. But he knew that he himself belonged to this Elect. His *Essay on Human Inequality* was "written only to serve as preface" for his researches in his own family tree, researches which he published in 1879 as *The History of Ottar Jarl, Norwegian Pirate, Conqueror of Bray in Normandy, and of His Descendants*. It was a genealogy perhaps as well-authenticated as most genealogies which go back to the Vikings, and it was a labor of love which freed him of his own prosperous bourgeois father and established him as one of his "race of princes." It was the racial ancestry of the chosen few in which he believed, not the pure ancestry of a nation.

Gobineau's *Essay* is still the classic document of racism, and its argument is so universally read today as nationalistic propaganda that its place in history is misunderstood. Gobineau was neither pro-French nor pro-German—in spite of the vol-

umes his followers have written claiming the one or the other
—he was pro-aristocracy. He hated patriotism, which he
scorned as a Latin provincialism unworthy of his Elect. He
wrote that nationalism had been the chief cause of French
defeat in the War of 1870. He was, during his later years, un-
waveringly anti-government, and for this reason French racialists today borrow from his arguments without acknowl-
edging the source; they do not like the bitterness with which
he described the conduct of France in the War of 1870. Gobineau's message was that of the incomparable worth of the
patricians and their culture, and his eyes were fastened on
a lost golden age when their worth had not been contested.
He had the aristocrat's contempt for commerce—which was
due to the "poison of racial intermixture"—and for the tech-
nological inventions of modern civilization; printing, steam
power, and industrial discoveries, he wrote, were mere matters of routine which "Aryans" would not have concerned
themselves with. He left them to the mob.

Gobineau wrote in the early 1850's, when anthropomorphic
measurements were few and uncritical and before Darwin
had published the *Origin of Species*. He could not foresee the
distribution of racial traits as they are known today and he
could not foresee the laws of genetics. After Darwin the "survival of the fittest" was added to racist pronouncements, but
Gobineau had pictured his Aryans rather as fine flowers of
mankind and had often endowed them with the more fragile
virtues.

His successors have developed his doctrines, therefore,
along two lines: first, the interpretation of anthropometric
measurements, and, second, the "survival of the fittest." Because of this latter borrowing from Darwinism, racist theories
after Gobineau gave more and more weight to the sacredness
of conquest and of force. Conquerors—who might be pictured either as a privileged nobility or as a nation embracing

all classes—had succeeded because they were by nature the fittest; a "scientific" reason had been discovered which sanctified the old axiom that might makes right.

Another development of racism, that based on anthropometric measurements, was pushed vigorously in France during the latter half of the nineteenth century. Broca, Lapouge, and Ammon in Germany are the names that stand out in the energetic school that called itself anthropo-sociology. In contrast to the romantic Gobineau, they were prodigious collectors of measurements, avid statistical students, and they sought to find the answers to specific rather than to cosmic problems. Nevertheless, they were truly of the Boulainvilliers-Gobineau school of racists in that they too did not make nationalistic application of their material; they were concerned with class differences. They investigated the "two Frances" and the "two Germanies," the narrow-headed Nordics and the broad-headed Alpines; and their Elect were, as with the earlier racists, the Nordic narrow-heads. Their problem was to determine the inferiority or superiority of different strains within Western Europe. The lack of nationalism in their position even allowed this school to work in harmony on both sides of the Rhine: Ammon's work was done in Germany (Baden), and Broca's and Lapouge's in France.

They all used mass anthropomorphic measurements to show that the narrow-heads (Nordics) were the adventurous, aggressive race and the broad-heads (Alpines) the timid, submissive subject race. In Lapouge's figure of speech the narrow-heads are the hunting pack and the broad-heads the marauded sheep. In line with the sacred "survival of the fittest," which the school owed to Darwin, the Elect was clearly the hunting pack. Of course, skull measurements of European populations do not of themselves separate the hunting pack from the sheep, but a test case was propounded: Since cities are "advanced" as compared with rural populations, the Elect should be concentrated in the cities. This was indeed a fact which had been noted in south-central France, in northern Italy, and in Germany before the rise of the anthropo-sociological school, and in its earlier, more aristocratic form—nobles, instead of city dwellers—it had been recognized by Gobineau. Ammon interpreted this difference in average head form in city and country as evidence of social selection; the higher average of narrow-heads in the cities showed that their abilities were greater and had been "selected." "Social selection" he placed in the same position in human history as Darwin had placed "natural selection" in animal history. This urban concentration of long-heads to the disadvantage of broad-heads is known as Ammon's law, and was inter-preted as proving the racial superiority of long-heads.

Had it not been for the racist traditions and the hallowed claims of the fair, blue-eyed narrow-heads, the facts could have been interpreted, by the same arguments this school ad-vanced, as proving the exact opposite. For their data all showed that the cephalic index was increasing, that is, that narrow-heads were losing out to round-heads. Also com-plexions were growing darker. Since population was increas-ing more rapidly in cities than in the country, these changes were the more marked in the cities. Why not a social selec-tion of round-heads? The anthropo-sociological school con-fined itself to the statistics of cephalic indices and in no case set itself the task of showing that broad-heads were inferior in length of life or fertility.

It is unnecessary to choose between one interpretation of these facts and the other, for the universality of the facts themselves was soon disproved. Livi [1] in his military statistics of Italy showed that in some districts, like Piedmont, the city population was on the average more long-headed than that of the surrounding district, just as in Germany, but that in

---

[1] Livi, *Anthropometria militaire*, Rome, 1896.

other districts, like Palermo, it was the other way around. The explanation was simple: the city population was drawn from a wider area than the rural population and, therefore, whether the latter was long- or short-headed, differed from it. The inferiority or superiority of the strains was in no way involved.

The figures accumulated by the school of anthropo-sociology are more striking in their overlapping than in their significant differences. Both city-born and country-born have the same range; there are a few *more* narrow-heads than broad-heads in the cities, and that is all. To speak of "concentration of narrow-heads" in the cities, when the cephalic index of Heidelberg students from the country averaged 82.7 and from the city 81 is to mistake the situation. All the measurements established the fact that the same *range* of cephalic indices was found in the city and in the country; even if one could grant that all city dwellers were by heredity superior to all country dwellers, city people did not most of them have long heads.

The whole racist argument of the school of anthropo-sociology seems pretentious and distorted to modern investigators, and their sole reliance on the cephalic index is regarded as thoroughly unsatisfactory. The importance of this school in the history of racist dogmas is that it reflected changing conditions in Europe. It was still pre-nationalistic, and in no way anticipated the twentieth-century patriotic pronouncements; the problem it posed was a class problem of inferiority or superiority of different strata within the nation. But instead of seeing the problem in terms of feudalism or the well-born as Boulainvilliers and Gobineau had seen it, the students of 1850–1900 saw it in terms of urban prestige. They could, of course, have measured descendants of the nobility and compared them with the bourgeoisie or the peasants, and if conditions had been what they were in earlier generations they would no doubt have done so. In an urban age they arranged their material to show the characteristics of city dwellers and to argue from these traits their innate superiority.

Racism, the doctrine of the innate superiority of a class, became in Europe, about the time of the turn of the century, a doctrine of the superiority of nations; but in America it has maintained its earlier meaning. This is a reflection at once of the lesser menace of other armed nations in the New World and of the recency and the proportions of immigrations which have brought representatives of all European ethnic groups in great numbers to the United States. About 1890 the immigrants, who since the earliest colonization had been drawn from Northern and Western Europe, began to come, as a result of European conditions, chiefly from Southern and Eastern Europe. The racist literature which this called forth asserts the superiority of the Nordics and the inferiority of the non-Nordics, and derives from this that the United States is in danger because the blood of her older settlers is being contaminated by mixture with that of the later comers. The difficulties of the postwar years were ascribed en masse to the immigration policy the United States had pursued and to the groups that had most recently taken advantage of it. These immigrants were obviously poverty-stricken and employed mainly as unskilled labor. As a group they made a poor showing beside the immigrants who had settled in this country before 1890. The American racists cut, at one stroke, the Gordian knot of historical and sociological facts and ascribed the obvious condition of the Italian and Polish immigrant to his innate inferiority as a non-Nordic.

The arguments the American racists presented to uphold this interpretation were taken from Gobineau and Houston Chamberlain. In Europe, according to Madison Grant, "the amount of Nordic blood in each nation is a very fair measure of its strength in war and standing in civilization," [1] but his application of this principle would not recommend itself to German and French racialists. "The Germans of today are for the most part descendants of the peasants"—the author's alternative designation of the Alpine broad-heads—and this explains the present "ghastly rarity in the German armies of chivalry and generosity toward women and of knightly protection and courtesy toward the prisoners or wounded." [2] France has been ruined in the same manner: "Step by step, with the reappearance of these primitive and deep-rooted stocks [Alpine and Mediterranean] the Nordic element in France declined and with it the vigor of the nation." [3] The same substitution of one race for another accounts for "the superstitious and unintelligent Spaniard of today." In England too the Nordics are receding. This desperate state of affairs in Europe, however, since *The Passing of the Great Race* is written by an American, leads in its author's view to glorious prospects for the United States if the older immigrants keep their dominant position. For down to the time of the Civil War the white race in our country was "purely Nordic . . . not only Nordic but also purely Teutonic, a very large majority being Anglo-Saxon in the most limited meaning of that term." [4] Even at the date of writing he announces that the majority of Americans are Nordic. All that is needed in order that the United States shall take the glorious position Europe has lost is, in the words of Henry Fairfield Osborn in his Introduction to Grant's book, to combat "the gradual dying out among our people of those hereditary traits through which the principles of our religious, political or social foun-

---

[1] Grant, Madison, *The Passing of the Great Race*, New York, 1916, p. 175.
[2] *Ibid.*, pp. 167–8.
[3] *Ibid.*, p. 177.
[4] *Ibid.*, pp. 72–74.

dations were laid down, and their insidious replacement by traits of less noble character." [1] In later racist books in America, Nordic racial hygiene, the obligation of the chosen race to keep its blood free from contamination with that of lesser breeds, was raised to the pinnacle of patriotic duty.

The application of these time-worn doctrines to America was inept in the extreme. The gratuitous assumption of the superiority of the Nordic in Europe we have already examined in considering the racist volumes written in Europe. Grant merely repeated these claims. The identification of all older American immigrants as Nordic, however, was a contention not advanced among European racists. Grant arrived at it not by use of any anthropomorphic measurements, but by the perusal of lists of nationalities from which immigrants were drawn before 1860. He himself made the point that Great Britain and Germany, the two chief sources of this immigration, were at that time losing or had already lost their Nordic pre-eminence. Hence it would seem necessary for him to have proved that some factors had brought about a *racial* selection in these populations so that those who took passage to America were Nordic and those who stayed behind were non-Nordic. This he failed to do. It would have been impossible. Whatever selection occurred, it did not operate to make English blonds emigrate and English brunets stay in Europe. The motive was generally economic and operated in the same manner for blonds and brunets.

An anthropomorphic analysis of "Old Americans" has been made by Aleš Hrdlička [2] which shows clearly the fallacy of Grant's supposition. This study examines two thousand Americans whose four grandparents were all born on American soil. "Light" hair color was found in only 5.3 per cent of the Old American men studied, "light-brown" in only 16 per

---

[1] *Ibid.*, p. ix.
[2] Hrdlička, Aleš, *The Old Americans*, Baltimore, 1925.

which has as a subbasis

$$\{ \Uparrow x : x \in S \} \cup \{ S \backslash \uparrow t : x \in S \}$$

2.26 Lemma Let S be a continuous semilattice. If $w \ll x \ll y \leq z$ in S, then $w \ll z$. In particular, $\ll$ is transitive.

Proof: Let D be a directed set such that $z \leq sup\ D$. Then $y \leq sup\ D$, and since $x \ll y$, there exists $d \in D$ such that $x \leq d$. Since $w \leq x$, we have $w \leq d$, and hence $w \ll z$. ∎

2.27 Lemma Let S be a continuous semilattice. If $x \ll y$ in S, then there exists $w \in S$ such that $x \ll w \ll y$.

Proof: Let $A = \{ q : q \ll p \ll y$ for some $p \in S \}$. We first show that A is up-directed. Let $q_1, q_2 \in A$. Then there exist $p_1, p_2 \in S$ such that $q_1 \ll p_1 \ll y$ and $q_2 \ll p_2 \ll y$. Now $\Downarrow y$ is directed, so there exists $p \in \Downarrow y$ such that $p_1 \leq p$ and $p_2 \leq p$. Again, $\Downarrow p$ is directed, so there exists $q \in \Downarrow p$ with $q_1 \leq q$ and $q_2 \leq q$, and $q \in A$.

We claim that $y = sup\ A$. Now $x = sup \Downarrow x \leq sup\ A$ and $x \ll y$, so that $y = sup \Downarrow y \leq sup\ A$.

To complete the proof observe that $x \ll y$, $y = sup\ A$, and A is up-directed. Thus $x \leq a$ for some $a \in A$, and there exists $w \in S$ such that $a \ll w \ll y$ from the definition of A. We obtain that $x \leq a \ll w \ll y$, and from 2.25, $x \ll w \ll y$. ∎

The result of 2.27 is called the *interpolation property* of continuous semilattices.

2.28 Lemma Let S be a compact semilattice and let $x \in S$.
(a) If $A = \Uparrow x$, then $A = \uparrow A$.
(b) If $a,b \in \Downarrow x$, and $c = sup\ \{a,b\}$, then $c \in \Downarrow x$.

Proof: To prove (a), let $a \in A$. Then $x \ll a$. Let $b \in \uparrow a$. Then $a \leq b$, and if D is a directed set with $b \leq sup\ D$, then $a \leq sup$

D. Since $x \ll a$, there exists $d \in D$ such that $x \leq d$. It follows that $x \ll b$, $\uparrow a \subseteq A$, and hence $A = \uparrow A$.

To prove (b), let D be a directed set with $x \leq \sup D$. Then $a \leq d_1$, and $b \leq d_2$ for some $d_1, d_2 \in D$. Since D is directed, there exists $d \in D$ with $d_1, d_2 \leq d$. Thus $a, b \leq d$ and hence $c \leq d$. It follows that $c \ll a$, i.e., $c \in \Downarrow x$. ∎

2.29   Theorem   If S is a continuous semilattice, then S is a compact Lawson semilattice with respect to the Lawson topology on S. Conversely, if S is a compact Lawson semilattice, then S is a continuous semilattice and S has the Lawson topology.

Proof: First assume that S is a continuous semilattice and endow S with the Lawson topology.

To see that S is compact, let $\mathcal{U}$ be an open cover of S with subbasic open sets. We will use the Alexander subbase lemma to establish compactness. Consider those subbase elements of this cover of the form $S \setminus \uparrow x$. If $\uparrow x_1 \cap \cdots \cap \uparrow x_n = \square$ for some finite number of these, then $S \setminus \uparrow x_1, \ldots, S \setminus \uparrow x_n$ covers S and hence is a finite subcover of $\mathcal{U}$. We can assume then that $\uparrow x_1 \cap \cdots \cap \uparrow x_n \neq \square$ for all choices of $x_1, \ldots, x_n$. Thus $\sup\{x_1, \ldots, x_n\}$ exists for each such choice. The set D of these *sups* forms an up-directed set. Let $y = \sup D$. Then $y \in \uparrow x$ for all x such that $S \setminus \uparrow x \in \mathcal{U}$, and hence $y \in \Uparrow$ for some $\Uparrow x \in \mathcal{U}$. Since $x \ll y$ and $y = \sup D$, there exists $\{x_1, \ldots, x_n\}$ such that $x \leq d$, where $d = \sup\{x_1, \ldots, x_n\}$. We have $S \setminus (S \setminus \uparrow x_1 \cup \cdots \cup S \setminus \uparrow x_n) = \uparrow x_1 \cap \cdots \cap \uparrow x_n = \uparrow d \subseteq \Uparrow x$. Thus $S \setminus \uparrow x_1, \ldots, S \setminus \uparrow x_n, \Uparrow x$ is a finite open cover of $\mathcal{U}$, and S is compact.

To see that S is Hausdorff, let $x \neq y$ in S. We can assume that $x \nleq y$, and hence there exists $z \ll x$ such that $z \nleq y$. Then $x \in \Uparrow z$, $y \in S \setminus \uparrow z$ and $\Uparrow z \cap (S \setminus \uparrow z) = \square$. It follows that S is Hausdorff.

For the purpose of showing that multiplication is continuous on S, let $z = xy$. Now if $z \in \Uparrow w$, then $w \ll z$, and from 2.27, there exists $q \in S$ such that $w \ll q \ll z$, so that $z = xy \in \uparrow q \cdot \uparrow q \subseteq \uparrow q \subseteq \Uparrow w$. If $z \in S \setminus \uparrow b$, then $b \nleq z$, so that either $b \nleq x$ or $b \nleq y$. We can assume that $b \nleq x$, and hence $xy \in (S \setminus \uparrow b) \cdot S \subset S \setminus \uparrow b$.

To see that S is a Lawson semilattice, first observe that $S \setminus \uparrow b$

is a subsemilattice for each $b \in S$. If $x \in \Uparrow z$ in S, then by 2.27, there exists $p \in S$ such that $z \ll p \ll x$. Then $x \in \Uparrow p \subseteq \uparrow p \subseteq \Uparrow z$, and $\uparrow p$ is a semilattice. This completes the proof of the first half of the theorem.

To prove the converse, let S be a compact Lawson semilattice. We will show that S is a continuous semilattice and that S has the lawson topology.

Now S is up-complete from Appendix B.4.

Let $x \in S$. To show that $\downarrow x$ is directed, let $a, b \in \Downarrow x$. Then $\{a, b\}$ is bounded above in S by x, so that from 2.1(b), $\sup\{a, b\} = c$ exists. From 2.28(b), $c \in \Downarrow x$, and $\Downarrow x$ is directed.

We claim that if $x \in (\uparrow y)^\circ$, then $y \ll x$ for $x, y \in S$. Suppose that $x \in (\uparrow y)^\circ$ and let D be a directed set with $x \leq \sup D = d$. Now $D \to d$ as a net, so that $xD \to xd = x$. Thus $xD \in^e (\uparrow y)^\circ \subseteq \uparrow y$. Then $y \leq xd$ for some $d \in D$, and $xd \leq d$ in S, so that $y \leq d$, and $y \ll x$.

We next claim that if $x \nleq z$ in S, then there exists $w \in S$ such that $w \nleq z$ and $w \ll x$. To see this, suppose that $x \nleq z$. Then $S \backslash \downarrow z$ is an open set containing x. Since S is a regular space and has small subsemilattice, there exists a semilattice neighborhood N of x such that $\overline{N} \subseteq S \backslash \downarrow z$. Now $\overline{N}$ is a compact semilattice. Let w be the zero of $\overline{N}$. Then $\overline{N} \subseteq \uparrow w$. Now $x \in (\overline{N})^\circ \subseteq (\uparrow w)^\circ$, and from the previous paragraph, $w \ll x$. Since $w \in \overline{N} \subseteq S \backslash \downarrow z$, we have that $w \nleq z$.

Now let $q = \sup \Downarrow x$. Then $q \leq x$. Suppose that $q < x$. Then $x \nleq q$, so that from the previous paragraph there exists $w \ll x$ such that $w \nleq q$. This contradiction proves that $q = x$, and the proof that S is a continuous semilattice is complete.

It remains only to show that S has the Lawson topology. Now from the first part of the theorem and the part that has been established toward the converse, S with its given topology and S with the Lawson topology are both compact Hausdorff spaces. In view of this, to complete the proof, we need only demonstrate that each type of Lawson-open set is open in the given topology of S.

Now $S \backslash a \uparrow x$ is open for each $x \in S$ from 2.1(d).

Let $x \in S$. We want to show that $\Uparrow x$ is open in S. Let $a \in \Uparrow x$. Then $x \ll a$, and from 2.27, there exists $p \in S$ such that $x \ll p \ll a$. Let $D = \{w \in S: a \in (\uparrow w)^\circ\}$. Then D is bounded above by a and hence has a *sup* according to 2.1(b). Moreover, $a = sup\ D$, since $\uparrow sup\{w_1, w_2\} = \uparrow w_1 \cap \uparrow w_2$. Since $a \le sup\ D$ and $p \ll a$, there exists $w \in D$ such that $p \le w$. Now $x \ll p \le w$ and hence $x \ll w$ from 2.26. We conclude that $a \in (\uparrow w)^\circ \subseteq \uparrow w \subseteq \Uparrow x$, and $\Uparrow x$ is open. ∎

BREADTH OF A SEMILATTICE

In this section we present a brief discusssion of the notion of breadth of a semilattice. Results are derived from Lawson [1971] and Brown and Stepp [1982].

If S is a semilattice and $e \in S$, then $F = \{e_1, e_2, \ldots, e_n\} \subseteq S$ is called an *irreducible representation* of e provided $e = e_1 e_2 \cdots e_n$ and the product of the elements of no proper subset of F is e. The *breadth* of e is $sup\{\#F{:}F$ is an irreducible representation of $e\}$, where $\#F$ denotes the number of elements of F. Observe that the breadth of e need not be finite. We definite the *breadth* of S to be $Br\ S = sup\{$breadth of $e{:}e \in S\}$.

2.30   Theorem   Let S be a topological semilattice with finite breadth. Then S is a Lawson semilattice.

Proof: Let $n = Br\ S$. Let U be open in S and let $e \in U$. Then $e = e^n$, so that in view of the continuity of multiplication in S we see that there exists an open set V in S with $e \in V$ and $V^n \subseteq U$. Let T be the subsemilattice of S generated by V. Then $e \in T$.

We claim that $T \subseteq V^n$. Let $v \in T$. Then $v = v_1, \ldots, v_n \in V$ since T is generated by V and $Br(v) \le n$. Thus $T \subseteq V^n$.

We have that $T \subseteq U$, and T is the required subsemilattice. ∎

We mention the next result along this line by way of exposition. It appears in Lawson [1971].

2.31   Theorem   If S is a locally compact semilattice, then $cd\ S \le Br\ S$.

To conclude this section, we present a sequence of lemmas and a theorem from Brown and Stepp [1982].

2.32 Lemma Let X be an acyclic space. Then $x \in X$ is a 0-middle point of X if and only if there exists an open set U containing x such that for each open set V containing x, $V \subseteq U$, the homomorphism induced by the inclusion map $j:X\backslash U \to X\backslash V$ is nonzero in some dimension.

Proof: By the acyclicity of X and the exactness of the pairs $(X,X\backslash U)$ and $(X,X\backslash V)$, the horizontal arrows in the diagrams below are isomorphisms in all dimensions:

$$H^p(X\backslash V) \to H^{p+1}(X,X\backslash V)$$
$$j^* \downarrow \qquad\qquad i^* \downarrow$$
$$H^p(X\backslash U) \to H^{p+1}(X,X\backslash U)$$

The conclusion follows from the fact that this diagram commutes and the observation that x is a 0-middle point if and only if i^* is nonzero in some dimension. ∎

2.33 Lemma Let X be a compact Hausdorff space, A a closed subset of X, and let $cdX = n$, with $H^n(X) = 0 = H^{n-1}(A)$. If x is a 0-middle point in dimension $n-1$ relative to A, then x is a 0-middle point relative to X (in the same dimension).

Proof: From 2.32, there exists a set U which is open in A and contains x such that $j^*:H^{n-1}(A\backslash V) \to H^{n-1}(A\backslash U)$ is not trivial for every A-open set $V \subseteq U$ such that $x \in V$.

Let U_1 be an open set in X such that $U_1 \cap A = U$, and let V_1 be any open set in X such that $x \in V_1 \subseteq U_1$. Consider the Mayer–Vietoris sequence

$$H^{n-1}(X\backslash V_1) \times H^{n-1}(A) \to H^{n-1}((X\backslash V_1) \cap A) \to H^n(A \cup (X\backslash V_1))$$

Since $cd\, X = n$ and $H^n(X) = 0$, the final group in the above triple is zero. Since $H^{n-1}(A) = 0$, we have that i_1^*, the homomorphism induced by the inclusion of $A \backslash V_1$ into $X \backslash V_1$, is onto $H^{n-1}(A \backslash V_1)$. Since $A \cap V_1$ is an A-open set contained in U and containing x, j^* is not zero. Finally, from the diagram

$$H^{n-1}(X \backslash V_1) \xrightarrow{i_1^*} H^{n-1}(X \backslash U_1)$$

$$j_1^* \downarrow \qquad\qquad i_U^* \downarrow$$

$$H^{n-1}(A \backslash V_1) \xrightarrow{j^*} H^{n-1}(A \backslash U)$$

we have $0 \neq j^* i_1^* = i_U^* j_1^*$, so that $j_1^* \neq 0$, which shows that x is a 0-middle point relative to X. ∎

2.34 Lemma Let $\{A_i\}_{i=1}^n$ be a collection of acyclic sets such that $\bigcap_{i \in I} A_i$ is acyclic for every nonempty $I \subseteq \{1, \dots, n\}$. Then $\bigcup \{A_i: i = 1, \dots, n\}$ is acyclic.

Proof: Each A_i is connected, as are pairwise intersections; this proves the lemma in dimension 0, for all n. If $n = 2$, the result follows from the Mayer–Vietoris sequence in all dimensions. If $n > 2$, the lemma follows from a direct application of induction. ∎

2.35 Lemma Let S be a compact chainwise connected semilattice with $cd\, S = n$. Let z be an element of breadth $n + 1$, with irreducible representation $z = x_1 x_2 \cdots x_{n+1}$. Let $y_i = x_1 x_2 \cdots \hat{x}_i \cdots x_{n+1}$. Then, for any proper subset $I \subset \{1, \dots, n + 1\}$, we have $\bigcap \{\uparrow y_i: i \in I\} \neq \square$ and $\bigcap \{\uparrow y_i: i = 1, \dots, n + 1\} = \square$.

Proof: Choose $j \in \{1, \dots, n + 1\} \backslash I$. Then $x_j \geq y_i$ for every $i \in I$. Hence $\bigcap \{\uparrow y_i: i \in I\} \neq \square$.

Next, suppose there exists $a \in \bigcap \{\uparrow y_i: i = 1, \dots, n + 1\}$. Let $b_i = ax_i; i = 1, \dots, n + 1$. If $b_i = b_j, j \neq i$, then $ax_i x_j = ax_j$, so that $z = x_1 \cdots x_{n+1}$. Hence all of the b's are distinct. Now $b_1 b_2 \cdots b_{n+1} = a(x_1 \cdots x_n) = az = z$. The chainwise connected semilattice aS has identity a and is of codimensions less than or equal to n; as mentioned before, $Br\ aS = n$, so that z may be written as the product of a proper subset of $\{b_1, \ldots, b_{n+1}\}$. Without loss of generality, assume $z = b_1 \cdots b_n$. Then $z = a(x_1 \cdots x_n) = ay_{n+1} = y_{n+1}$. This again contradicts the irreducible representation of z as the product of $x_1 \cdots x_{n+1}$. ∎

2.36 Lemma Let $\{A_1, \ldots, A_{n+1}\}$ be a collection of distinct, compact acyclic sets such that $\bigcap\{A_i : i \in I\}$ is acyclic and nonempty for each I properly contained in $\{1, \ldots, n + 1\}$, but $\bigcap\{A_i : i = 1, 2, \ldots, n + 1\} = \square$. Then $H^{n-1}(A_1 \cup \cdots \cup A_{n+1}) \neq 0$.

Proof: Note that $I \neq J \subseteq \{1, \ldots, n + 1\}$ implies $\bigcap\{A_i : i \in I\} \neq \bigcap\{A_j : j \in J\}$.

If $n = 1$, then $H^0(A_1 \cup A_2) \neq 0$, since $A_1 \cap A_2 = \square$. Suppose the conclusion is valid for all families of k sets satisfying the hypothesis, and let $\{A\}_{i=1}^{k+1}$ be a family of $k + 1$ sets which satisfy the hypothesis. Consider the Mayer–Vietoris sequence

$$H^{k-2}\left(\bigcup_{i=1}^{k} A_i\right) \times H^{k-2}(A_{k+1}) \to H^{k-2}\left(\bigcup_{i=1}^{k} (A_i \cap A_{k+1})\right)$$

$$\Delta\diagdown$$

$$H^{k-2}\left(\bigcup_{i=1}^{k+1} A_i\right) \to H^{k-1}\left(\bigcup_{i=1}^{k} A_i\right) \times H^{k-1}(A_{k+1})$$

By 2.34, $\bigcup\{A_i : i = 1, \ldots, k\}$ is acyclic, so that Δ is an isomorphism. For $i = 1, \ldots, k$ set $B_i = A_i \cap A_{k+1}$ and note that if $i \neq j$, then $B_i \neq B_j$. Let $I \subseteq \{1, \ldots, k\}$; then $\bigcap\{B_i : i \in I\} = \bigcap\{A_j : j \in I \cup \{k + 1\}\}$. Hence $\bigcap\{B_i : i = 1, \ldots, k\} = \square$ and $\bigcap\{B_i : i \in I\}$ is acyclic (and nonempty) for every I properly contained in $\{1, \ldots, k\}$. By the inductive hypothesis, $H^{k-2}(\bigcup_{i=1}^{k} B_i) \neq 0$, so that $H^{k-1}(\bigcup_{i=1}^{k+1} A_i) \neq 0$. ∎

2.37 Theorem. Let S be a compact chainwise connected semilattice of codimension n. If $Br\ S = n + 1$, then any point of breadth $n + 1$ is a 0-middle point (and hence is a middle point).

Proof: Let X be a compact chainwise connected topological semilattice with $cd\ X = n$. Let z be an element of breadth $n + 1$ with irreducible representation $z = x_1 x_2 \cdots x_{n+1}$. We first reduce the size of X. Fix $i \in \{1, \ldots, n + 1\}$; for $j \neq i$, let C_{ij} be an arc-chain with endpoints x_i and $x_i x_j$. Let $A_i = \Pi\{C_{ij}: j \neq i\}$. Note that each A_i contains all finite products of the x_j's which contain x_i as a factor. Now let S be the semilattice generated by $\bigcup\{A_i: i = 1, \ldots, n + 1\}$. Then S is a compact chainwise connected semigroup with maximal elements $x_1, \ldots, x_{n+1}$ and minimal element z. Since $Br\ S = n + 1$, $cd_S = n$. We will show that z is a 0-middle point in S and use 2.33 to complete the argument.

As in the Proof of 2.35, let $y_i = x_1 x_2 \cdots \hat{x}_i \cdots x_{n+1}$ and let $B = \bigcup\{\uparrow y_i: i = 1, \ldots, n + 1\}$ By 2.35 and 2.36 we have $H^{n-1}(B) \neq 0$. Let $U = S \backslash B$; we show that this set satisfies the hypothesis of 2.32. For any open set W with $z \in W \subseteq U$, there exists an open set V such that $z \in V \subseteq W$ and $S \backslash V = \bigcup\{\uparrow q_j: j = 1, \ldots, n\}$ (Stepp [1971]). As $S \backslash U = B \subseteq S \backslash W \subseteq S \backslash V$, it suffices to show that $j^*: H^{n-1}(S \backslash V) \to H^{n-1}(S \backslash U)$ is not trivial.

To simplify the notation some, let $a = x_1$ henceforth. Let $\lambda_a: S \to aS$ be the left translation defined by $\lambda_a(t) = at$, let $\lambda_1 = \lambda_a | S \backslash V$, and let $\lambda = \lambda_a | B$. Consider the diagram

$$
\begin{array}{ccc}
H^{n-1}(a(S \backslash V)) & \xrightarrow{\lambda_1^*} & H^{n-1}(S \backslash V) \\
\downarrow{\scriptstyle j_1^*} & & \downarrow{\scriptstyle j^*} \\
H^{n-1}(aB) & \xrightarrow{\lambda^*} & H^{n-1}(B)
\end{array}
$$

In order to have $j^* \neq 0$, it suffices to show that λ^* is an isomorphism and that $j_1^* \neq 0$. To prove that λ^* is an isomorphism, we apply the Vietoris mapping theorem to λ (see Appendix A.29), and will invoke a similar technique to prove that $j_1^* \neq 0$.

To show that λ^* is an isomorphism, fix $x \in aB$; we show that $\lambda^{-1}(x)$ is an acyclic subset of B. Clearly, $\lambda^{-1}(x) \cap \uparrow y_i = \lambda_a^{-1}(x) \cap \uparrow y_i$. Let $A \subseteq \{2, \ldots, n + 1\}$ be defined by $i \in \Lambda$ if and only if $\lambda^{-1}(x) \cap \uparrow y_i \neq \square$. Thus $\lambda^{-1}(x) = [\lambda^{-1}(x) \cap \uparrow y_1] \cup [\bigcup_{i \in \Lambda}(\lambda^{-1}(x) \cap \uparrow y_i)]$. Note that the second of the two bracketed sets is, in fact, $\lambda^{-1}(x) \cap (\bigcap_{i \in \Lambda} \uparrow y_i)$. To see this, fix $t \in \bigcup_{i \in \Lambda}[\lambda^{-1}(x) \cap \uparrow y_i]$; it suffices to show that $t \geq y_i$ for each $i \in \Lambda$. Fix $i \in \Lambda$, and let $s \in \lambda^{-1}(x)$ $\cap \uparrow y_i$. Then, since $i \neq 1$, $a \in \uparrow y_i$ also, so that $x = as \in \uparrow y_i$. Thus y_i $\leq x = at \leq t$. Since $\lambda^{-1}(x) \cap \uparrow y_i = \lambda_a^{-1}(x) \cap \uparrow y_i$ and $\lambda_a^{-1}(x)$ is a compact chainwise connected semilattice, we have $\lambda^{-1}(x) \cap \uparrow y_i$ is a principal filter in $\lambda_a^{-1}(x)$ and is therefore acyclic. In a similar manner, $\lambda^{-1}(x) \cap (\bigcap_{i \in \Lambda} \uparrow y_i)$ is acyclic provided it is not empty. Finally, if both $\lambda^{-1}(x) \cap \uparrow y_i$ and $\lambda^{-1}(x) \cap (\bigcap_{i \in \Lambda} \uparrow y_i)$ are nonempty, then choose t in the first set and choose s in the second. Since, $x = at = as$, and $a \in \bigcap_{i \in \Lambda} \uparrow y_i$, we have $x \in \bigcap_{i \in \Lambda} \uparrow y_i$ from which it follows that $t \in \bigcap_{i \in \Lambda} \uparrow y_i \cap \lambda^{-1}(x)$. Hence, in this case the first set is a subset of the second, so that the intersection is again acyclic. By 2.34, $\lambda^{-1}(x)$ is acyclic. We conclude from the Vietoris mapping theorem that λ^* is an isomorphism in all dimensions.

We proceed to show that $j_1^* \neq 0$. Since λ^* is an isomorphism and $H^{n-1}(B) \neq 0$, it suffices to show that j_1^* is surjective. By exactness of the pair sequence $(a(S \backslash V), aB)$, this can be accomplished by showing that $H^n(a(S \backslash V), aB) = 0$. From the strong excision theorem (see Appendix A.14), decomposing $a(S \backslash V)$ as $[(S \backslash V) \cap \uparrow a] \cup aB$, $H^n(a(S \backslash V), aB) \approx H^n((S \backslash V) \cap \downarrow a, (S \backslash V) \cap aB)$. We show the latter group to be trivial by showing that each factor is acyclic and again appealing to the exactness of pair sequences.

(i) We claim that $a(S \backslash V) = ((S \backslash V) \cap \uparrow a) \cup aB$. This is a consequence of the construction of S. Let $x = at$, with $t \in S \backslash V$. If $t \in \downarrow a$, then $x = at = t$; hence it must be shown that if $t \notin \downarrow a$, then $at \in aB$. Let $t = t_1 \cdots t_m$, where each t_k belongs to some C_{ij}, an arc-chain with endpoints x_i and $x_i x_j$. Since $t \notin \downarrow a$, $i \neq 1$ for each upper endpoint of x_i. If, for some j, $x_j = 1$, then $a(x_i x_j) \leq at_k \leq ax_i$, so that $at_k = ax_i \in a \uparrow y_1$. If $x_j \neq a$, then $y_1 \leq x_i x_j$, so again $at_k \in a \uparrow y_1$. Thus $at = at_1 \cdots t_m = (at_1) \cdots (at_m) \in a \uparrow y_1 \subseteq aB$. The other inclusion is immediate.

(ii) We claim that $(S \backslash V) \cap \downarrow a$ is acyclic. By construction, $S \backslash V$ is a finite union of principal filters; cut down to $\downarrow a$, a chainwise connected semilattice, they retain this property. The intersection of all of these filters (which meet $\downarrow a$ at all) must contain a and is therefore itself a principal filter in $\downarrow a$. By 2.34, the set $(S \backslash V) \cap \uparrow a$ is acyclic.

(iii) We claim that $(S \backslash V) \cap aB$ is acyclic. If $n = 1$, then $B =$

$\{x_1 = a, x_2\}$, so that $(S \backslash V) \cap aB = \{a\}$ in this case. We assume henceforth that $n \geq 2$. Now for $2 \leq j \leq n + 1$, define

$$T_j = (S \backslash V) \cap a(\uparrow y_1 \cap \downarrow x_j)$$

and

$$S_j = \bigcup_{k \neq 1, j} (\uparrow y_k \cap \downarrow a) \qquad J_j = S_j \cup T_j$$

A direct argument establishes that $(S \backslash V) \cap aB = \bigcup \{J_j : j \geq 2\}$. We show that the family of J_j's satisfies the hypothesis of 2.34. Each S_j is the union of principal filters in $\downarrow a$, hence is acyclic by 2.34. In a similar manner, each T_j is the union of finitely many principal filters in the chainwise connected subsemilattice $a(\uparrow y_1 \cap \downarrow x_j)$, even though some of the $\downarrow q_i$'s which comprise $S \backslash V$ will fail to intersect this set. Thus T_j is also acyclic by 2.34. The set $S_j \cap T_j$ is, like T_j, the finite union of principal filters in $a(\uparrow y_1 \cap \downarrow x_j)$, and hence acyclic. Once more applying 2.34, we have that J_j is acyclic. Next fix Λ, a nonempty subset of $\{2, \ldots, n + 1\}$, and let $J_\Lambda = \bigcap \{J_j : j \in \Lambda\}$, $T_\Lambda = \bigcap \{T_j : j \in \Lambda\}$, and $S_\Lambda = \bigcap \{S_j : j \in \Lambda\}$. For each $\Lambda' \subseteq \Lambda$, define $F_{\Lambda'} = S_{\Lambda'} \cap T_{\Lambda \backslash \Lambda'}$. Then $J_\Lambda = \bigcup \{F_{\Lambda'} : \Lambda' \subseteq \Lambda\}$, and $F_\Lambda \cap F_\Omega = F_{\Lambda \cup \Omega}$ for any subsets $\Lambda, \Omega \subseteq \{2, \ldots, n + 1\}$. To prove that J_Λ is acyclic, it suffices to prove that each $F_{\Lambda'}$ is acyclic, that F_Λ is nonempty, then invoke 2.34 again. Now $S_{\Lambda'}$ is a finite union of principal filters in $\downarrow a$, and $T_{\Lambda \backslash \Lambda'} = (S \backslash V) \cap a[\uparrow y_1 \cap \downarrow w]$, where $w = \Pi \{x_j : j \in \Lambda \backslash \Lambda'\}$. Since $wa \leq a$, we may therefore regard $F_{\Lambda'} = S_{\Lambda'} \cap T_{\Lambda \backslash \Lambda'}$ as the union of principal filters in the chainwise connected semilattice $a[\uparrow y_1 \cap \downarrow w]$, and thus $F_{\Lambda'}$ is acyclic by 2.34. Since $a \in S_\Lambda = F_\Lambda$, the set F_Λ is nonempty. This establishes that the family $\{F_{\Lambda'} : \Lambda' \subseteq \Lambda\}$ satisfies the hypothesis of 2.34, so that J_Λ is itself acyclic. Hence the family $\{J_j : j \geq 2\}$ also satisfies the conditions of 2.34, from which we conclude that $(S \backslash V) \cap aB$ is acyclic.

We have then that $j_1^* \neq 0$, so that $j^* \neq 0$, and the proof is complete. ∎

3

Irreducible Semigroups

In this chapter we establish that each irreducible semigroup is abelian and has a trivial group of units. Most of the results are versions of results that appear in Hofmann and Mostert [1966]. The deep and difficult transformation group theorem (3.4) is presented here without proof. Our objective is to follow a more direct path leading from this result to the theorem that irreducible semigroups are abelian. In the presence of this result it was shown in Hunter [1963] that each irreducible semigroup has a trivial group of units. We modify the argument in Hofmann and Mostert [1966] so that the result does not employ the hormos construction. It is important to note that this construction allows one more insight into the structure of an irreducible semigroup. Related results appear in Mislove [1970], Carruth and Clark [1971], Mislove [1972], and Carruth, Hofmann, and Mislove [1973].

POWER SET SEMIGROUPS

In this section we briefly discuss the semigroup of closed subsets of a compact semigroup. This topic is of interest in itself, but is placed here because of its application to subsequent material on irreducible semigroups. Reference sources for the results of this section are Carruth [1961] and Hofmann and Mostert [1966].

Many of the topological results can be derived from Michael [1951].

If S is a compact semigroup, let $C(S)$ denote the family of all closed subsets of S with the Vietoris topology and multiplication defined by $(A,B) \mapsto AB = \{ab : a \in A, b \in B\}$.

3.1 Theorem If S is a compact semigroup, then $C(S)$ is a compact semigroup.

Proof: Now $C(S)$ is a compact Hausdorff space from Appendix B.2. Since the associativity of multiplication is clear, we need only establish its continuity. We will apply the result of Appendix B.1. Let $A_\alpha \to A$ and $B_\alpha \to B$ be nets in $C(S)$ and let $N(U,V)$ be a subbasic open set such that $AB \in N(U,V)$. Then $AB \subseteq U$ and $AB \cap V \neq \square$. Let U_1 and U_2 be open subsets of S such that $A \subseteq U_1, B \subseteq U_2$, and $U_1 U_2 \subseteq U$. Let $a \in A$ and $b \in B$ such that $ab \in V$, and let V_1 and V_2 be open sets such that $a \in V_1, b \in V_2$, and $V_1 V_2 \subseteq V$. Now let $\beta_1, \beta_2, \beta_3$, and β_4 be elements of the directed set of A_α and B_α such that if γ follows all of these, then $A_\gamma \subseteq U_1, B_\gamma \subseteq U_2, A_\gamma \cap V_1 \neq \square$, and $B_\gamma \cap V_2 \neq \square$. Then for such a γ, we have that $A_\gamma B_\gamma \subseteq N(U,V)$. ∎

Recall that a semigroup T is an $\mathcal{H}$-chain if $\leq_{\mathcal{H}}$ is a total quasi-order on T. For a semigroup S, we use $M(S)$ to denote the minimal ideal of S (if S has a minimal ideal).

3.2 Lemma Let S be a compact semigroup and let T_α be a net of compact subsemigroups of S with $T = \lim T_\alpha$. Then:

    (a) T is a compact subsemigroup of S.
    (b) If each T_α is abelian, then T is abelian.
    (c) If S is a monoid and $1 \in T_\alpha$ for each α, then $1 \in T$.
    (d) If each T_α is connected, then T is connected.
    (e) $M(T) = \lim M(T\alpha)$.
    (f) If each T_α is an $\mathcal{H}_S$-chain, then T is an $\mathcal{H}_S$-chain.

Proof: To prove (a), let $a,b \in T$ and suppose that $ab \notin T$. Then $ab \in S\backslash T$, and $S\backslash T$ is open in S. Let W be an open set such that $ab \in W \subseteq \overline{W} \subseteq S\backslash T$. Let U and V be open sets such that $a \in U$, $b \in V$, and $UV \subseteq W$. Then $U \cap T_\alpha \neq^e \square$, $V \cap T_\alpha \neq^e \square$, and since $T \subseteq S\backslash \overline{W}$, we have $T_\alpha \subseteq^e S\backslash \overline{W}$. Select α in the directed set of T_α so that all three of these hold. Let $u \in U \cap T_\alpha$; $v \in V \cap T_\alpha$, and observe that $uv \in T_\alpha$, so that $uv \in S\backslash \overline{W}$. But, $uv \in UV \subseteq W$, and we have a contradiction.

To prove (b), let $a,b \in T$, and suppose that $ab \neq ba$. Let P and Q be disjoint open sets such that $ab \in P$ and $ba \in Q$, and let U and V be open sets such that $a \in U$, $b \in V$, $UV \subseteq P$, and $VU \subseteq Q$. Now $U \cap T_\alpha \neq^e \square$ and $V \cap T_\alpha \neq^e \square$. Select α so that both of these hold, and $u \in U \cap T_\alpha$ and $v \in V \cap T_\alpha$. Then $uv = vu \in UV \cap VU \subseteq P \cap Q$. This contradicts the fact that P and Q are disjoint, and we conclude that $ab = ba$.

To prove (d), suppose that T is not connected. Then there exists disjoint closed set A and B such that $T = A \cup B$. Let U and V be disjoint open sets such that $A \subseteq U$ and $B \subseteq V$. Then $T \subseteq U \cup V$, so that $T_\alpha \subseteq^e U \cup V$. Now, since $A \subseteq U$ and $B \subseteq V$, we have $T_\alpha \cap U \neq^e \square$ and $T_\alpha \cap V \neq^e \square$. Select α so that all three of these hold. Then $T_\alpha = (T_\alpha \cap V) \cup (T_\alpha \cap U)$ is a separation of T_α, contradicting that T_α is connected.

The proofs of (e) and (f) are straightforward. ∎

IRREDUCIBLE SEMIGROUPS ARE ABELIAN

Recall that if S is a compact connected monoid, then a compact connected submonoid of T is irreducible provided $1 \in T$, $T \cap M(S) \neq \square$, and T is minimal with respect to these properties. A proof that each compact connected monoid contains an irreducible semigroup appears in 5.11 of Carruth, Hildebrant, and Koch [1983]. In this section we prove that irreducible semigroups are abelian.

If S is a monoid and G is a subgroup of $H(1)$, recall that the *centralizer* of G in S is defined by $Z(G) = \{x \in S : xg = gx$ for all $g \in G\}$.

For a compact monoid S, we use $\mathcal{U}(S)$ to denote the family of symmetric neighborhoods of the diagonal of $S \times S$. For $U \in \mathcal{U}(S)$ and $A \subseteq S$, recall that A is *U-connected* provided that for each $a, b \in A$, there exists $\{x_1, \ldots, x_n\}$ in S such that $x_1 = a, x_n = b$ and $(x_j, x_{j+1}) \in U$ for $j = 1, 2, \ldots, n - 1$.

3.3 Lemma Let S be a compact monoid, G a compact subgroup of $H(1)$, and let $\mathcal{A} = \{T : T$ is a compact abelian submonoid of S in $Z(G)$, T is an $\mathcal{H}$-chain, and $M(T)$ is connected$\}$. Suppose that for each $U \in \mathcal{U}(S)$ there exists a U-connected member of $\mathcal{A}$ which meets $M(S)$. Then S contains a compact connected abelian submonoid T such that $T \cap M(S) \neq \square$, T is an $\mathcal{H}$-chain, and $T \subseteq Z(G)$.

Proof: For each $U \in \mathcal{U}(S)$, let T_U be a U-connected member of $\mathcal{A}$. Then T_U clusters in the space of compact subsemigroups of S [$\mathcal{U}(S)$ is directed by inclusion]. We can assume that $T_U \to T$. In view of Appendix B.3, we see that T is connected. ∎

As we mentioned earlier we state the following important transformation group result without proof (see Hofmann and Mostert [1966]).

3.4 Theorem Let X be a compact connected space which is acyclic over the rationals and let $\psi : G \times X \to X$ be an action on X by a compact connected abelian group G. Then the set $F = \{x \in S : \psi(g, x) = x$ for all $g \in G\}$ of fixed points is nonempty and acyclic over the rational. In particular, F is connected.

3.5 Theorem Let S be a compact connected monoid and let G be a compact connected abelian subgroup of $H(1)$. Then $Z(G)$ is connected and $Z(G) \cap M(S) \neq \square$.

Proof: Let $R = \{(x, y) \in S \times S : x, y \in M(S)$ and $(x, y) \in \mathcal{H}\} \cup \Delta(S)$. Then R is a closed congruence on S and we let $\pi : S \to T = S/R$ be the natural map.

Now $M(T) \subseteq E(T)$, and hence T is acyclic from 1.6. The group $\pi(G)$ acts on T as follows: $\phi:\pi(G) \times T \to T$ is defined by $\phi(h,t) = hth^{-1}$. From 3.4 we have that $Z(\pi(G))$ is connected, since it is the fixed point set of ϕ. Observe that $M(T)$ is also acyclic from 1.2 and that ϕ maps $M(T)$ into itself. Again, by 3.4, the centralizer of $\pi(G)$ in $M(T)$ is nonempty and connected. Thus $Z(\pi(G)) \cap M(T)$ is nonempty and connected.

Now $\pi|Z(G):Z(G) \to Z(\pi(G))$ is a monotone surmorphism, so that $Z(G)$ is connected (see Carruth, Hildebrant, and Koch [1983]), and $Z(G) \cap M(T) \neq \square$, since $Z(\pi(G)) \cap M(T) \neq \square$. ∎

3.6 Theorem Let S be a compact connected monoid and let G be a compact connected abelian subgroup of $H(1)$. Then there exists a compact connected abelian submonoid T in S such that $T \subseteq Z(G)$, T is an $\mathcal{H}_S$-chain, and $T \cap M(S) \neq \square$.

Proof: Let $\mathcal{A} = \{T:T$ is a compact abelian submonoid of $S, T \subseteq Z(G)$, T is an $\mathcal{H}$-chain, and $M(T)$ is connected$\}$. We will apply 3.3. Let $U \in \mathcal{U}(S)$ and suppose that T is a maximal U-connected member of $\mathcal{A}$. We need only show that $T \cap M(S) \neq \square$. Since T is abelian, we have that $M(T)$ is a group. Let e denote the identity of $M(T)$. We claim that $e \in M(S)$.

Suppose that $e \notin M(S)$, and consider the compact connected monoid eSe. Let K denote the centralizer of $M(T)G$ in eSe. Then, by 3.5, K is compact and connected and meets $M(eSe) \subseteq M(S)$. Observe that $M(T) \subseteq K$ and consider two cases.

Case 1. Suppose that e is isolated in $E(S) \cap K$. Let $\sigma:\mathbf{H} \to K$ be a one-parameter semigroup such that $\sigma(0) = e$ and $\sigma(a) \notin H(e) \cap K$ for $a > 0$ in $\mathbf{H}$ (see 5.13 of Carruth, Hildebrant, and Koch [1983]). Now $\overline{\sigma(\mathbf{H})} \subseteq K$, so that $P = T \cup \overline{\sigma(\mathbf{H})}M(T)$ is a compact abelian submonoid of S contained in $Z(G)$ with $M(P)$ connected. Moreover, T is an $\mathcal{H}_S$-chain. In view of the maximality of T, we see that $P = T$, and hence $\sigma(\mathbf{H}) \subseteq T \cap K = M(T)$. This is a contradiction.

Case 2. Suppose that e is not isolated in $E(S) \cap K$. Let f be any idempotent in K with $f \neq e$ and $(e,f) \in U$. Then, since f commutes with all of the elements of $M(T)G$, we have that $Q =

$T \cup fM(T)$ is a compact abelian semigroup contained in $Z(G)$. Since $M(T)$ is connected and $(e,f) \in U$, we have that Q is U-connected. Moreover, the minimal ideal of $Q(M(Q) = fM(T))$ is connected. Now $fM(T)$ is an $\mathcal{H}$-class of Q, so that Q is totally quasi-ordered relative to the $\mathcal{H}$-order of S. In view of the maximality of T, we have that $Q = T$ and $f \in T \cap L = M(T)$. This is a contradiction. ∎

3.7 Corollary Each irreducible semigroup is abelian.

Recall that if S is a compact abelian semigroup, then $\mathcal{H}$ is a congruence on S.

3.8 Corollary If S is an irreducible semigroup, then S is an $\mathcal{H}$-chain.

3.9 Corollary Each irreducible semigroup is divisible.

Proof: Let S be an irreducible semigroup and let $n \in \mathbf{N}$. Then, since S is abelian, the map $x \mapsto x^n$ is a continuous homomorphism of S into itself. For $e \in M(S) \cap E(S)$, $e \mapsto e$, and $1 \mapsto 1$, so that $x \mapsto x^n$ is surjective, since S is irreducible. It follows that S is divisible. ∎

3.10 Corollary If S is an irreducible semigroup, then $H(e)$ is connected for each $e \in E(S)$.

Proof: This follows from 3.9 and from 5.5 of Carruth, Hildebrant, and Koch [1983]. ∎

In Hofmann and Mostert [1966] a more detailed description of irreducible semigroups was provided. They introduced the concept of a "hormos". In view of divisibility, we see that the atoms of a hormos are compact subunithetic semigroups. Hofmann and Mostert also proved that if S is an irreducible semigroup, then $S/\mathcal{H}$ is an I-semigroup.

3.11   Theorem   Let S be an irreducible semigroup and let $\phi:S \to$ T be a continuous monotone surmorphism of S onto a compact monoid T. Then T is irreducible.

Proof: Let Q be an irreducible subsemigroup of T. Then, since ϕ is monotone, $\phi^{-1}(Q)$ is connected, and hence $S = \phi^{-1}(Q)$. It follows that $Q = T$, and hence T is irreducible.   ∎

AN IRREDUCIBLE SEMIGROUP HAS A TRIVIAL GROUP OF UNITS

In this section we prove that if S is an irreducible semigroup, then $H(1) = \{1\}$. The techniques employed in this argument are modifications of those used in Hofmann and Mostert [1966] without dependence on the hormos construction and taking advantage of the fact that for an irreducible semigroup S and $e \in E(S)$, the group $H(e)$ is connected (see 3.10).

3.12   Lemma   Let S be a compact monoid and let $\mathscr{A} = \{A : A$ is a closed subset of S containing $1\}$. Suppose that for each $U \in \mathscr{U}(S)$, if A is a maximal U-connected member of $\mathscr{A}$, then $A \cap M(S) \neq \square$. Then S contains a closed connected subset C such that $1 \in C$ and $C \cap M(S) \neq \square$.

Proof: For each $U \in \mathscr{U}(S)$, let A_U be a maximal U-connected member of $\mathscr{A}$ (use the Hausdorff maximality principal and the closure of members of a maximal chain). Then A_U clusters in $C(S)$, so we can assume that $A_U \to A$. In view of Appendix B.3, we see that A is connected.   ∎

3.13   Lemma   Let S be a compact monoid and suppose that for each $e \in E(S) \setminus M(S)$, $H(e)$ is not open in eSe. Then the component of 1 in S meets $M(S)$.

Proof: We will employ the result of 3.12 and the technique used in the proof of 3.6. Let $\mathscr{A} = \{A : A$ is a closed subset of S containing $1\}$, let $U \in \mathscr{U}(S)$, and let A be a maximal U-connected member of $\mathcal{A}$. Let e be a minimal idempotent in A and suppose that $e \notin M(S)$. We consider two cases:

Case 1. Suppose that e is isolated in $E(S) \cap eSe$. Let $\sigma : \mathbf{H} \to eSe$ be a one-parameter semigroup with $\sigma(0) \in H(e)$ and $\sigma(a) \notin H(e)$ if $0 < a$. Then $B = A \cup \overline{\sigma(\mathbf{H})}$ is U-connected, and $B \in \mathcal{A}$. In view of the maximality of A, we have that $A = B$, and $\overline{\sigma(\mathbf{H})} \subseteq A \cap eSe \subseteq H(e)$. Thus we have a contradiction in this case.

Case 2. Suppose that e is not isolated in $E(S) \cap eSe$. Let $f \in E(S) \cap eSe$ with $f \neq e$ and $(e,f) \in U$. Let $B = A \cup \{f\}$. Then $B \in \mathcal{A}$ and B is U-connected. From the maximality of A, we have $B = A$, so that $f \in A \cap eSe \subseteq H(e)$, and we have a contradiction. ∎

3.14 Lemma Let S be a compact monoid and suppose that for each $e \in E(S) \backslash M(S)$, $H(e)$ is not open in eSe. Then S contains an irreducible semigroup T such that $1 \in T$ and $T \cap M(S) \neq \square$.

Proof: From 3.13, the component C of 1 in S meets $M(S)$. Now C is a compact connected monoid. The result follows by letting T be an irreducible subsemigroup of C. ∎

If S is a compact abelian monoid and G is a closed subgroup of $H(1)$, then $\sigma = \{(x,y) \in S \times S : Gx = Gy\}$ is a closed congruence on S. The quotient semigroup S/σ is denoted S/G, and for $x \in S$, the congruence class Gx is called the *G-orbit* of x.

3.15 Lemma Let S be an irreducible semigroup and let G be a closed subgroup of $H(1)$. Then S/G is an irreducible semigroup.

Proof: Suppose that T is a compact subsemigroup of S such that $TG = T$ and T/G is a compact connected subsemigroup of S/G containing the identity and meeting the minimal ideal. Let $e \in E(T) \backslash M(T)$.

Suppose that $x \in T \cap eSe$ and $Gx = Gh$ for some $h \in T \cap H(e)$. We claim that $x \in T \cap H(e)$. To see this, observe that $h = gx$ for some $g \in G$. Thus $h = gx = g(ex) = (ge)x$, so that $h = eh = (ege)x$, and $x = ex = (ege)^{-1}x = (ege)^{-1}h$. It follows that $x \in H(e)$.

Now $(T \cap H(e))/G$ is not open in $(T \cap eSe)/G$, since T/G is connected, and hence, in view of the preceding paragraph, we see that $T \cap H(e)$ is not open in $T \cap eSe$. From 3.14, T contains an irreducible semigroup Q such that $1 \in Q$ and $Q \cap M(S) \neq \square$. Since $Q \subseteq T \subseteq S$, and S is irreducible, we have $Q = T = S$. It follows that S/G is irreducible. ∎

The next lemma (3.16) is a reduction in the proof that each irreducible semigroup has a trivial group of units. Observe that the only compact connected subgroups of $\mathbf{R/Z}$ are $\{1\}$ and $\mathbf{R/Z}$. We use this fact in the proof of 3.16.

3.16 Lemma If there is an irreducible semigroup S such that $H(1)$ is nontrivial, then there exists an irreducible semigroup with $\mathbf{R/Z}$ as group of units.

Proof: Let $\phi:H(1) \to \mathbf{R/Z}$ be a nontrivial character of $H(1)$ (see 5.8 of Carruth, Hildebrant, and Koch [1983]). From 3.10, $H(1)$ is connected and hence ϕ is surjective. Let $G = ker\phi$. Then $H(1)/G$ is topologically isomorphic to $\mathbf{R/Z}$ (see 1.49 of Carruth, Hildebrant, and Koch [1983]) and is the group of units of the irreducible semigroup S/G (3.15). ∎

If S is a compact abelian semigroup, then $M(S)$ is a group (see 1.21 of Carruth, Hildebrant, and Koch [1983]). Let e denote the identity of $M(S)$ and define $\phi_S:S \to M(S)$ by $\phi_S(x) = ex$. Then ϕ_S is a continuous homomorphism of S onto $M(S)$, and is called the *Clifford–Miller endomorphism*.

3.17 Lemma Let S be a compact abelian monoid such that $H(1) = \mathbf{R/Z}$ and $\phi_S|H(1)$ is injective. Then S is topologically isomorphic to $H(1) \times S/H(1)$.

Proof: Since $\phi|H(1)$ is injective, we have that $\mathbf{R/Z}$ is a subgroup of $M(S)$. Consider the sequence

$$0 \to \mathbf{R/Z} \hookrightarrow M(S) \xrightarrow{\gamma} \mathbf{R/Z} \to 0$$

where γ is the extension to $M(S)$ of the identity character on $\mathbf{R/Z}$.

In view of 2.12 of Carruth, Hildebrant, and Koch [1983], we see that $M(S)$ is topologically isomorphic to $Q \times \mathbf{R/Z}$ for some compact subgroup Q of $M(S)$. Let $\beta:M(S) \to eH(1)(= \mathbf{R/Z})$ be the extension of the identity character on $eH(1)$ to $M(S)$, and let $\alpha:M(S) \to H(1)$ be the continuous homomorphism such that $\alpha(m) = h$ if $\beta(m) = eh$. Define $\psi:S \to H(1) \times S/H(1)$ by $\psi(x) = (\alpha(ex),\delta(x))$, where $\delta:S \to S/H(1)$ is the natural continuous homomorphism. Then ψ is a continuous homomorphism of S into $H(1) \times S/H(1)$.

To see that ψ is surjective, let $(h,xH(1)) \in H(1) \times S/H(1)$ and let $t = xh(\alpha(ex))^{-1}$. Then $\alpha(et) = \alpha(e(xh(\alpha(ex))^{-1})) = \alpha(ex)\alpha(eh)\alpha(e(\alpha(ex))^{-1}) = \alpha(ex)\alpha(eh)(\alpha(ex))^{-1} = \alpha(eh) = h$ and $tH(1) = xH(1)$. Thus ψ is surjective.

To see that ψ is injective, let $\psi(x) = \psi(t)$. Then $\alpha(ex) = \alpha(et)$ and $xH(1) = tH(1)$. Thus $x = th$ for some $h \in H(1)$, $\alpha(et) = \alpha(ex) = \alpha(eth) = \alpha(et)\alpha(eh) = \alpha(et)h$, and $h = 1$ and $x = t$. ∎

3.18   Theorem   If S is an irreducible semigroup, then $H(1) = \{1\}$.

Proof: Suppose that $H(1)$ is nontrivial. Then, in view of 3.16, we can assume that $H(1) = \mathbf{R/Z}$, and from 5.13 of Carruth, Hildebrant, and Koch [1983], we can assume that 1 is not isolated in $E(S)$. If $e \le 1$ in $E(S)$, define $\alpha_e:H(1) \to H(e)$ by $\alpha_e(h) = eh$. Then α_e is a continuous homomorphism. Note that for $f \le e \le 1$ in $E(S)$, the diagram

$$h \mapsto fh$$
$$H(1) \xrightarrow{\alpha_e} H(e) \to H(f)$$
$$\underset{\alpha_f}{\longrightarrow}$$

commutes, and hence $ker\ \alpha_e \subseteq ker\ \alpha_f$.

In view of the facts that S is an $\mathcal{H}$-chain, that 1 is not isolated in $E(S)$, and that each proper closed subgroup of $\mathbf{R/Z}$ has only a finite number of closed subgroups, there exists a proper closed subgroup K of $\mathbf{R/Z}$ and $g \in E(S)$ with $g < 1$ such that $ker\ \alpha_f = K$ for $g \le f(\le$ is the $\mathcal{H}$-order on S). Let $x \in K$ and let f_γ be a net in $\uparrow g$ in $E(S)$ with

$f_\gamma \to 1$. Then, by continuity of multiplication in S, $f_\gamma x \to x$. Since $x \in \ker \alpha_{f_\gamma}$ for each γ, $f_\gamma x = \alpha_{f_\gamma}(x) = f_\gamma \to 1$, and hence $x = 1$. We obtain that $K = \{1\}$, and thus $H(f) = \mathbf{R}/\mathbf{Z}$ for $g < f$.

Now fix $e \in E(S)$ such that $g < e < 1$, and let $T = \{y \in S : e \le y\}$. Then T is a compact monoid with group of units $H(1)$ and $M(T) = H(e)$. To see that T is irreducible, we need only show that T is connected.

Suppose that T is not connected. Then there are disjoint closed (compact) subsets A and B of T such that $T = A \cup B$. Now $H(e) \subseteq T$ and $H(e)$ is connected (3.10). We can assume that $H(e) \subseteq B$. Then $S = A \cup B \cup \{x \in S : x \le e\}$ is a separation of S. This contradiction proves that T is connected, and hence T is an irreducible semigroup with $H(1) = \mathbf{R}/\mathbf{Z}$ and $M(T) = \mathbf{R}/\mathbf{Z}$.

We now have that $\phi_T|H(1)$ is injective. From 3.17, T is topologically isomorphic to $H(1) \times T/H(1)$, contradicting that T is irreducible. ∎

KOCH'S THREAD THEOREM

In this section we present a proof of the theorem that in a compact connected monoid S which is not a group and which has totally disconnected subgroups, there is a standard thread (I-semigroup) from the identity of S to the minimal ideal of S [Koch, 1964]. One could prove this theorem using results on irreducible semigroups. However, the earlier proof given by Koch provides an interesting alternative approach and does not employ the transformation group theorem of Hofmann and Mostert [1966] (see 3.4).

Recall from 3.1 that if S is a compact semigroup, then the semigroup $C(S)$ of closed subsets of S is compact.

3.19 Koch's Thread Theorem Let S be a compact connected monoid which is not a group such that each subgroup of S is totally disconnected. Then there is an I-semigroup T in S such that $1 \in T$ and $T \cap M(S) \ne \square$.

Proof: For each open cover δ of S, let $\mathcal{M}_\delta = \{A \in C(S) : A$ is an abelian $\mathcal{H}$-chain in S, $1 \in A$; and if $g,h \in E(S) \cap A$, with $g \neq h$, and if there is no element t in A with $g <_{\mathcal{H}} t <_{\mathcal{H}} h$, then there exists $N \in \delta$ such that $g,h \in N$}.

We show first that for each open cover δ of S, there exists $A_\delta \in \mathcal{M}_\delta$ with $A_\delta \cap M(S) \neq \square$. Choose $V \in \delta$ with $1 \in V$ and $V \cap M(S) = \square$. If $V \cap E(S) = \{1\}$, then there exists a one-parameter semigroup T_1 such that $1 \in T_1$, $\partial V \cap T_1 \neq \square$ [Mostert and Shields, 1957], and such that $M(T_1)$ is a connected group and hence (from the hypothesis) is degenerate. Let $\{e\} = M(T_1)$. If, on the other hand, $V \cap E(S) \neq \{1\}$, then we consider two cases: (a) some idempotent $f \in V$ is a local minimum in $E(S)$. In this case $V \cap fSf$ is a neighborhood of f in the semigroup fSf, and as above we get an I-semigroup from e to f. (b) each idempotent in V is not a local minimum in $E(S)$. In this case there is an I-semigroup of idempotents from 1 to ∂V from Koch's arc theorem (see 2.23). Thus in any case, there is an I-semigroup $T_1 = [e_1,f_1]$. Let $T_0 = \{1\}$, and let $A_1 = T_0 \cup T_1$. Then $A_1 \in \mathcal{M}_\delta$. If $e \notin M(S)$, we repeat the process in eSe (which is a semigroup satisfying the hypothesis of the theorem) and proceed by induction. Let Θ denote the least ordinal whose cardinal exceeds that of S. Suppose that the I-semigroup $T_\alpha = [e_\alpha, f_\alpha]$ has been constructed for each $\alpha < \zeta$ so that $A_\alpha = \bigcup_{\gamma \leq \alpha} T_\gamma$ is in $\mathcal{M}_\delta$. (Here $\alpha, \gamma, \zeta < \Theta$.) If ζ is not a limit ordinal, define T_ζ from $T_{\zeta-1}$ (where $\zeta - 1$ denotes the immediate predecessor of ζ) by repeating the process above in $e_{\zeta-1} S e_{\zeta-1}$ [assuming that $e_{\zeta-1} \notin M(S)$; clearly $A_\zeta \in \mathcal{M}_\delta$]. If ζ is a limit ordinal, consider

$$B_\zeta = \overline{\bigcup_{\alpha < \zeta} T_\alpha}$$

We show that $M(B_\zeta)$ is a single element, which we define to be T_ζ. Note that $M(B_\zeta)$ is a group (with unit e_ζ). Now $e_\zeta e_\alpha = e_\alpha$ for each $\alpha < \zeta$, so $e_\zeta[e_\alpha, f_\alpha] = e_\zeta$ for each α. It follows that $e_\zeta B_\zeta = e_\zeta$ and hence $\{e_\zeta\} = M(B_\zeta)$. It remains to show that $A_\zeta \in \mathcal{M}_\delta$; we show only that A_ζ is closed, the other properties being clear. Note that

$$\overline{A_\zeta} = A_\zeta \cup \overline{\bigcup_{\alpha < \zeta} A_\alpha} = e_\zeta \cup B_\zeta = B_\zeta$$

For each $\alpha \leq \zeta$, $A_\zeta = A_\alpha \cup \bigcup_{\alpha < \beta \leq \zeta} T_\beta$, so

$$\overline{A_\zeta} = A_\alpha \cup \overline{\bigcup_{\alpha < \zeta \leq \zeta} T_\beta}$$

and $\overline{A_\zeta} \backslash A_\zeta \subseteq e_\zeta Se_\zeta \cap \overline{A_\zeta} = M(\overline{A_\zeta}) = M(B_\zeta) = e_\zeta$. But $e_\zeta \in A_\zeta$, so $\overline{A_\zeta} \backslash A_\zeta = \square$ and A_ζ is closed. Hence, by transfinite induction, for each open cover δ there exists $A_\delta \in \mathcal{M}_\delta$ with $A_\delta \cap M(S) \neq \square$.

Let $\mathcal{D} = \{\delta : \delta$ is an open cover of $S\}$ and define $\delta_1 < \delta_2$ in $\mathcal{D}$ if δ_2 is a refinement of δ_1. Then the net $\{A_\delta : \delta \in \mathcal{D}\}$ clusters to some A in $C(S)$.

We claim that A is an I-semigroup from 1 to $M(S)$ in S. It is easy to show that A is a compact abelian semigroup with $1 \in A$ and $A \cap M(S) \neq \square$.

We show next that the principal ideals of A are ordered by inclusion, i.e., A/J_A is an ordered space (here J_A is the $\mathcal{H}$ relation on A defined by $J_A = \{(a,b) \in A \times A : aA = bA\}$). For, suppose $a,b \in A$ with $a \notin bA$ and $b \notin aA$; then there exist open sets U, V and P in S such that $a \in U$, $b \in V$, $A \subseteq P$, $U \cap PV = \square$, and $V \cap PU = \square$. Then $N = K(P,U) \cap K(P,V)$ (see the second paragraph of Appendix B) is an open set in $C(S)$ such that $A \in N$. Since $A_\delta \xrightarrow{f} A$, there exists $\delta \in \mathcal{D}$ such that $A_\delta \in N$. But if $a' \in A_\delta \cap U$ and $b' \in A_\delta \cap V$, then $a' \notin b'A_\delta$ and $b' \notin a'A_\delta$ contrary to the fact that the principal ideals of A_δ are ordered.

We next show that A is connected. Suppose to the contrary; then there are open sets P and Q with $\bar{P} \cap \bar{Q} = \square$, $A \subseteq P \cup Q$, and $A \cap P \neq \square \neq A \cap Q$. Now let $N = K(P \cup Q, P \cup Q)$; then N is open and $A \in N$. Further, there exists δ_0 in $\mathcal{D}$ such that $\delta_0 < \delta$ implies that $V \in \delta$ misses either P or Q. Thus there exists $\delta_0 < \delta$ such that $A_\delta \in N$ and we may suppose that $inf\ A_\delta \in$ P. Let $a = inf(A_\delta \cap Q)$ and $b = sup(P \cap \downarrow a)$. Note that $a^2 = a$, for otherwise $a \in (e_\alpha, f_\alpha) \subseteq A_\delta$ which leads to a disconnection of the interval (e_α, f_α). Also $b^2 = b$, as follows: $b \in [e_\alpha, f_\alpha]$, so $e_\alpha \leq b < a$ and $e_\alpha \in$ P. If $a \leq f_\alpha$, then $f_\alpha \in$ Q and $[e_\alpha, f_\alpha]$ is disconnected. Thus $f_\alpha \leq a$, so $f_\alpha \in$ P and $sup(P \cap \downarrow a) = b < f_\alpha$, a contradiction. Thus some member of δ contains both a and b, and hence meets both P and Q, contrary to the choice of δ. This contradiction shows that A is connected, and it follows that A/J_A is an I-semigroup. We conclude that A contains an I-semigroup from 1 to $M(S)$ (see Hunter [1960]). $\blacksquare$

The original definition of a hormos is found in Hofmann and Mostert [1966]. We give an equivalent definition for compact monoids in order to present an application of Koch's thread theorem that appears in Carruth and Clark [1972].

A compact monoid S is said to be a *hormos* provided $\mathcal{H}$ is a congruence on S and $S/\mathcal{H}$ is an I-semigroup.

3.20 Lemma.   Let S be a compact semigroup and let T be a subsemigroup of S such that $\bigcup\{H(e):e \in E(S)\} \subseteq T$. Then $\mathcal{H}_T = \mathcal{H}_S \cap (T \times T)$. Moreover, T is $\mathcal{H}_S$ saturated.

Proof: For the first part we need only show that $\mathcal{H}_S \cap (T \times T) \subseteq \mathcal{H}_T$. However, we prove both parts by fixing $x \in T$, letting H be its $\mathcal{H}_S$ class, and show that $H \times H \subseteq \mathcal{H}_T$. Let $T(H) = \{s \in S^1 : Hs \subseteq H\}$ and let $T'(H) = \{s \in S^1 : sH \subseteq H\}$. Let K be a maximal subgroup of $M(T(H))$ and let L be a maximal subgroup of $M(T'(H))$. Then $H = xK = Lx$ for each $x \in H$. Hence $H \subseteq xT^1 \cap T^1x$ for each $x \in H$ and it follows that $H \times H \subseteq \mathcal{H}_T$. $\blacksquare$

3.21 Theorem   If S is a compact connected abelian monoid, then S contains a hormos that contains 1 and meets $M(S)$.

Proof: Now, since S is abelian, $\mathcal{H}_S$ is a congruence on S. Since $S/\mathcal{H}_S$ has trivial groups, it follows from Koch's thread theorem (3.19) that there is an I-semigroup I in $S/\mathcal{H}_S$ from its zero to its identity. Let $\eta:S \to S/\mathcal{H}_S$ denote the natural map and let $S_1 = \eta^{-1}(I)$. Then, as above, $S_1/\mathcal{H}_{S_1}$ contains an I-semigroup J from its zero to its identity. Now, if $\{f\} = E(S_1) \cap M(S)$ and $e \in E(S_1)\setminus\{1,f\}$, then $I\setminus\{\eta(e)\} = P \cup Q$ (disjoint union). It follows that $(S_1/\mathcal{H}_{S_1})\setminus\{\eta_1(e)\} = \eta_1(\eta^{-1}(P)) \cup \eta_1(\eta^{-1}(Q))$. Hence, $\eta_1(e) \in J$ and $H(e) \subseteq S_2 = \eta_1^{-1}(J)$. Obviously, $H(1) \cup H(f) \subseteq S_2$. It now follows from 3.20 that $S_2/\mathcal{H}_{S_2}$ is topologically isomorphic to J, and we obtain the result of the theorem. $\blacksquare$

4

The Translational Hull and Ideal Extensions

In this chapter we develop the concept of the translational hull of a topological semigroup. Many of the results are valid for semitopological semigroups, but we will restrict our attention to locally compact (and mostly compact) semigroups.

Most of the material in this chapter is derived from Hildebrant, Lawson, and Yeager [1976] and Hildebrant [1982] with earlier contributions from Christoph [1970] and Bowman [1970]. The algebraic theory was developed in Clifford and Preston [1961], Petrich [1970], and Petrich [1973]. A discussion of background topological concepts appears in Arens and Dugundji [1951] and Kelly [1955].

BASIC CONSTRUCTION

In this section we present the basic concepts needed to construct the translational hull of a locally compact semigroup.

If S is a semigroup, the a function $\lambda:S \to S$ [$\rho:S \to S$] is called a *left [right] translation* of S provided $\lambda(xy) = (\lambda x)y[(xy)\rho = x(y\rho)]$ for each $x, y \in S$. It is convenient to express the image of $x \in S$ under the right translation ρ as $x\rho$.

A pair (λ, ρ) of functions of a semigroup S into itself is said to be *linked* provided $x(\lambda y) = (x\rho)y$ for each $x, y \in S$. If we write $\omega = (\lambda, \rho)$, then we write $\omega a = \lambda x$ and $a\omega = a\rho$ for each $a \in S$. We refer

49

to ω as a *bitranslation* or simply *translation* of S, if λ is a left translation of S and ρ is a right translation of S.

If S is a topological semigroup, $\lambda:S \to S$ is a continuous left translation of S and $\rho:S \to S$ is a continuous right translation of S such that $\omega = (\lambda,\rho)$ is linked, then we say that ω is a *continuous bitranslation* of S.

For a topological semigroup S, if $a \in S$, then $\lambda_a:S \to S[\rho_a:S \to S]$ defined by $\lambda_a(x) = ax[x\rho_a = xa]$ for each $x \in S$ is a continuous left [right] translation of S, and $\omega_a = (\lambda_a,\rho_a)$ is a continuous bitranslation of S. We refer to ω_a as the *inner bitranslation* of S defined by a.

Recall that if X is a locally compact Hausdorff space and $C(X,X)$ is the set of all continuous functions from X into X, then under composition and with the compact-open topology, $C(X,X)$ is a topological semigroup (see 2.6 of Carruth, Hildebrant, and Koch [1983]). If we let $R(X,X)$ be the semigroup of continuous functions from X into X under reverse composition, then it is equally clear that $R(X,X)$ is a topological semigroup.

Let S be a locally compact semigroup and let $\Omega(S)$ denote the set of all continuous bitranslations of S. We introduce multiplication on $\Omega(S)$ by declaring that $(\lambda_1,\rho_1)(\lambda_2,\rho_2) = (\lambda_1 \circ \lambda_2, \rho_1 \circ \rho_2)$. Note that multiplication in the second factor is reverse composition, since right translations act on the right. Observe that $x,y \in S$ yields $x(\lambda_1\lambda_2 y) = x(\lambda_1(\lambda_2 y)) = (x\rho_1)(\lambda_2 y) = (x\rho_1\rho_2)y$, so that $\Omega(S)$ is a subsemigroup of $C(S,S) \times R(S,S)$, and with the relative topology $\Omega(S)$ is a topological semigroup.

For $\omega = (\lambda,\rho) \in \Omega(S)$, and $x \in S$, we write $\omega x = \lambda x$ and $x\omega = x\rho$.

A net ϕ_α in a space $C(X,X)$ is said to *converge continuously* to $\phi \in C(X,X)$ provided for each $x_\beta \to x$ in X, we have $\phi_\alpha(x_\beta) \to \phi(x)$. Observe that if ω_α is a net in $\Omega(S)$, then ω_α converges continuously to $\omega \in \Omega(S)$ if and only if for each $x_\beta \to x$ in S, we have $\omega_\alpha x_\beta \to \omega x$ and $x_\beta \omega_\alpha \to x\omega$.

4.1 Lemma Let X be a locally compact Hausdorff space and let ϕ_α be a net in $C(X,X)$. Then $\phi_\alpha \to \phi$ in $C(X,X)$ if and only if ϕ_α converges continuously to ϕ.

Proof: Suppose first that $\phi_\alpha \to \phi$, and let $x_\beta \to x$ in X. Take U to be an open set in X such that $\phi(x) \in U$, and let W be an open set in X such that $x \in W$, $\overline{W}$ is compact and $\phi(\overline{W}) \subseteq U$ (from the continuity of ϕ). Then $\phi \in N(\overline{W}, U)$ [recall that $N(\overline{W}, U)$ is the set of all functions which take $\overline{W}$ into U], and thus $\phi_\alpha \in^e N(\overline{W}, U)$. Now $x_\beta \in^e \overline{W}$, so that $\phi_\alpha(x_\beta) \in^e U$, and $\phi_\alpha(x_\beta) \to \phi(x)$. We conclude that ϕ_α converges continuously to ϕ.

Suppose now, on the other hand, that ϕ_α converges continuously to ϕ. Let $\phi \in N(K, U)$, where K is compact and U is open in X. Then $\phi(K) \subseteq U$. We want to demonstrate that $\phi_\alpha \in^e N(K, U)$. Assume to the contrary that $\phi_\alpha \in^f C(X, X) \backslash N(K, U)$. Then $\phi_\alpha(K) \cap (X \backslash U) \neq^f \square$. Let $x_\alpha \in K$ with $\phi_\alpha(x_\alpha) \in^f X \backslash U$. Now x_α clusters to some x in K, since K is compact. We can assume that $x_\alpha \to x$. Then $\phi_\alpha(x_\alpha) \to \phi(x)$, so that $\phi(x) \in X \backslash U$. This contradicts $\phi(K) \subseteq U$. ∎

4.2 Theorem Let S be a locally compact semigroup. Then $\Omega(S)$ is a topological semigroup. If ω_α is a net in $\Omega(S)$, then $\omega_\alpha \to \omega$ in $\Omega(S)$ if and only if ω_α converges continuously to ω.

Proof: This follows from 4.1. ∎

A semigroup S is said to be *left* [*right*] *reductive* if $xa = xb[ax = bx]$ for all $x \in S$ implies $a = b$. If S is both left and right reductive, then S is said to be *reductive*. If $xa = xb$ and $ax = bx$ for all $x \in S$ implies that $a = b$, then S is said to be *weakly reductive*. It is clear that a reductive semigroup is also weakly reductive.

If S is a topological semigroup, then S is said to be *left* [*right*] *net reductive* if $xa_\alpha \to xa[a_\alpha x \to ax]$ for all $x \in S$ implies $a_\alpha \to a$. If S is both left and right net reductive, then we say that S is *net reductive*. By considering a constant net, it is clear that each net reductive topological semigroup is reductive.

4.3 Theorem Let S be a net reductive topological semigroup. Then each bitranslation of S is continuous.

Proof: Let ω be a bitranslation of S, and let $y_\alpha \to y$ in S.

Then for each $x \in S$, we have $x(\omega y_\alpha) = (x\omega)y_\alpha \to (x\omega)y = x(\omega y)$, and since S is net reductive, $\omega y_\alpha \to \omega y$. Likewise, $y_\alpha \omega \to y\omega$, and hence ω is continuous. ∎

4.4 Theorem Let S be a compact semigroup. Then S is reductive if and only if S is net reductive.

Proof: That net reductive implies reductive is clear. Suppose that S is reductive. Let y_α be a net in S and assume that $xy_\alpha \to xy$ for all $x \in S$. Now $y_\alpha \xrightarrow{f} z$ for some $z \in S$, so that for each $x \in S$, $xy_\alpha \xrightarrow{f} xz$. It follows that $xy = xz$ for each $x \in S$, and since S is reductive, $y = z$, and $y_\alpha \to y$. ∎

4.5 Corollary Each bitranslation of a compact reductive semigroup is continuous.

Proof: This follows from 4.3 and 4.4. ∎

If ω_α is a net of bitranslations of a topological semigroup S and ω is a bitranslation of S, then ω_α *converges pointwise* to ω provided $\omega_\alpha x \to \omega x$ and $x\omega_\alpha \to x\omega$ for each $x \in S$.

4.6 Theorem Let S be a net reductive topological semigroup, ω a bitranslation of S, and ω_α a net of bitranslations of S. Then ω_α converges to ω pointwise if and only if ω_α converges to ω continuously.

Proof: It is clear that continuous convergence implies pointwise convergence. Suppose that ω_α converges pointwise to ω. Let $x_\beta \to x$ in S. Then for each $y \in S$, we have $y(\omega_\alpha x_\beta) = (y\omega_\alpha) x_\beta \to (y\omega)x = y(\omega x)$, and since S is net reductive, $\omega_\alpha x_\beta \to \omega x$. ∎

4.7 Corollary Let S be a compact reductive semigroup, ω_α a net of bitranslations of S, and ω a bitranslation of S. Then these are equivalent:
   (a) $\omega_\alpha \to \omega$ in $\Omega(S)$.
   (b) ω_α converges continuously to ω.
   (c) ω_α converges pointwise to ω.

Proof: The equivalence of (a) and (b) follows from 4.2, and the equivalence of (b) and (c) follows from 4.4 and 4.6. ∎

4.8 **Lemma** Let S be a reductive semigroup and $\alpha,\beta:S\to S$ such that (α,β) is linked. Then (α,β) is a bitranslation of S.

Proof: We need to show that α is a left translation and β is a right translation of S. To see that α is a left translation, let $x,y \in S$. Then for each $t \in S$, we have $t(\alpha x)(y) = (t(\alpha x))y = (t\beta)(x)y = (t\beta)(xy) = t(\alpha(xy))$. Since S is reductive, $(\alpha x)y = \alpha(xy)$, and α is a left translation. A similar argument shows that β is a right translation. ∎

4.9 **Theorem** Let S be a compact reductive semigroup. Then $\Omega(S)$ is a compact semigroup.

Proof: For each $a \in S$, let $T_a = S \times S$, $\pi_1, \pi_2:S \times S \to S$ first and second projections, $T = \Pi\{T_a : a \in S\}$, and $\phi_a:T \to T_a$ projection. If $\omega \in \Omega(S)$, let $\omega' \in T$ such that $\phi_a\omega' = (\omega a, a\omega)$ for each $a \in S$.

Let ω_α be a net in $\Omega(S)$. Then, since T is compact, $\omega'_\alpha \xrightarrow{f} \sigma$ for some $\sigma \in T$. We can assume that $\omega'_\alpha \to \sigma$ in T. Define ω by $\omega a = \pi_1\phi_a\sigma$ and $a\omega = \pi_2\phi_a\sigma$ for each $a \in S$.

To see that ω is a bitranslation of S, in view of 4.8, we need only verify that ω is linked. Let $a,b \in S$. Then $b(\omega_\alpha a) = (b\omega_\alpha)a$ for each α, $b(\omega_\alpha a) = b(\pi_1(\omega_\alpha a, a\omega_\alpha)) = b\pi_1\phi_a\omega'_\alpha \to b\pi_1\phi_a\sigma = b(\omega a)$ and $b(\omega_\alpha)a = (\pi_2(\omega_\alpha b, b\omega_\alpha))a = (\pi_2\phi_b\omega'_\alpha)a \to (\pi_2\phi_b\sigma)a = (b\omega)a$. It follows that $b(\omega a) = (b\omega)a$, and from 4.3 and 4.4, we have $\omega \in \Omega(S)$.

To show that $\Omega(S)$ is compact, it remains to show that $\omega_\alpha \to \omega$ in $\Omega(S)$ (assuming that $\omega'_\alpha \to \sigma$). In view of 4.7, we need only show that convergence is pointwise. Now for $x \in S$, we have $\omega_\alpha x = \pi_1(\omega_\alpha x, x\omega_\alpha) = \pi_1\phi_x\omega'_\alpha \to \pi_1\phi_x\sigma = \omega x$ and likewise $x\omega_\alpha \to x\omega$. ∎

If S is a locally compact semigroup, define $\pi:S \to \Omega(S)$ by $\pi(a) = \omega_a$ for each $a \in S$. It is clear that π is a homomorphism. We will show that it is continuous. We call π the *canonical homomorphism* and $\pi(S)$ is called the *inner translational hull* of S. Observe that if S is weakly reductive, then π is injective. In any case, $\pi(S)$ is an ideal of $\Omega(S)$.

4.10 Theorem Let S be a locally compact semigroup and $\pi : S \to \Omega(S)$ the canonical homomorphism. Then π is continuous.

Proof: Let $a_\alpha \to a$ in S. Then for $x_\beta \to x$ in S, we have $\omega_{a_\alpha} x_\beta = a_\alpha x_\beta \to ax = \omega_a x$, and likewise $x_\beta \omega_{a_\alpha} \to x\omega_a$. In view of 4.2, we have $\omega_{a_\alpha} \to \omega_a$, i.e., $\pi(a_\alpha) \to \pi(a)$ and π is continuous. ∎

4.11 Corollary Let S be a compact weakly reductive semigroup. Then $\pi : S \to \Omega(S)$ is an embedding.

If S is an abelian semigroup, then S is reductive if and only if S is weakly reductive. Moreover, if (λ, ρ) is a bitranslation of S and $x, y \in S$, we have $(\lambda x)y = y(\lambda x) = (y\rho)x = x(y\rho) = (xy)\rho = (yx)\rho = y(x\rho) = (x\rho)y$, so that $\lambda x = x\rho$ for all $x \in S$. In this case we also have for bitranslations ω and ω', and $x \in S$, $\omega\omega'x = \omega(x\omega') = (x\omega')\omega = x(\omega'\omega) = \omega'\omega x$, so that $\omega\omega' = \omega'\omega$. Thus if S is a locally compact abelian semigroup, then $\Omega(S)$ is an abelian topological semigroup of (left) translations of S under composition.

EXTENSIONS OF BITRANSLATIONS

If T is a subsemigroup of a semigroup S and ω is a bitranslation of T, then a bitranslation $\bar\omega$ of S is called an *extension* of ω to S provided $\bar\omega x = \omega x$ and $x\bar\omega = x\omega$ for each $x \in T$, and we write $\bar\omega | T = \omega$.

4.12 Theorem Let S be a compact reductive semigroup and let T be a dense subsemigroup of S. Then each bitranslation of T has a unique continuous extension to S.

Proof: Let ω be a bitranslation of T. Let $x \in S$ and let a_α and b_β be nets in T with $a_\alpha \to x$ and $b_\beta \to x$. Let p be a cluster point of the net ωa_α and let q be a cluster point of ωb_β. Then for each $t \in T$, $t(\omega a_\alpha) = (t\omega)a_\alpha \overset{f}{\to} tp$ and $t(\omega b_\beta) = (t\omega)b_\beta \overset{f}{\to} tq$. On the other hand, from the continuity of multiplication in S, we have $(t\omega)a_\alpha \to (t\omega)x$ and $(t\omega b_\beta) \to (t\omega)x$. Thus $tp = (t\omega)x = tq$. Thus $tp = tq$ for all $t \in T$, and since T is dense in S, $zp = zq$ for all $z \in S$. Since S is reductive, we have $p = q$. We conclude that for each $x \in S$ with any choice of the net t_α in T converging to x, the net ωt_α converges to a unique limit. We define $\bar{\omega}x = lim\, \omega t_\alpha$, and likewise $x\bar{\omega} = lim\, t_\alpha \omega$. It is clear that $\bar{\omega}|T = \omega$ and $\bar{\omega}$ is unique. In view of 4.5 and 4.3, we need only show that $\bar{\omega}$ is linked. For this purpose, let $x, y \in S$, and x_α and y_α nets in T such that $x_\alpha \to x$ and $y_\beta \to y$. Then $(x\bar{\omega})y = lim(x_\alpha \omega)y_\beta = lim(x_\alpha)(\omega y_\beta) = x(\bar{\omega}y)$. ∎

4.13   Theorem   Let S be a semigroup, T a reductive semigroup, $\phi : S \to T$ a surmorphism, and let ω be a bitranslation of S. Then there exists a unique bitranslation ω' of T such that for each $x \in S$, $\omega'\phi(x) = \phi(\omega x)$ and $\phi(x)\omega' = \phi(x\omega)$.

Proof: For $t \in T$, let $s \in S$ such that $\phi(s) = t$, and define $\omega't = \phi(\omega s)$ and $t\omega' = \phi(xw)$. The remainder of the argument is straightforward. ∎

4.14   Theorem   Let S be a topological semigroup, T a compact reductive semigroup, $\phi : S \to T$ a dense continuous homomorphism and ω a bitranslation of S. Then there exists a unique continuous bitranslation ω' of T such that $\omega'\phi(x) = \phi(\omega x)$ and $\phi(x)\omega' = \phi(x\omega)$ for all $x \in S$.

Proof: This follows from 4.12 and 4.13. ∎

4.15   Theorem   Let S be a locally compact semigroup, T a compact reductive semigroup, and $\phi : S \to T$ a dense continuous homomorphism. Then there exists a unique continuous homomorphism $\phi^*:\Omega(S) \to \Omega(T)$ such that the diagrams

$$\Omega(S) \overset{\phi^*}{\to} \Omega(T) \qquad\qquad S \overset{\phi}{\to} T$$

$$\pi\uparrow \qquad \uparrow\pi \qquad\qquad \omega\uparrow \qquad \uparrow\phi^*\omega$$

$$S \xrightarrow[\phi]{} T \qquad\qquad S \underset{\phi}{\to} T$$

commute.

Proof: We define $\phi^*\omega = \omega'$ from 4.14. To see that the first diagram commutes observe that for $x \in S$, $\phi^*(\omega_x) = \omega_{\phi(x)}$. That ϕ^* is a homomorphism follows from 4.14.

To see that ϕ^* is continuous, let $\omega_\alpha \to \omega$ in $\Omega(S)$. Then ω_α converges continuously to ω (4.2), and in particular, for $x \in S$, $\omega_\alpha x \to \omega x$, so that $\phi(\omega_\alpha x) \to \phi(\omega x)$, and $\phi^*\omega_\alpha(\phi x) = \phi(\omega_\alpha x) \to \phi(\omega x) = \phi^*\omega(\phi x)$. In view of 4.7, we have $\phi^*\omega_\alpha \to \phi^*\omega$ and ϕ^* is continuous. ∎

DIVISIBILITY

In this section we use the translational hull to demonstrate a partial solution of the conjecture that each compact semigroup can be embedded in a compact divisible semigroup.

Note that if S is a reductive abelian semigroup and $(\lambda,\rho) \in \Omega(S)$, then $\lambda x = x\rho$ for each $x \in S$. To see this, let $x \in S$. Then for each $t \in S$, we have $t(\lambda x) = (t\rho)x = x(t\rho) = (xt)\rho = (tx)\rho = t(x\rho)$, and hence $\lambda x = x\rho$.

Observe that a power cancellative abelian semigroup S is reductive. To see this, let $a, b \in S$, and suppose that $ax = bx$ for all $x \in S$. Then, in particular, for $x = a$, $a^2 = ba = ab$, and for $x = b$, $ab = b^2$, so that $a^2 = b^2$. It follows that $a = b$, and S is reductive.

4.16 Lemma   Let S be a power-cancellative abelian semigroup. Then $\Omega(S)$ is a power-cancellative abelian semigroup.

Proof: Let $\alpha, \beta \in \Omega(S)$ and suppose that $\alpha^n = \beta^n$ for some $n \in \mathbf{N}$. Then for $x \in S$, $(\alpha x)^n = \alpha^n x^n$ (using induction and $x\alpha = \alpha x$). Thus $(\alpha x)^n = \alpha^n x^n = \beta^n x^n = (\beta x)^n$ and, since S is power cancellative, $\alpha x = \beta x$ and $\alpha = \beta$. $\blacksquare$

If S is a locally compact semigroup, and $A \subseteq S$, then

$$A^* = \{\omega \in \Omega(S): \omega A \cup A\omega \subseteq A\}$$

Note that $A^* \neq \square$, since 1_S (the identity on S) is in A^*

4.17 Lemma Let S be a locally compact semigroup and I a closed ideal of S. Then I^* is a closed subsemigroup of $\Omega(S)$ containing $\pi(S)$ and 1_S.

Proof: That $\pi(S) \subseteq I^*$ and that I^* is a subsemigroup of $\Omega(S)$ are transparent. To see that I^* is closed, let $\omega_\alpha \to \omega$ in $\Omega(S)$. Then ω_α converges continuously (and hence pointwise) to ω by 4.2. Thus for $x \in I$, we have $\omega_\alpha x \to \omega x$, $\omega_\alpha x \in I$, and since I is closed $\omega x \in I$. Similarly, $x\omega \in I$, and $\omega \in I^*$. $\blacksquare$

A semigroup S is called a *power ideal semigroup* if for each $n \in \mathbf{N}$, the image of S under $x \mapsto x^n$ is an ideal of S.

4.18 Theorem Let S be a compact power cancellative power ideal abelian semigroup. Then there exists a compact uniquely divisible abelian subsemigroup T of $\Omega(S)$ such that $\pi: S \to \Omega(S)$ is an embedding of S into T.

Proof: For each $n \in \mathbf{N}$, let $S_n = \{x^n : x \in S\}$, and let $T = \bigcap\{S_n^* : n \in \mathbf{N}\}$. Then, from 4.17 and 4.9, T is a compact subsemigroup of $\Omega(S)$ containing $\pi(S)$. From 4.16, we have that $\Omega(S)$ is power cancellative, and from 4.11, $\pi: S \to \Omega(S)$ is an embedding of S into T. It remains to show that T is divisible.

Let $\omega \in T$ and $n \in \mathbf{N}$. Then for each $x \in S$, $\omega x^n \in S_n$, since $\omega \in$

S_n^*. Since S is power cancellative, there exists a unique $x_0 \in S$ such that $x_0^n = \omega x^n$. Define $\tau x = x_0$ for each $x \in S$. Let $a, b \in S$. Then $[a(\tau b)]^n = a^n(\tau b)^n = a^n b_0^n = a^n(\omega b^n) = (a^n \omega) b^n = a_0^n b^n = (a_0 b)^n = [(a\tau)b]^n$, and hence $a(\tau b) = (a\tau)b$. From 4.8 and 4.3, we have $\tau \in \Omega(S)$.

For the purpose of showing that $\tau^n = \omega$; let $x \in S$, and observe that $[\tau^n x]^n = (\omega x)^n$, and $\tau^n \omega = \omega x$, so that $\tau^n = \omega$.

Finally to see that $\tau \in T$, let $k \in \mathbf{N}$ and $x \in S$. Then $[\tau x^k]^n = (x^k)_0^n = \omega x^{kn} = u^{kn}$ for some $u \in S$, since $\omega \in T \subseteq S_{kn}^*$. Thus $[\tau x^k]^n = [u^k]^n$, so that $\tau x^k = u^k \in S_k$, and $\tau \in T$. ∎

COMPUTATIONAL TECHNIQUES

In this section we present results which allow one to determine the structure of the translational hull from some compact semigroups.

An element x in a semigroup S is called a *left [right] cancellative element* of S provided $xa = xb [ax = bx]$ implies $a = b$ in S. If x is both left cancellative and right cancellative, then x is said to be a *cancellative element* of S.

If x is an element of a semigroup S and $xS = Sx$, then x is called a *normal element* of S.

4.19   Theorem   Let S be a compact monoid and x a cancellative normal element of S. Then $\Omega(Sx)$ is topologically isomorphic to S.

Proof: Define $\phi: S \to \Omega(Sx)$ by $\phi(a) = \omega_a | Sx$. If $a \in S$ and $t \in S$, then $\omega_a(tx) = atx \in Sx$, so that ϕ is well defined.

To see that ϕ is surjective, let $\omega \in \Omega(Sx)$. Then $\omega x \in Sx$, so that $\omega x = ax$ for some $a \in S$. Let $y \in Sx$. Then $y = tx = xt'$ for some $t, t' \in S$, since x is normal. Thus $(\omega y)x = \omega(yx) = \omega(xt'x) = (\omega x)t'x = (ax)(t'x) = ayx = (\omega_a y)x$, and, since x is cancellative, $\omega y = \omega_a y$. We obtain that $\omega = \phi(a)$, and ϕ is surjective.

Now for $a, b \in S$, we have $\phi(ab) = \omega_{ab} | Sx = (\omega_a | Sx) \circ (\omega_b | Sx) = \phi(a)\phi(b)$, and ϕ is a homomorphism.

If $a_\alpha \to a$ in S, then since $\pi: S \to \Omega(S)$ is continuous, $\omega_{a_\alpha} \to \omega_a$, and hence $\phi(a_\alpha) \to \phi(a)$. It follows that ϕ is continuous.

To see that ϕ is injective, suppose that $\phi(a) = \phi(b)$. Then

$\omega_a|Sx = \omega_b|Sx$, and in particular $\omega_a x = \omega_b x$, $ax = bx$, and hence $a = b$, since x is cancellative. ∎

Example To illustrate 4.19, let $S = I_u = [0,1]$ with the usual topology and multiplication, and let $x = 1/2$. Then $Sx = [0,1/2]$ and hence $\Omega([0,1/2]) = [0,1]$.

Example If we modify the preceding example to let $S = [0,1/2] \cup \{1\}$, and let $x = 1/2$, then $Sx = [0,1/4] \cup \{1/2\}$ and $\Omega([0,1/4] \cup \{1/2\}) = [0,1/2] \cup \{1\}$.

A subset B of a semigroup S is called a *separating subset* of S provided that for each $x \neq y$ in S, there exist $a,b \in B$ such that $ax \neq ay$ and $xb \neq yb$. A minimal separating subset of a semigroup S is called a *bitranslational basis* (or simply a *basis*) for S. Observe that a semigroup S is reductive if and only if S contains a separating subset.

If x is a cancellative normal element of a semigroup S, then $\{x\}$ is a basis for S.

4.20 Lemma Let S be a semigroup and B a separating subset of S. If ω and ω' are bitranslations of S such that $\omega|B = \omega'|B$, then $\omega = \omega'$.

Proof: Let $x \in S$. Now for each $b \in S$, $b\omega = b\omega'$ and hence $b(\omega x) = (b\omega)x = (b\omega')x = b(\omega'x)$. It follows that $\omega x = \omega'x$, and likewise $x\omega = x\omega'$, so that $\omega = \omega'$. ∎

4.21 Theorem Let S be a compact reductive abelian semigroup and B a separating subset of S such that $B \subseteq E(S)$. Define $\phi:\Omega(S) \to \Pi\{Se:e \in B\}$ by $\pi_e\phi(\omega) = \omega e$, where π_e is projection onto Se. Then ϕ is an embedding.

Proof: Now $\Omega(S)$ is a compact abelian semigroup and $x\omega = \omega x$ for each $\omega \in \Omega(S)$ for each $x \in S$. Now ϕ is continuous, since its composition with each projection is continuous, and injectivity follows from 4.20. To see that ϕ is a homomorphism, let $\omega, \omega' \in \Omega(S)$ and $e \in B$. Then $\pi_e\phi(\omega\omega') = \omega\omega'e = \omega(e\omega') = \omega(ee\omega') = \omega(e(e\omega')) = (\omega e)(\omega'e) = \pi_e\phi(\omega)\pi_e\phi(\omega')$. ∎

Observe that if S is an abelian semigroup such that $S = ES$, then S is reductive and E is a separating subset of S. To see this, let $x \neq y$ in S, and suppose that $e, f \in E$ such that $x = ex$ and $y = fy$. Now if $xe = ye$, then $xf = yef = ye = x$, and since $yf = y$, we have $xf \neq yf$. Moreover, if B is a subset of E such that $S = BS$, then B is a separating subset of S.

4.22 Theorem Let S be a compact abelian semigroup such that $S = ES$, and let $B \subseteq E$ such that $S = BS$. Let $K = \{x \in \Pi\{Se:e \in B\}:\pi_e(x)f = \pi_f(x)e$ for each $e, f \in B\}$. Then K is a compact subsemigroup of $\Pi\{Se:e \in B\}$ and K is topologically isomorphic to $\Omega(S)$.

Proof: Let $\phi:\Omega(S) \to \Pi\{Se:e \in B\}$ be the embedding of S in 4.21. We will show that $K = \phi(\Omega(S))$. Let $x \in K$. Let $t \in S$ with $t \in Se$ and define $\omega t = \pi_e(x)t$. Then $\omega \in \Omega(S)$, and $\phi(\omega) = x$. Now let $\omega \in \Omega(S)$. Then for $e, f \in B$, $\pi_e(\phi(\omega))f = (\omega e)f = \omega(ef) = \omega(fe) = (\omega f)e = \pi_f(\phi(\omega))e$, and hence $\phi(\omega) \in K$. ∎

Example To illustrate 4.22, let $P = I_m \times I_m$ and let $S = \{(0,b):b \in I_m\} \cup \{(a,0):a \in I_m\} \cup \{(a,1):a \leq 1/2\} \cup \{(1,b):b \leq 1/2\} \cup \{(a,b) \in P:a \leq 1/2, b \leq 1/2\}$. Let $e = (1/2,1)$ and $f = (1,1/2)$. Then S is a compact connected subsemilattice of P and $S = Se \cup Sf$. We illustrate S:

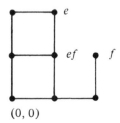

(0, 0)

Let $S^1 = S \cup \{(1,1)\}$ and let $K = \{(a,b) \in Se \times Sf : af = be\}$. Then, according to 4.22, $\Omega(S)$ is topologically isomorphic to K. Now $\psi : S^1 \to K$ defined by $\psi(t) = (te, tf)$ is a topological isomorphism, and hence $\Omega(S)$ is topologically isomorphic to S^1.

FINITE SEMIGROUPS

We discuss in this section some of the results which appear in Hildebrant [1984]. These results pertain to a broader class of semigroups which contain finite semigroups, but our applications are mostly to finite semigroups. Computer generated examples serve both to illustrate results and to demonstrate their limitations.

For a set A, recall that $\#A$ denotes the cardinal number of A, and for a semigroup S we use $\leq$ to denote $\leq_{\mathcal{H}}$, i.e., the $\mathcal{H}$ quasi-order on S. If $x \in S$, then $\downarrow x = \{y \in S : y \leq x\}$, and $\uparrow x = \{y \in S : x \leq y\}$.

The following result demonstrates the special nature of finite abelian semigroups.

4.23 Theorem   Let S be a finite reductive abelian semigroup. Then S has an idempotent translational basis.

Proof: Let $S = \{a_1, \ldots, a_n\}$ and let $n_i = min\{k : a_i^k \in E\}$, $1 \leq i \leq n$, where E denotes the set of idempotents of S. Then $a_i^{n_i} \in E$ for $1 \leq i \leq n$. Let $x \neq y$ in S. Then, since S is reductive, $t_1 x \neq t_1 y$ for some $t_1 \in S$. We obtain a sequence $\{t_n\}$ in S in such that $t_n t_{n-1} \cdots t_1 x \neq t_n t_{n-1} \cdots t_1 y$, and hence $a_1^{m_1} \cdots a_n^{m_n} x \neq a_1^{m_1} \cdots a_n^{m_n} y (m_i \leq 0)$. Eventually, since S is finite $m_j = n_j$ for some j, $a_n^{n_j} = e \in E$, $rex \neq rey$ for $r \in S$, and $ex \neq ey$.   ∎

If S is an abelian semigroup and $a \leq b$ in S, then for each $\omega \in \Omega(S)$, $\omega a \leq \omega b$. To see this note that $a = bx$ for some $x \in S^1$, so that $\omega a = \omega(bx) = (\omega b)x$ and $\omega a \leq \omega b$. Thus an bitranslation on an abelian semigroup is $\mathcal{H}$-order preserving.

If S is a semigroup and $A \subseteq S$, then for $\omega : S \to S$, we use $\omega | A$ to denote the restriction of ω to A.

4.24 Theorem Let S be an abelian semigroup such that $S = ES$, and let A and B be subsemigroups and I an ideal of S such that $S = A \cup B$, and $A \cap B = AB = I$. If $\omega:S \to S$, then $\omega \in \Omega(S)$ if and only if there exist $\alpha \in \Omega(A)$ and $\beta \in \Omega(B)$ such that $\alpha|I = \beta|I$, $\omega|A = \alpha$, and $\omega|B = \beta$.

Proof: Suppose that $\omega \in \Omega(S)$. We show that $\omega|A \in \Omega(A)$. Let $x \in S$ and let $e \in E$ such that $x = ex$. If $e \in B$, then $x = ex = xe \in AB = I$, and hence $\omega x = \omega(ex) = (\omega e)x \in I \subseteq A$. Thus we can assume that $e \in A$. If $\omega e \in B$, then $\omega e = (\omega e)e = e\omega e \in AB = I$, $\omega x = \omega(ex) = (\omega e)x \in I$, and hence $\omega x \in A$ in any case. Similarly, $\omega|B \in \Omega(B)$.

To prove the converse, let $\alpha \in \Omega(A)$ and $\beta \in \Omega(B)$, such that $\alpha|I = \beta|I$. Define $\omega:S \to S$ by $\omega x = \alpha x$ if $x \in A$, and $\omega x = \beta x$ if $x \in B$. If $a,b \in S$, then $\omega(\omega b) = a(\omega b)$ is clear if a and b are either both in A or both in B. Suppose that $a \in A$ and $b \in B$. Let $f \in E$ such that $b = bf$. If $f \in A$, then $b = bf \in AB = I$, and $b \in A$. If $f \in B$, then $\omega(ab) = \omega(afb) = \beta(afb) = (af)\beta(b) = a\beta(b) = a(\omega b)$. ∎

The following is a corollary of 4.24.

4.25 The Product Theorem Let S be a finite abelian semigroup with zero 0 such that $S = ES$, and let A and B be subsemigroups of S such that $S = A \cup B$, and $A \cap B = AB = \{0\}$. Then $\#\Omega(S) = \#\Omega(A) \cdot \#\Omega(B)$.

If S is a weakly reductive semigroup, then we have observed that $\pi:S \to \Omega(S)$ is an isomorphism of S into $\Omega(S)$. In this case, the *translational degree* of S is defined by $deg\ S = \#(\Omega(S)\backslash\pi(S))$.

4.26 Theorem Let S be an abelian semigroup, A a subsemigroup of S with zero e, and let B be a subsemigroup of S such that e is the identity of B and $S \stackrel{.}{=} A \cup B$. If $\omega:S \to S$, then $\omega \in \Omega(S)$ if and only if either $\omega|A \in \Omega(A)$ and $\omega|B = 1_B$; or $\omega A = \omega e$ and $\omega|B \in \Omega(B)$. In particular, if S and A are reductive, then $deg\ S = deg\ A$.

Proof: Suppose that $\omega \in \Omega(S)$. If $\omega e = e$, then since $e \le a$

for each $a \in A$, $e = \omega e \leq \omega a$ for each $a \in A$, and $\omega|A \in \Omega(A)$. Clearly, $\omega|B = 1_B$, since $\omega e = e$.

Suppose that $\omega \in \Omega(S)$ and $\omega e \neq e$. Since $\omega e = \omega e^2 = (\omega e)e$, $\omega e \leq e$. Now if $\omega a \in A$ for some $a \in A$, we have $e = e \cdot \omega a = \omega(ea) = \omega e$, which contradicts $\omega e \neq e$. Thus $\omega A \subseteq B$, and for $a \in A$, we have $\omega a = e(\omega a) = \omega(ea) = \omega e$.

Suppose that $\omega|A \in \Omega(A)$ and $\omega|B = 1_B$. Let $a, a' \in A$ and $b \in B$. Then $\omega(aa') = \omega e = \omega(ea) = a(\omega e) = a(\omega a')$, $\omega(ab) = \omega(a \cdot eb) = \omega((ae)b) = \omega(eb) = \omega b = a(\omega b)$, and $\omega(ba) = \omega((be)a) = \omega(b(ea)) = b\omega(ea) = b(\omega e) = b(\omega a)$. We conclude that $\omega \in \Omega(S)$. ∎

The following is a corollary of 4.26.

4.27 The Sum Theorem Let S be a finite abelian semigroup, A a subsemigroup of S with zero e, and B a subsemigroup of S such that e is the identity of B and $S = A \cup B$. Then $\#\Omega(S) = \#\Omega(A) + \#B - 1$.

For a semigroup S, it is clear that $deg\ S = 0$ if and only if S is a monoid. If S is not a monoid, then $deg\ S = 1$ if and only if $\Omega(S) = S^1$. We will characterize the finite trees S satisfying $S = ES$ and $deg\ S = 1$.

We will call an abelian semigroup S a *tree* provided $\downarrow x$ is an $\mathcal{H}$-chain for each $x \in S$. It is evident that each tree is a holoid; i.e., $\leq$ is a partial order, and hence S is $\mathcal{H}$-trivial.

If S is a semigroup, $A \subseteq S$, then $a \in A$ is said to be $\mathcal{H}$-*maximal* in A provided $a \leq x$ and $x \in A$ implies $(a,x) \in \mathcal{H}$.

4.28 Lemma Let S be a finite tree, and $M = \{e_1, \ldots, e_n\}$ $(n \geq 2)$ the set of maximal idempotents of S, and let $g = e_1 e_2 \cdots e_n$. Then there exists subsets P and Q of M such that $M = P \cup Q$ and $PQ = \{g\}$.

Proof: Suppose that w is a product of members of M and $e, f \in M$ such that $ew \neq g$ and $ewf = g$. We claim that $ef = g$. To see this, observe that $ew \leq e$ and $ef \leq e$, and hence either $ew \leq ef$ or

$ef \leq ew$. Now if $ew \leq ef$, then $ew \leq ewf = g$ and $ew = g$; which is a contradiction to our assumption. Thus $ef \leq ew$, $ef \leq ewf = g$ and $ef = g$.

We enumerate M so that $e_1 \cdots e_m$ is a word of members of M of maximum length such that $e_1 e_2 \cdots e_m \neq g$. Let $1 \leq j \leq m$, and let $w_j = e_1 \cdots \hat{e}_j \cdots e_m$ (the product excluding e_j). Let $m < k \leq n$. Then $e_j w_j = e_1 e_2 \cdots e_m \neq g$ and $e_j w_j e_k = g$ from the choice of $e_1 \cdots e_m$. According to the previous paragraph, $e_j e_k = g$. Let $P = \{e_1, \ldots, e_m\}$ and $Q = \{e_{m+1}, \ldots, e_n\}$. ∎

4.29 Theorem Let S be a finite tree such that $S = ES$. Then $deg\ S = 1$ *if and only if* S has exactly two maximal idempotents e and f such that $\uparrow ef = \{e, f, ef\}$.

Proof: Suppose that the condition holds, and let $A = \{e, f, ef\}$ and let $B = \{x \in S : x \leq ef\}$. Then the product theorem applies to show that $\#\Omega(A) = 4$, and the sum theorem yields that $\#\Omega(S) = 4 + \#B - 1 = 3 + \#B$. Since S is a tree, $\#S = 2 + \#B$, and hence $deg\ S = 1$.

To prove the converse, let $M = \{e_1, \ldots, e_n\}$ be the set of maximal idempotents of S and assume for the purpose of proof by contradiction that $n \geq 3$. Let $g = e_1 e_2 \cdots e_n$, and let P and Q be subsets of M such that $M = P \cup Q$ and $PQ = \{g\}$. We enumerate M so that $P = \{e_1, \ldots, e_m\}$ and $Q = \{e_{m+1}, \ldots, e_n\}$. Then, according to 4.22, $(e_1, \ldots, e_m, g, \ldots, g)$ is an element of $\Omega(S)$ which is neither inner nor the identity of S. This contradicts $deg\ S = 1$, and hence $n = 2$. To complete the proof, let e and f denote the two maximal idempotents, and suppose that $ef \leq x \leq e$. Then, $(x, f) \in \Omega(S)$, and since $deg\ S = 1$, either $x = ef$ or $x = e$. ∎

The result of 4.29 is illustrated in the following typical example:

Example Let S be the semilattice which has the following $\leq$ graph:

Then, as proved in 4.29, *deg S* = 1.

Example To demonstrate that the tree condition is 4.29 is not necessary, let *S* be the semilattice with ≤ graph

Then ↑ *ef* = {*ef,e,f*} and *S* has exactly two maximal idempotents *e* and *f*. Although *S* is not a tree, *deg S* = 1.

Example To demonstrate further the limitations of 4.29, let *S* be a semilattice with ≤ graph

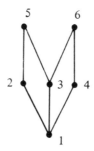

Then S has exactly two maximal idempotents 5 and 6, and $3 = 5 \times 6$ is just below both 5 and 6. However, $deg\ S = 2$.

IDEAL EXTENSIONS

The fundamental problem one considers in ideal extension theory is one of starting with a semigroup S, an ideal I of S, and the structure of I and S/I, and recovering the structure of S by replacing the zero of S/I with I.

Let I and Q_0 be topological semigroups, with Q_0 having a zero 0. A topological semigroup S is said to be an *ideal extension* of I by Q_0 provided S contains a closed ideal J such that J is topologically isomorphic to I and S/J is topologically isomorphic to Q_0.

A *partial homomorphism* of a subset M of a semigroup H into a semigroup T is a function $\phi:M \to T$ such that if $x\ y$, and xy are in M, then $\phi(xy) = \phi(x)\phi(y)$.

A set P of bitranslations of a semigroup S is said to be *permutable* provided $(\omega x)\omega' = \omega(x\omega')$ for each $\omega,\omega' \in P$ and each $x \in S$.

Let I and Q_0 be a disjoint compact semigroups such that Q_0 has a zero 0, let $Q = Q_0 \setminus \{0\}$, and let $P_Q = \{(a,b) \in Q \times Q : ab = 0\}$. Let $\theta:Q \to \Omega(I)$ be a continuous partial homomorphism. A function $\phi:P_Q \to I$ is called a *ramification* provided:
(a) $\theta(a)\theta(b) = \pi\phi(a,b)$ for each $(a,b) \in P_Q$,
(b) $\phi(ab,c) = \phi(a,bc)$ if $abc = 0$, $ab \neq 0$, $bc \neq 0$,
(c) $\phi(ab,c) = \theta(a)\phi(b,c)$ if $ab \neq 0$, $bc = 0$,
(d) $\phi(a,bc) = \phi(a,b)\theta(c)$ if $ab = 0$, $bc \neq 0$,
(e) $\phi(a,b)\theta(c) = \theta(a)\phi(b,c)$ if $ab = bc = 0$.

Let $\delta:Q_0 \times Q_0 \to Q_0$ and $\beta:I \times I \to I$ denote the multiplications on Q_0 and I, and let $S = Q \cup I$ (disjoint union). We define $*:S \times S \to S$ as follows: For $a,b \in S$, let

$$(1) \qquad a * b = \begin{cases} a\theta(b) & \text{if } a \in I,\ b \in Q \\ \theta(a)b & \text{if } a \in Q,\ b \in I \\ \phi(a,b) & \text{if } a,b \in Q,\ (a,b) \in P_Q \\ \delta(a,b) & \text{if } a,b \in Q,\ (a,b) \notin P_Q \\ \beta(a,b) & \text{if } a,b \in I \end{cases}$$

(2) We define a base for a topology on S by declaring that U is a basic open set in S if either U is open in Q in the relative topology of Q_0 or $U = \pi^{-1}(W) \cup (\theta^{-1}(W) \setminus K)$, where W is open in $\Omega(I)$ and K is a compact subset of Q in the relative topology of Q_0.

Observe that with the topology given S by (2), if U is open in Q, then $U \cap Q$ is open in Q and $U \cap I$ is open in I.

We say that $\theta: Q \to \Omega(I)$ is π-*proper* provided that for each subset of C of $\Omega(I)$ such that $C \cap \pi(I) = \square$, we have that $\theta^{-1}(C)$ is compact in Q.

4.30 Lemma If p_α is a net in Q, $p \in I$, and $p_\alpha \to p$, then $\theta(p_\alpha) \to \pi(p)$.

Proof: Let $\pi(p) \in W$, where W is open in $\Omega(I)$. Then $p \in \pi^{-1}(W) \cup \theta^{-1}(W)$, and hence $p_\alpha \in^e \theta^{-1}(W)$. Thus $\theta(p_\alpha) \in^e W$, and $\theta(p_\alpha) \to \pi(p)$. ∎

Let I be a compact reductive semigroup, and let Q_0 be a compact semigroup with zero 0. If $\theta: Q \to \Omega(I)$ is a continuous π-proper partial homomorphism of Q onto a set of permutable bitranslations of I, $\phi: P_Q \to I$ a continuous ramification, and $S = Q \mathbin{\dot\cup} I$ with multiplication and topology defined by (1) and (2), then we write $S = \langle I, Q_0, \theta, \phi \rangle$.

4.31 Theorem Let I be a compact reductive semigroup and let Q_0 be a compact semigroup with zero 0. Then S is a compact ideal extension of I by Q_0 if and only if there exists a continuous π-proper partial homomorphism $\theta: \to \Omega(I)$ and a continuous ramification $\phi: P_Q \to I$ such that S is topologically isomorphic to $\langle I, Q_0, \theta, \phi \rangle$.

Proof: Let us first suppose that $S = \langle I, Q_0, \theta, \phi \rangle$. We need to establish that S is a Hausdorff space, I is a closed ideal of S, S is compact, $*: S \times S \to S$ is continuous, and that S/I is topologically isomorphic to Q_0.

To prove that S is Hausdorff, let p and q be distinct points of S. If p and q are both in Q or both in I, the argument is straightforward using that π is injective in the latter case. We can assume then that $p \in I$ and $q \in Q$. Let W be an open set in $\Omega(I)$ containing $\pi(p)$ and let U be an open set in Q containing q with $\bar{U}$ (closure in Q) compact. Then $p \in \pi^{-1}(W) \cup (\theta^{-1}(W) \backslash \bar{U})$, $q \in U$, and these are disjoint open subsets of S. It follows that S is Hausdorff.

To see that I is closed in S, we need only observe that $S \backslash I = Q$ is open in S. It is evident from the definition of multiplication on S that I is an ideal of S.

To prove that S is compact, let x_α be a net in S. We will show that x_α clusters in S. Now if $x_\alpha \in^f I$, then $\pi(x_\alpha)$ clusters in $\Omega(I)$ to some $\pi(x)$, so that $x_\alpha \xrightarrow{f} x$. We can assume then that $x_\alpha \in Q$. Now $\theta(x_\alpha) \xrightarrow{f} \omega$ for some $\omega \in \Omega(I)$, since $\Omega(I)$ is compact, and again we can assume that $\theta(x_\alpha) \to \omega$. If $\omega \notin \pi(I)$, let U be an open set in $\Omega(I)$ with $\omega \in U \subseteq \bar{U} \subseteq \Omega(I) \backslash \pi(I)$. Then $\theta(x_\alpha) \in^e U$, $x_\alpha \in^e \theta^{-1}(\bar{U})$, and $\theta^{-1}(\bar{U})$ is compact, since θ is π-proper, so that x_α clusters in $\theta^{-1}(\bar{U})$ in this case. On the other hand, if $\omega \in \pi(I)$, then $\omega = \pi(p)$ for some $p \in I$. Let $\pi^{-1}(W) \cup (\theta^{-1}(W) \backslash K)$ be a basic open set containing p. Then $\omega = \pi(p) \in W$, $\theta(x_\alpha) \in^e W$, and hence $x_\alpha \in^e \theta^{-1}(W)$. Now if $x_\alpha \in^f K$, then x_α clusters in K, since K is compact. Otherwise, $x_\alpha \in \theta^{-1}(W) \backslash K$, and $x_\alpha \to p$. We conclude that S is compact.

To prove that $*: S \times S \to S$ is continuous, let $(a,b) \in S \times S$, and (a_α, b_α) a net in $S \times S$ with $a_\alpha \to a$ and $b_\alpha \to b$. We need to show that $a_\alpha * b_\alpha \xrightarrow{f} a * b$. In view of the complexity of the definition of $*$ in (1), we see that there are a number of cases to consider. We demonstrate the argument in two of the more complicated cases and leave the remaining cases to the reader.

Suppose that $a \in I$ and $b \in Q$. We can assume that $b_\alpha \in Q$, since Q is open in S. Let us consider the subcase in which $a_\alpha \in^e Q$ and $(a_\alpha, b_\alpha) \in^e (Q \times Q) \backslash P_Q$. We can assume that $a_\alpha \in Q$ and $(a_\alpha, b_\alpha) \notin P_Q$. Then $\theta(a_\alpha * b_\alpha) = \theta\delta(a_\alpha, b_\alpha) = \theta(a_\alpha)\theta(b_\alpha) \to \pi(a)\theta(b) = \pi(a\theta(b)) = \pi(a * b)$. Let $a * b \in \pi^{-1}(W) \cup (\theta^{-1}(W) \backslash K)$, where W is open in $\Omega(I)$ and K is compact in Q. Then $\pi(a * b) \in W$ and $\theta(a_\alpha * b_\alpha) \in^e W$, so that $a_\alpha * b_\alpha \in^e \theta^{-1}(W)$. Now a_α does not cluster in Q and hence $a_\alpha \to 0$ in Q_0. Thus $\delta(a_\alpha, b_\alpha) \to \delta(0,b) = 0$ in Q_0. It follows that $a_\alpha * b_\alpha = \delta(a_\alpha, b_\alpha) \in^e \theta^{-1}(W) \backslash K$, and $a_\alpha * b_\alpha \to a * b$.

Consider the case in which $a,b \in I$; $a_\alpha, b_\alpha \in Q$, and $(a_\alpha, b_\alpha) \notin P_Q$. Then $a * b = \beta(a,b)$ in this case and $\theta(a_\alpha * b_\alpha) = \theta \delta(a_\alpha, b_\alpha) = \theta(a_\alpha)\theta(b_\alpha) \to \pi(a)\pi(b) = \pi\beta(a,b) = \pi(a * b)$. Let $\pi^{-1}(W) \cup (\theta^{-1}(W)\backslash K)$ be a basic open set in S containing $a * b$. Then $\pi(a * b) \in W$, and $\theta(a_\alpha * b_\alpha) \in^e W$. It follows that $a_\alpha * b_\alpha \in^e \theta^{-1}(W)$. Now $\delta(a_\alpha, b_\alpha) \to 0$ in Q_0, since $a_\alpha \to a$ and $b_\alpha \to b$, and hence $a_\alpha * b_\alpha = \delta(a_\alpha, b_\alpha) \in^e Q\backslash K$. Thus $a_\alpha * b_\alpha \in^e \theta^{-1}(W)\backslash K$, and $a_\alpha * b_\alpha \to a * b$.

To see that S/I is topologically isomorphic to Q_0, let $\gamma : S \to S/I$ be the natural map and let $\psi : Q \hookrightarrow S$ be inclusion. Define $\sigma : Q \to S/I$ by $\sigma(x) = \gamma\psi(x)$ if $x \in Q$ and $\sigma(0) = \gamma(I)$. Then σ is a topological isomorphism.

To prove the converse, we can assume that I is a closed ideal of S, $Q_0 = S/I$, and identify Q with $S\backslash I$. Let $*$ denote multiplication on S. Define $\theta : Q \to \Omega(I)$ by $\theta(p) = \omega_p | I$ for each $p \in Q$. Then θ is a partial homomorphism of Q onto a set of permutable bitranslations of I.

To verify that θ is continuous, let $p_\alpha \to p$ in Q. Then for $x \in I$, $\omega_{p_\alpha} x = p_\alpha * x \to p * x = \omega_p x$, and similarly $x\omega_{p_\alpha} \to x\omega_p$, so that $\omega_{p_\alpha} | I$ converges pointwise to $\omega_p | I$. From 4.7, we have $\omega_{p_\alpha} | I \to \omega_p | I$. It follows that θ is continuous.

To prove that θ is π-proper, let C be a compact subset of $\Omega(I)$ such that $C \cap \pi(I) = \square$. Then $\theta^{-1}(C)$ is closed in Q, since θ is continuous. We will show that $\theta^{-1}(C)$ is closed in S and hence is compact. Let x_α be a net in $\theta^{-1}(C)$ with $x_\alpha \to x$ in S. We want to prove that $x \in Q$. Assume to the contrary that $x \in I$. Now $\theta(x_\alpha) = \omega_{x_\alpha} | I$ clusters to some ω in C, since C is compact. Then $\omega_{x_\alpha} t = x_\alpha * t \to x * t$ for each $t \in I$. Thus $\omega t = x * t$, and similarly $t\omega = t * x$ for each $t \in I$. We have that $\omega = \pi(x) \in C$, contradicting that $C \cap \pi(I) = \square$. We conclude that θ is π-proper.

Now define $\phi : P_Q \to I$ by $\phi(a,b) = a * b$, where we identify P_Q with $\{(a,b) \in Q \times Q : a * b \in I\}$. Then ϕ is a continuous ramification of S and S is topologically isomorphic to $\langle I, Q_0, \theta, \phi \rangle$. ∎

If Q_0 is a compact semigroup with zero 0 and has no proper zero divisors, i.e., $P_Q = \square$, then using Q_0 to extend a compact semigroup I is simplified considerably. Let $\theta : Q \to \Omega(I)$ be a continuous π-proper homomorphism and $S = Q \overset{.}{\cup} I$. For $x \in Q$

and $y \in I$, we define $x * y = \theta(x)y$, and $y * x = y\theta(x)$. Moreover, if I is a monoid, then any continuous homomorphism $\theta:Q \to \Omega$ (I) is π-proper, since $\pi:I \to \Omega(I)$ is a topological isomorphism. In fact, in this case, we can replace $\Omega(I)$ by I and let $\theta:Q \to I$ be a continuous homomorphism.

Example As an example of the construction just described let G be a compact solenoidal group and let $\theta:\mathbf{H} \to G$ be a dense continuous homomorphism. Then the extension of G using $\mathbf{H}^*$ as described above is the compact monoid with the copy of $\mathbf{H}$ winding down on G.

The following example illustrated the need to assume that $\pi:Q \to \Omega(I)$ is π-proper in the statement of 4.31.

Example Let $I = [0,1/2]$ and $Q_0 = [0,1] = I_u$. Then, from the example following 4.19, $\Omega(I) = [0,1] = I_u$, and $\pi:I \hookrightarrow \Omega(I)$. Let $\phi = \square$, since $P_Q = \square$, and let $\theta:Q \to \Omega(I)$ be defined by $\theta(x) = 1$ for all $x \in Q$. Then $1 \notin \pi(I)$, and $\theta^{-1}(1) = Q$ is not compact, so that θ is not π-proper. Note that $S = I \dot{\cup} Q$ with the topology in (2) and multiplication in (1) is not compact. We illustrate S below:

$$S = \quad \underset{0}{\bullet}\!\!-\!\!-\!\!-\!\!\underset{\frac{1}{2}}{\bullet} \quad \overset{I}{} \qquad \underset{0}{\circ}\!\!-\!\!-\!\!-\!\!\bullet \quad \overset{Q}{}$$

Example For our next example illustrating 4.31, let $S = \mathbf{H}^*$ and let $Q_0 = S/I$, where $I = [1,\infty]$. Then, from 4.19, $\Omega(I) = S$ and $\pi:I \to \Omega(I)$ is inclusion. We can realize Q_0 as $[0,1]$ with addition $a \oplus b = \min\{1, a + b\}$, where $a + b$ is the usual sum. Then $Q = [0,1)$ and $= \{(a,b) \in Q \times Q : a + b \geq 1\}$. Let $\theta:Q \to \Omega(I) = [0,\infty]$ be inclusion and $\phi:P_Q \to I$ be defined by $\phi(a,b) = a + b$. Then S is topologically isomorphic to $\langle I,Q,\theta,\phi \rangle$.

Example For our final example of this section, we demonstrate that ideal extensions need not be unique. Let $I = [0,1/2]$ and let

$Q_0 = [0,1]$ (usual). Let $\theta_1 : Q \to \Omega(I) = [0,1]$ be the identity and let $\theta_2 : Q \to \Omega(I)$ be the zero map, i.e., $\theta(x) = 0$ for all $x \in Q$. Then the space of $S_1 = \langle I, Q, \theta_1, \phi \rangle$ and $S_2 = \langle I, Q, \theta_2, \phi \rangle$ is illustrated by

If in S_1 we have $x \in I$ and $y \in Q$, then xy is the usual product of x and y in I. In S_2 this product is 0.

5

Semigroups on Continua

In this chapter we consider the problem of starting with a continuum X (a compact connected Hausdorff space) and introducing a continuous multiplication so that X satisfies some prescribed set of algebraic conditions.

Material in the literature which relates to that in this chapter appears in Cohen and Koch [1956], Eberhart [1966], Friedberg and Mahavier [1968], Hudson [1963], Hunter [1959, 1961], Koch and Krule [1960], Koch and McAuley [1962, 1964], Madison [1969], McCharen [1969], Selden and Madison [1967], Wallace [1955], Ward [1957], Williams [1969], Koch [1970], and Friedberg [1972].

FRIEDBERG'S CONSTRUCTIONS

In this section we describe and illustrate two of the constructions from Friedberg [1972]. These examples answered earlier questions of A. D. Wallace, H. Cohen, and D. R. Brown regarding whether certain continua would admit the structure of a monoid.

Throughout this section $C = \mathbf{H} \times \mathbf{H}$. Then C is a locally compact σ-compact connected divisible abelian monoid.

If I is a closed ideal in C, define $R(I) = \Delta(C) \cup \{((a,b), (c,d)) \in C \times C : (a,b), (c,d) \in I$ and $(a + b) - (c + d)$ is an integer$\}$. Then $R(I)$ is a closed congruence on C and $C/R(I)$ is a connected divisible abelian monoid (see 1.56 of Carruth, Hildebrant, and Koch [1983]).

Let L be a compact subset of C and let $I = L + C$. Then I is a closed ideal of C. If $S = C/R(I)$, $\phi : C \to S$ is the natural map, and there exists a compact subset M of C such that $\phi(M) = S$, then S is a compact connected divisible abelian monoid.

Example We illustrate this construction with Friedberg's *French Army Hat* example. Let $L = \{(x,1) : 0 \le x \le 1\} \cup \{(1,y) : 0 \le y \le 1\}$, $I = L + C$, $S = C/R(I)$, and let $\phi : C \to S$ be the natural map. Let $M = \{(x,y) : 0 \le x \le 1, 0 \le y \le 1\}$.

We claim first that $\phi(M) = S$. Let $(a,b) \in C \backslash M$. If $1 < a$, let $n \in \mathbf{N}$ such that $b/n \le 1$. Then $(a,b) = (a-1, (n-1)b/n) + (1,b/n) \in C + L$. A similar argument works if $1 < b$. In any case $(a,b) \in I$. Let $a = \bar{a} + a'$ and $b = \bar{b} + b'$, where $\bar{a}, \bar{b} \in \mathbf{N} \cup \{0\}$, and $0 \le a' < 1, 0 \le b' < 1$. Let $c = a + b$. Then $1 < c$, since either $1 < a$ or $1 < b$. Now let $m \in \mathbf{N} \cup \{0\}$ and $0 \le \varepsilon < 1$ such that $c = 1 + \varepsilon + m$. Then $(1,c) \in M$, $(1,\varepsilon)$, $(a,b) \in I$, and $(a+b) - (1+\varepsilon) = c - 1 - \varepsilon = m \in \mathbf{N} \cup \{0\}$, so that $((a,c), (1,\varepsilon)) \in R(I)$. It follows that $\phi(M) = S$.

We will illustrate S by determining which elements of M are identified under $R(I)$. Now if $(a,b) \in M \backslash L$, then $(a,b) \notin I$, so that the $R(I)$ class of (a,b) is degenerate. Now clearly each point of L is a point of I. Thus, is $((a,b), (b,1)) \in R(I)$, then $(a+1) - (b+1) = a - b$ is an integer, so that either $a = b$ or one of a or b is 0 and the other is 1. Now if $((1,a), (1,b)) \in R(I)$, we also conclude that either $a = b$ or one of a or b is 0 and the other is 1. If $((a,1), (1,b)) \in R(I)$, then $(a+1) - (b+1) = a - b$, so again either $a = b$ or one of a or b is 0 and the other is 1. Thus the classes of L are of the form $\{(a,1), (1,a)\}(0 < a < 1)$ and $\{(0,1), (1,1), (1,0)\}$. The following diagram illustrates M and S:

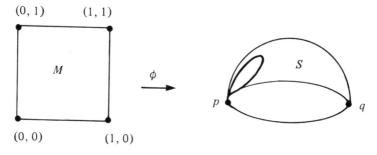

We have that $\phi(0,1) = \phi(1,1) = \phi(1,0) = p$ and $\phi(0,0) = q$. Moreover, q is the identity of S.

Example We now turn to another construction of Friedberg, which is termed *Pasting Cones Together*. Let $M = [1/2,1]$ with multiplication $x \cdot y = max \{1/2, xy\}$ (the nil interval), $J = [-1,1]$ under usual multiplication and let K be the Cantor set in $[0,1]$ with min multiplication. Let R be the decomposition on $M \times J \times K$ whose only nondegenerate elements are the closed sets $\{t\} \times \{0\}$ $\times K$ for $1/2 \leq t \leq \sqrt{1/2}$. Then R is a closed congruence on $M \times J \times K$ and $S = (M \times J \times K)/R$ is a compact monoid whose space consists of a Cantor set of cones attached along a line segment.

ADMISSIBILITY

We consider in this section the problem of determining whether a given continuum admits the structure of a compact monoid. In addition to cohomology, there are other results which can be used as tools in attacking this problem. We develop some of these here.

Example Consider the continuum S which consists of two 1-spheres attached at a single point:

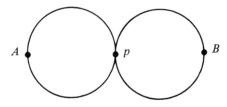

$S = A \cup B$ and $A \cap B = \{p\}$. Now let G be a coefficient group. Then $H^1(A) = H^1(B) = G$. Consider the Mayer-Vietoris sequence

$$\to H^0(p) = 0$$

$$\Delta$$

$$H^1(S) \to H^1(A) \oplus H^1(B) \to H^1(p) = 0$$
$$\quad J^* \qquad\qquad\qquad\qquad I^*$$

Now $Im(\Delta) = ker\, J^* = 0$, so that J^* is an isomorphism. Since $Im(J^*) = ker\, I^* = H^1(A) \oplus H^1(B) = G \oplus G$, we have $H^1(S) = G \oplus G$.

Suppose that S is a compact monoid. Then $H^1(M(S)) = G \oplus G$ according to 1.2. This is not possible if $M(S)$ is a proper subset of S. Thus $S = M(S)$ is a group. Since S is not homogeneous, we condlude that S does not admit a compact monoid.

The following result has some interesting consequences in regard to the admissibility problem:

5.1 Theorem Let X be a continuum, $p \in$ edge (X), and let U be an open neighborhood of p. Then there exists an open set V such that $p \in V \subseteq U$ and $X \backslash V$ is connected.

Proof: Since $p \in$ edge (X), there exists an open set V such that $H^0(X) \approx H^0(X \backslash V)$. Since X is connected, $H^0(X) = 0$, and hence $H^0(X \backslash V) = 0$. It follows that $X \backslash V$ is connected. ∎

The property of 5.1 is sometimes expressed by saying that X is 1-semilocally connected at p.

5.2 Corollary If X is a continuum, then each cutpoint of X is a middle point of X.

5.3 Corollary If S is a compact monoid, then 1 is not a cutpoint of S.

The results of 5.2 and 5.3 are valid if "cutpoint" is replaced by "weak cutpoint". In view of 1.8, we see that a stronger version of 5.3 is valid:

5.4 Corollary If S is a compact monoid, then no point of $H(1)$ is a cutpoint of S.

We employ 5.3 in the next example.

Example   Let S denote the space of the closed-up $\sin(1/x)$ curve as in the following diagram:

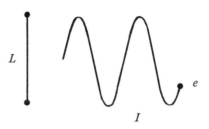

Suppose that S admits the structure of a compact monoid. Then, in view of 5.3, we see that either $1 \in L$ or $1 = e$. There are various methods to rule out that $1 \in L$. One of these is based on the fact that there are small neighborhoods of $H(1)$ whose complements are connected ideals. We conclude that e is the identity of S.

We consider the location and structure of $M(S)$. From 3.21 of Carruth, Hildebrant, and Koch [1983], $M(S)$ must be a trivial cartesian product. Since the connected subgroups of S must be degenerate, $M(S)$ must consist of either left zeros of S or right zeros of S. We can assume that $fx = f$ for all $f \in M(S)$ and all $x \in S$.

Suppose that $M(S) \cap I \neq^e \square$, and let $p \in M(S) \cap I$. Then $p = pL \subseteq IL \supset L$. Now I and L are pathwise connected, so that $I \times L$ is pathwise connected. Since IL is the continuous image of $I \times L$ under multiplication, we have that IL is a pathwise connected subspace of S containing L and meeting I. From this contradiction, we have that $M(S) \cap I = \square$, and hence $M(S) \subseteq L$. Now let $x \in M(S)$ and $x_n \in I$ such that $x_n \to x$. Then $\lim x_n S = xS = x$, and $x_n S$ is a continuum containing x_n and meeting $M(S)$ for each $n \in \mathbf{N}$. It follows that $L \subseteq x_n S$ for each $n \in \mathbf{N}$, since $M(S) \subseteq L$. We have then $L \subseteq x_n S \to xS = x$. With this contradiction, we conclude that S does not admit the structure of a monoid.

The result of 5.3 can be obtained from a more elementary approach using the following result in Faucett [1955].

5.5   Theorem   Let S be a compact connected semigroup and let p be a cutpoint of S in $S \backslash M(S)$. Let A and B be nonempty closed connected subsets of S such that $S = A \cup B$, $A \cap B = \{p\}$, and $M(S) \subseteq A$. Then $J(p) \subseteq A$.

   Proof: Now $M(S) \subseteq A \setminus \{p\}$ is open. Thus $M(S) \subseteq J_0(A \setminus \{p\}) \subseteq A \setminus \{p\}$, and $K = J_0(A \setminus \{p\})$ is an ideal of S containing p. Since A is closed, we have $J(p) \subseteq K \subseteq A$.   ∎

   An alternative proof of 5.3 is as follows: Let S be a compact connected monoid and suppose that 1 is a cutpoint of S. Let $S = A \cup B$ as in 5.5 with $p = 1$. Then $J(1) = S \subseteq A$, so that $B = \square$. This contradiction yields the result.

5.6   Theorem   Let S be a compact connected semigroup and let p be a cutpoint of S in $S \setminus M(S)$. If A and B are nonempty closed connected subsets of S such that $S = A \cup B$, $A \cap B = \{p\}$, and $M(S) \subseteq A$, then for each $e \in B \cap E(S)$, $ep = pe = p$.

   Proof: Now $ep \in J(p) \subseteq A$ from 5.5, so that $p \in eB$. Now $p = eb$ for some $b \in B$ and hence $p = ep$.   ∎

   Admissibility of continua to algebraic structures other than monoids has received some attention in the literature. A comparison of these structures was presented in Koch [1970]. We give a brief version of this comparison here.
   Below we have listed a table of symbols which will be used to designate the class of continuum semigroups satisfying the given algebraic properties in the diagram that follows.

G	group
$(E,1)$	semilattice with identity
E	semilattice
$(1,0)$	monoid with zero
(1)	monoid
ESE	semigroup S satisfying $S = ESE$
$(ESE,0)$	semigroup S with zero satisfying $S = ESE$
S^2	semigroup S satisfying $S = S^2$
$(S^2,0)$	semigroup S with zero satisfying $S = S^2$

In the diagram below $A \Rightarrow B$ indicated that each continuum that admits A also admits B.

$$(E,1) \Rightarrow (1,0) \Rightarrow (1) \Leftarrow G$$

$$\Downarrow \qquad \Downarrow \qquad \Downarrow$$

$$E \Rightarrow (ESE,0) \Rightarrow ESE$$

$$\Downarrow \qquad \Updownarrow$$

$$(S^2,0) \Rightarrow S^2$$

The left trivial multiplication $(x,y) \mapsto x$ is continuous on any continuum X and hence ESE and S^2 include all continua.

A retract of a two-cell is in $(E,1)$ [Williams, 1969]. Eberhart and Madison have settled a question of Koch in the negative by showing that a two-cell with a radius identified with the boundary cannot be in (1); this space is an absolute retract without edge-points. Another such example is Bing's house of two rooms. Borsuk's example of a retract of a 3-cell which contains no two-cell has been shown by Lawson not to be in E; in fact, he shows that each member of E is either one-dimensional or contains a two-cell. The analogous result for $(1,0)$ is conjectural.

One-dimensional members of $(1,0)$ have the fixed point property [Hunter, 1959]. Locally connected finite dimensional members of $(E,1)$ have the fixed point property because the diagonal is a symmetric retract of the product space [Kelley, 1955]. It was shown in Cohen [1960] that Kinoshita's "can with a roll of toilet paper" example is in $(1,0)$ (and does not have the fixed-point property). The ruled space of Koch and McAuley are in $(1,0)$, and it is conjectural that these spaces have the fixed-point property.

The powerful results 1.10 and 1.11 are useful tools in the classification problem. Lawson and McCharen have shown that weak cutpoints and local cutpoints must be middle points; thus if $S \in (1) \backslash G$, then 1 is not a local cutpoint or a weak cutpoint. In particular, S cannot be indecomposable (in the metric case). A continuum S that is floored in dimension n must consist of middle points, so if $S \in (1)$, then $S \in G$. It is natural to ask whether a maximal idempotent of a semigroup S in ESE or S^2 is an edge point. If $S \in (1)$ and S is a coset space of a compact connected group, then S is a group (see Madison [1969], and Selden and Madison [1967]). It would be of interest to know whether coset spaces have middle points.

Examples to illustrate that the arrows in the diagram above cannot be reversed appear in a number of the papers cited at the beginning of this chapter. We present some of these examples. The symbol $A \nRightarrow B$ means that a continuum exists that admits A and does not admit B.

We say that the continuum X belongs to $(*)$ if X admits the structure of a topological semigroups S satisfying $(*)$. For example, $X \in (1,0)$ if and only if X admits the structure of a topological semigroup S with identity and zero.

Example $(1) \nRightarrow (1,0)$: In the examples following 1.5 it is shown that the space S consisting of a circle C with a sticker with endpoint e (not on the circle) admits the structure of a monoid and that e must be the identity and C the minimal ideal. It follows that $S \notin (1,0)$.

Example $ESE \nRightarrow (1)$: In the example preceding 5.1, we have seen that the space X which consists of two circles that meet in one point does not admit the structure of a compact monoid. Since any space admits left trivial multiplication $(x,y) \mapsto x$, we see that $X \notin ESE$.

We develop some results that will be useful in our next example.

If X and Y are spaces, $R \subseteq X \times Y$, and $y \in Y$, then $L(y) = \{x \in X : (x,y) \in R\}$. For $B \subseteq Y$, we let $L(B) = \cup \{L(y) : y \in B\}$.

The following appears in Wallace [1961].

5.7 Lemma Let X and Y be compact Hausdorff spaces and R a closed subset of $X \times Y$ such that $L(A) \cap L(B)$ is connected for each pair of closed subsets A and B of Y, and $H^1(L(y)) = 0$ for each $y \in Y$. Then $H^1(L(C)) = 0$ for each closed subset C of Y.

Proof: Let C be a closed subset of Y and suppose that $H^1(L(C)) \neq 0$. Let $h \in H^1(L(C))$ with $h \neq 0$. Let $\mathcal{K} = \{K : K$ is a closed subset of Y and $h|L(K) \neq 0\}$. Then $\mathcal{H} \neq \square$, since $C \in K$. Let $\mathcal{M}$ be a maximal tower in $\mathcal{H}$ and let $M = \cap \, \mathcal{M}$.

We claim that $h|L(M) \neq 0$. If $h|L(M) = 0$, then there exists an open set U in X such that $L(M) \subseteq U$ and $h|U = 0$ from Appendix A.15. Now there exists an open set V in Y such that $M \subseteq V$ and $L(V) \subseteq U$. Thus $h|L(V) = 0$, and there exists $M' \in \mathcal{M}$ such that $M' \subseteq V$ and hence $h|L(M') = 0$. This contradiction proves that $h|L(M) \neq 0$.

Now M is not degenerate, since $H^1(L(y)) = 0$ for each $y \in Y$. Let $p \neq q$ in M. Let U and V be disjoint open sets such that $p \in V$, $q \in U$, and $U \cap V = \square$. We have $M = P \cup Q$, where $P = Y \backslash U$ and $Q = Y \backslash V$, $p \in P$, $q \in Q$, and P and Q are closed.

Now $L(P) \cap L(Q)$ is connected, so that $H^0(L(P) \cap L(Q)) = 0$. Consider the Mayer-Vietoris sequence for this decomposition of M:

$$H^0(L(M))$$

$$\|$$

$$H^0(L(P) \cup L(Q)) \rightarrow H^0(L(P)) \oplus H^0(L(Q)) \rightarrow H^0(L(P) \cap L(Q)) = 0$$

$$\swarrow$$

$$H^1(L(P) \cup L(Q)) \underset{J^*}{\rightarrow} H^1(L(P)) \oplus H^1(L(Q)) \rightarrow$$

$$\|$$

$$H^1(L(M))$$

Now J^* is an isomorphism, and since $h|L(M)) \neq 0$, $H^1(L(M)) \neq 0$, so that either $h|L(P) \neq 0$ or $h|L(Q) \neq 0$. In either case we contradict the minimality of M. ∎

We remark that 5.7 can be improved if some additional conditions are assumed. In particular, if for each pair A and B of closed subsets of Y, $L(A) \cap L(B) = L(C)$ for some closed subset C

of Y and if $H^p(L(A)) = 0$ for $1 \le p \le q$ and each closed subset A of Y. The argument involves proceeding to lower levels of the Meyer-Vietoris diagram. Observe that if $X = Y$ and R is a closed quasi-order on X, then these conditions hold.

Our next results appear in Cohen and Koch [1965].

5.8 Lemma Let S be a compact connected semigroup with zero 0, let L be a closed left ideal of S, and let $e \in E(S)$. Then $H^*(eL) = 0$.

Proof: Define $F:eL \times S \to el$ by $F(ex,t) = etex$. Let $f,g:eL \to eL$, where f is the identity map on eL and $g(ex) = 0$ for all $x \in L$. Then $F(ex,e) = ex = f(ex)$, and $F(ex,0) = 0 = g(ex)$, so that from Appendix A.9, $f^* = g^*:H^*(eL) \to H^*(eL)$. Now f^* is the identity of $H^*(eL)$ and g^* is the 0-map. It follows that $H^*(eL) = 0$. ∎

5.9 Theorem Let S be a compact connected semigroup with zero 0 such that $S = ESE$ and let I be a closed ideal of S. Then $H^1(AI) = 0$ for each closed subset A of E. In particular $H^1(I) = 0$.

Proof: Let $R = \{(t,e) \in S \times E : t \in eI\}$. Then $L(A) \cap L(B) = AI \cap BI$ is a right ideal in $S = SE$ and is therefore connected for each A and B which are closed. From 5.8, $H^1(eI) = 0$ for each $e \in E$, and thus from 5.7, $H^1(AI) = 0$ for each closed subset A of E. ∎

5.10 Corollary Let S be a compact connected semigroup with $S = ESE$, and let I be a closed ideal in S. Then $H^1(I) \approx H^1(M(S))$.

Proof: Let $\phi:S \to S/M(S)$ be the natural map and let E_0 be the set of idempotents in $S/M(S)$. Then $\phi(E) = E_0$, and $\phi(S) = \phi(E)\phi(S)\phi(E)$. Now $\phi(S)$ has a zero and $M(S) \subseteq I$, so that $\phi(I)$ is an ideal in $\phi(S) = S/M(S)$ and $\phi(E)\phi(I) = \phi(EI) = \phi(I) = I/M(S)$. It follows that $H^1(I/M(S)) = 0$ from 5.9, and $H^1(I,M(S)) \approx H^1(I/M(S)) = 0$. Consider from Appendix A.4, the sequence

$$H^1(I,M(S)) \to H^1(S) \xrightarrow{i^*} H^1(M(S))$$

where $i:M(S) \hookrightarrow I$. Now $M(S)$ is a retract of S, so that i^* is surjective. Since $H^1(I,M(S)) = 0$, i^* injective. ∎

5.11 Corollary Let S be a compact connected semigroup with zero 0 such that $S = ESE$. Then $H^1(S) = 0$.

Example $(S^2,0) \not\Rightarrow (ESE,0)$: We construct one of the examples in Hudson [1963]. The space X of this example will be a circle with two intervals attached at one point to the circle. The semigroup does satisfy $S = ES$ with 0, and hence X supports $(S^2,0)$. Since $H^1(X) \neq 0$, it follows from 5.11 that $X \notin (ESE,0)$.

For real numbers a and b, let $a \vee b = max\{a,b\}, a \wedge b = min\{a,b\}$, and let ab be the usual product. To construct this example, we will begin with a subset of the plane $\mathbf{R} \times \mathbf{R}$, define a multiplication so that this subset becomes a compact semigroup, and then take a quotient semigroup.

Let $A = \{(x,2): 0 \leq x \leq 1\}$, $B = \{(2,y): 0 \leq y \leq 1\}$, $D = \{(x,0): 0 \leq x \leq 1\} \cup \{(x,1): 0 \leq x \leq 1\} \cup \{(0,y): 0 \leq y \leq 1\} \cup \{(1,y): 0 \leq y \leq 1\}$, and let $\theta = (0,-1)$. Let $T = A \cup B \cup D \cup \{0\}$. We illustrate T:

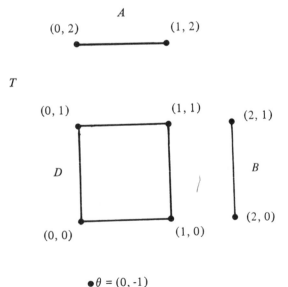

Define multiplication on T as follows: If $(x,2)$, $(y,2) \in A$, then $(x,2)(y,2) = (xy,2)$, and if $(2,x)$, $(2,y) \in B$, then $(2,x)(2,y) = (2,xy)$, so that each of A and B are topologically isomorphic to I_u. For $(\times,y) \in D$ and $(a,2) \in A$, define $(x,y)(a,2) = ((x \wedge y)a, x \vee y)$, and for $(a,b) \in B$ define $(x,y)(2,b) = (x \vee y, (x \wedge y)b)$. Then $D(A \cup B) \subseteq D$. Now define all other products to be θ. Then with this multiplication T is a compact semigroup. The idempotents of T are θ, $(0,2)$, $(1,2)$, $(2,0)$ and $(2,1)$. Let $I = \{(0,2), (2,0), \theta\} \cup \{(x,0): 0 \leq x \leq 1\} \cup \{(0,y): 0 \leq y \leq 1\}$. Then I is an ideal of T. Let $S = T/I$. Then $S = ES$ and the image of I is a zero for S.

We mention briefly other examples without providing explicit details. More examples will be considered in the next section. An example which illustrates that $(ESE, 0) \not\Rightarrow E$ appears in Hudson, [1963]. The underlying space is a 2-sphere with 4 stickers. An example appears in Lawson and Williams [1970] which illustrates that $E \not\Rightarrow (1)$. It is a subsemilattice of $I_m \times I_m$.

Questions regarding admissibility for spheres were inspired (as was A. D. Wallace) by the result of E. Cartan which states that if an n-sphere is a group, then $n = 0, 1$, or 3. Wallace showed (using results on floors) that if an n-sphere is a monoid, then it is a group (and hence $n = 0, 1$, or 3). This is immediate from the later result of Hudson and Mostert [1963] that a finite dimensional homogeneous compact connected monoid (clan) is a group (see 1.10).

There are other tools (which we will not explore) that one could use in attacking the admissibility question. For example, the fundamental group of a monoid must be abelian. Since the fundamental group of two tangent circles in the plane is the free group on two generators, this space does not admit a continuous multiplication with identity.

Since $n = 2$ is the missing sphere in the Cartan result, some researchers have been led to investigate the structures which the 2-sphere will admit. S.T. Hu asked the question: Can a semigroup on the 2-sphere contain the circle group $\mathbf{R}/\mathbf{Z}$? This question was answered in the affirmative in Mostert and Shields [1956]. In Cohen and Koch [1965] it was established that if S is a compact connected 2-manifold without boundary such that $S = ESE$, then $S = M(S)$. They also showed that if $S^2 = S$, then there are no circle subgroups, from which it follows that each subgroup must be totally disconnected. This result was extended in McCharen [1969] using the results in Koch [1964]. Koch's thread theorem states that if S is a compact connected monoid such that $S \neq M(S)$ and each subgroup of S is totally disconnected, then there exists an I-semigroup T in S such that $1 \in T$ and $T \cap M(S) \neq \square$.

The space S of tangent circles converging to a point was considered in McCharen [1974]. It was established that if S admits a multiplication such that $S^2 = S$, then $S = M(S)$.

SEMIGROUPS ON RULED CONTINUA

This section is concerned with results and examples that appear in Koch and McAuley [1964]. A set of sufficient conditions are obtained for a metric continuum to admit a multiplication with a zero and identity. In this section we write $[0,e]$ for an arc in a metric continuum. Observe that $[0,e]$ is homeomorphic to the real unit interval $[0,1]$.

If S is a metric continuum and $[0,e]$ is an arc in S, a metric d on S is said to be *radially convex* with respect to $[0,e]$ provided $d(0,a) \neq d(0,b)$ when $a \neq b$ in $[0,e]$. If $\mathcal{A}$ is a collection of arcs in S, then we say that S admits a *radially convex metric* with respect to $\mathcal{A}$ provided there is a metric d on S which is radially convex with respect to each arc in $\mathcal{A}$ and the metric topology of d is the topology of S.

A metric continuum S is said to be *ruled* provided there exists an element $0 \in S$ and a subset I of S such that the following conditions are satisfied:

(1) For each $e \in I$, there is a unique arc $[0,e]$ from 0 to e in S.
(2) $S = \bigcup \mathcal{A}$, where $\mathcal{A} = \{[0,e]:e \in I\}$.
(3) If $e \neq f$ in I, then $[0,e] \cap [0,f]$ is a proper subarc of both $[0,e]$ and $[0,f]$.

For $x \in S$, we denote by $[0,x]$ the subarc of $[0,e]$ with endpoints 0 and x, where $x \in [0,e]$, $e \in I$.

(4) If $x_n \to x$, then $[0,x_n] \to [0,x]$ (see Appendix B.1).
(5) S admits a radially convex metric d with respect to $\mathcal{A}$.

From (5) and (2) there exists $u \in I$ such that $d(0,u) = sup\{d(0,e):e \in I\}$. Without loss of generality, we assume that $d(0,u) = 1$.

(6) There is a function $x \mapsto e_x$ from S into I such that $x \in [0,e_x]$ and $e_x = u$ if $x \in [0,u]$.

(7) There is a total order $\leq$ on I such that u is $\leq$-maximal and if $x_n \to x, y_n \to y, e_x < e_y < u, x \notin [0,y]$, and $y \notin [0,x]$, then there exists a subsequence x_{n_k} of x_n and a subsequence y_{n_k} of y_n such that $e_{x_{n_k}} < e_{y_{n_k}}$ for each k.

Let $K_1 = \{y \in [0,u]$: there exists $a \in [0,u]$ and sequences $y_n \to y$ and $a_n \to a$ such that $e_{y_n} \leq e_{a_n}$ for each $n\}$. Let $K = \{0\} \cup K_1, k = sup\, K$ (in the natural order of $[0,u]$), and let $C = [0,k]$.

(8) If $C \neq \{0\}$, then S admits a radially convex metric d with respect to $\mathcal{A}$ such that $d(0,u) = 1, d(0,k) = 1/2$, and if $e \in I$, with $[0,e] \cap [0,u] = [0,p]$, then $d(e,p) \leq 1/2$.

Note that condition (8) implies that $u \notin C$.

If S is a ruled continuum [using the notation in (1)-(8)] for $x \in S$, we write $|x| = d(0,x)$. Define $\psi:S \to [0,1] \times I$ by $\psi(x) = (|x|,e_x)$. If $x \neq y$ and $e_x = e_y$, then $|x| \neq |y|$, since S is radially convex with respect to $[0,e_x]$, and we obtain that ψ is injective. Thus each $x \in S$ has a unique coordinate representation $(|x|, e_x)$. Observe that if t is a real number and $0 \leq t \leq |x|$ for $x \in S$, then (t,e_x) represents a point on $[0,e_x]$.

5.12 Lemma Let S be a ruled continuum and $x_n \to x$ in S. Let t_n be a sequence of real numbers such that $0 \leq t_n \leq 1$ and $t_n \to t$ with $t_n \leq |x_n|$ for each $n \in \mathbf{N}$. Then $(t_n, e_{x_n}) \to (t, e_x)$.

Proof: Now $(t_n, e_{x_n}) \in [0,x_n] \to [0,x]$ from condition (4). Hence there is a subsequence $(t_{n_k}, e_{x_{n_k}})$ which converges to an element of $[0,x]$, i.e., $(t_{n_k}, e_{x_{n_k}}) \to (t,e_x)$. Since each such subsequence converges to (t, e_x), we have that (t,e_x) is the only cluster point of (t_n, e_{x_n}), and hence $(t_n, e_{x_n}) \to (t,e_x)$. ∎

5.13 Theorem Let S be a ruled continuum. Then S admits the structure of a compact abelian monoid with zero.

Proof: For $x = (|x|, e_x)$ and $y = (|y|, e_y)$ in S let $\alpha(x, y) = max(|x| + |y| - 1, 0)$ and let $\beta(x, y) = min(e_x, e_y)$ we define $xy = (\alpha(x, y), \beta(x, y))$ To see that this multiplication is well defined, observe that for $x, y \in S$, $|x| + |y| \le |e_x| + |e_y| \le |e_x| + 1$ so that $|x| + |y| - 1 \le |e_x|$ and similarly $|x| + |y| - 1 \le |e_y|$. It is straightforward to see that this multiplication is associative and that $0 = (0, u)$ is a zero and $u = (1, u)$ is an identity. It remains to show that multiplication is continuous.

Let $x, y \in S$, $x_n \to x$, and $y_n \to y$ in S. We will show that $x_n y_n \to xy$. Without loss of generality, we can assume that $e_x \le e_y$ in I. By considering subsequence, we can also assume that either $e_{x_n} \le e_{y-n}$ or $e_{y_n} \le e_{x_n}$ for each $n \in \mathbf{N}$. The remainder of the proof will be resolved by cases. Let $p_n = max(|x_n| + |y_n| - 1, 0)$ for each $n \in \mathbf{N}$ and let $p = max(|x| + |y| - 1, 0)$. Then $0 \le p_n \le 1$ for each $n \in \mathbf{N}$ and $p_n \to p$ by the continuity of max and the metric d. Observe that $p_n \le |x_n|$ and $p_n \le |y_n|$ for each $n \in \mathbf{N}$.

Case 1. Suppose that $x \ne y$, $x \in [0, y]$ and $e_{x_n} \le e_{y_n}$ for all $n \in \mathbf{N}$. Then $x_n y_n = (|x_n|, e_{n_n})(|y_n|, e_{y_n}) = (p_n, e_{x_n}) \to (p, e_x)$ by 5.12 and $(p, e_x) = (|x|, e_x)(|y|, e_y) = xy$, since $e_x \le e_y$. Thus $x_n y_n \to xy$ in this case.

Case 2. Suppose that $x \ne y$, $x \in [0, y]$, and $e_{y_n} \le e_{x_n}$ for all $n \in \mathbf{N}$. Then $x_n y_n = (p_n, e_{y_n}) \to (p, e_y)$ by 5.12. Since $x \in [0, y]$, $(p, e_y) = (p, e_x)$ from $p \le |x|$, so that $(p, e_x) = xy$ and $x_n y_n \to xy$.

Case 3. Suppose that $x = y$. If $e_{x_n} \le e_{y_n}$ for each $n \in \mathbf{N}$, then $x_n y_n = (p_n, e_{x_n}) \to (p, e_x) = xy$, and if $e_{y_n} \le e_{x_n}$ for each n, then $x_n y_n = (p_n, e_{y_n}) \to (p, e_y) = xy$.

Case 4. Suppose that $x \notin [0, y]$, $y \notin [0, x]$, and $e_x < e_y < u$. Then, from (7) and taking subsequences we can assume that $e_{x_n} < e_{y_n}$ for each $n \in \mathbf{N}$. Then $x_n y_n = (p_n, e_{x_n}) \to (p, e_x) = xy$.

Case 5. Suppose that $x \notin [0, y]$, $y \notin [0, x]$, and $e_x < e_y = u$. Now if $e_{x_n} < e_{y_n}$ for each $n \in \mathbf{N}$, then $x_n y_n = (p_n, e_{x_n}) \to (p, e_x) = xy$. Assume then that $e_{y_n} < e_{x_n}$ for each n. Since $x \notin [0, u]$, we have $y \in C$. Assume that $y \ne 0$. Now $C = [0, k]$ where $d(0, k) = 1/2$ from (8). Using (3), let $[0, q] = [0, e_x] \cap [0, u]$. Then $|x| = d(0, x) \le d(0, e_x) \le d(0, q) + d(q, e_x) \le |q| + 1/2$. Since $y \in C$, $|y| \le 1/2$, so that $p \le max(|q|, 0) = |q|$. Therefore, $x_n y_n = (p_n, e_{y_n}) \to (p, u) = (pe_x) = xy$.

Observe that $(p,u) = (p,e_x)$, since $p \le |q|$, and p can be marked off either along $[0,u]$ or $[0,e_x]$ with the same final position. Now if $y = 0$, then $x_n y_n = (p_n, min(e_{x_n}, e_{y_n})) \to 0 = xy$ by 5.12. ∎

Example The motivating continuum for 5.13 was Haskel Cohen's example of a monoid with zero on the *Cantorian swastika* in the plane:

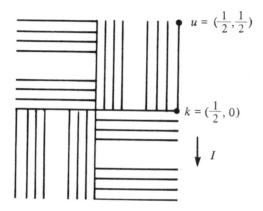

$u = (\frac{1}{2}, \frac{1}{2})$

$k = (\frac{1}{2}, 0)$

I

Now I is the collection of endpoints of the arcs erected on the Cantor set on each of the axis intervals, and I is ordered clockwise with u maximal. The metric d is the rectangular metric in the plane $0 = (0,0)$, and $C = [0,k]$ along the x-axis.

Example Two Cantor fans tangent along a segment is another continuum to which 5.13 applies:

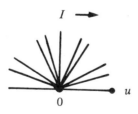

$I \longrightarrow$

u

0

The ordering on I is clockwise and $C = \{0\}$.

Example Two cones tangent along a line segment is a continuum to which 5.13 applies:

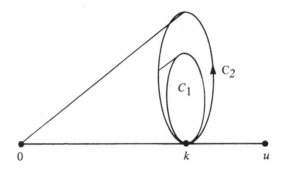

Here $I = ((C_1 \cup C_2)\backslash\{k\}) \cup \{u\}$, with C_1 and C_2 ordered as indicated and with the points of C_1 below those of C_2, and u maximal. Now $C = [0,k]$. Recall that Friedberg's construction also allows one to construct a monoid on two tangent cones.

Example The "closed up" $\sin(1/x)$ curve, toegether with interior admits the structure of a compact monoid with zero.

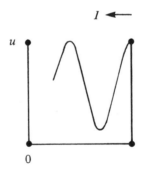

To apply 5.13, take I to be u together with the graph of $y = \sin(1/x)$ for $0 < x \leq 1$ ordered from right to left. In this example $C = \{0\}$.

Example The unit square in the first quadrant of the plane:

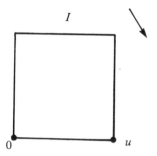

Here I is the set of points with at least one coordinate 1 and is ordered in the clockwise direction. The arcs are the line segments from 0 to points of I. Again, in this example, $C = \{0\}$.

SEMIGROUPS ON THE TWO-CELL

The two-cell has received considerable attention in the literature as the underlying continuum of a compact semigroup. Here the questions are of the nature as to what kind of algebraic structures does the two-cell admit, and given this structure, where is the minimal ideal, the set of idempotents, etc.? In this section we discuss some of the early results which appear in Hudson [1961], Brown [1965], Ferguson [1967], Hildebrant [1967], DeVun [1970], Cohen and Koch [1981], and Cohen and Koch [1982].

Probably the most significant contribution to semigroups on the two-cell is the above cited paper of Anne Lester Hudson. Her results on the divisibility properties of such semigroups have been quoted in a number of results and the so-called "backward Γ theorem" has been used in dealing with divisibility in a much larger class of compact semigroups.

One of the early problems in compact semigroup theory was the so-called "skin problem" posed by A. D. Wallace. Does there exist a continuous multiplication on the two-cell such that the boundary is the set of idempotents? The question was answered in the negative in Ferguson [1967]. In view of the length of the argument, we will not attempt to establish Ferguson's result, but will discuss some of his more interesting early results of that dissertation, since these are of a more general nature.

Recall that a space X has the *fixed-point property* provided that for each continuous function $\phi: X \to X$, there exists $p \in X$ such that $\phi(p) = p$. The point p is called a *fixed point* of ϕ. It is well known than an n-cell has the fixed-point property.

5.14 Theorem Let S be a compact semigroup with the fixed-point property. Then $M(S) \subseteq E(S)$.

Proof: Let $e \in M(S) \cap E(S)$. Then $H(e) = eSe$ is a retract of S, so that $H(e)$ has the fixed-point property. Now if $y \in H(e)\backslash\{e\}$, then the map $h \mapsto hy$ has no fixed point. We conclude that $H(e) = \{e\}$ and $M(S) = \bigcup\{H(e): e \in M(S) \cap E(S)\} \subseteq E(S)$. ∎

The next result is a slight generalization of a lemma of Ferguson, but the proof employs his technique.

5.15 Theorem If S is a semigroup on the two-cell such that ∂S is a uniquely divisible subset of S, then S is divisible.

Proof: Let $n \in \mathbf{N}$ and let $\phi: S \to S$ be the map defined by $\phi(x) = x^n$. Assume that ϕ is not surjective, and let $a \in S\backslash\phi(S)$. Let $r: S\backslash\{a\} \to \partial S$ be a retraction of $S\backslash\{a\}$ onto ∂S along radial lines. Then, since ∂S is uniquely divisible, $\phi|\partial S$ is a homeomorphism of S onto itself. We obtain that $\phi^{-1} \circ r \circ \phi: S \to \partial S$ is a retraction of S onto ∂S. This contradiction yields that ϕ is surjective, and hence S is divisible. ∎

5.16 Corollary If S is a semigroup on the two-cell such that ∂S is uniquely divisible, then $H(e)$ is connected for each $e \in E(S)$.

For a semigroup S on the two-cell, we use ∂S to denote the bounding one-sphere of S in $\mathbf{R}^2$. Now if S is a semigroup on the two-cell with $\partial S = E(S)$, then from 5.14, we have $M(S) \subseteq \partial S$ and hence $M(S)$ in an arc in ∂S. Thus $S/M(S)$ is a semigroup on the two-cell with 0 on the boundary. We therefore can assume that S has a zero element 0.

An important lemma to Ferguson's solution to the skin problem was the fact that if S is a semigroup on the two-cell such that $E(S) = \partial S$, then $H(e) = \{e\}$ for each $e \in E(S)$. We present his argument here:

If $H(e)$ is two dimensional, then $H(e)$ contains an open set. In view of the homogeneity of $H(e)$, we see that $H(e)$ is open. Since $H(e)$ is also closed and S is connected, we have $S = H(e)$ (which is a contradiction).

If $H(e)$ is one-dimensional, then $H(e)$ is either a circle group or a solenoidal group (see Pontryagin [1966]). From Bing [1951] only the circle is embeddable in the plane, and hence $H(e)$ is the circle group.Now $I = eSe \backslash H(e)$ is an ideal of eSe, and the ideals of a connected semigroup are connected. Since I is connected, it must lie in either the bounded or the unbounded component C of $\mathbf{R}^2 \backslash H(e)$. Now $0 \notin H(e)$ and $0 \in eSe$. Since $0 \in I$ and I is connected, we have $I \subseteq C$. Let B denote the bounded component of $\mathbf{R}^2 \backslash H(e)$. Then B does not lie in eSe and eSe has nontrivial cohomology. This contradiction yields that $H(e)$ is zero dimensional. Since from 5.16, $H(e)$ is connected, we have that $H(e) = \{e\}$.

We now present a result of Brown [1965], which characterizes a semilattice S on the two-cell in which $0 \in \partial S$ and such that $\uparrow x$ is connected for each $x \in S$. A similar characterization for $0 \in S \backslash \partial S$ is given in that paper, but will not be discussed here.

The following is a slight generalization of a result in Anderson and Ward [1961].

5.17   Theorem   If S is an arcwise connected idempotent semigroup with zero 0, then S is homotopically trivial.

Proof: Let I^n denote the cartesian product of n copies of [0,1]. Let $\phi : I^n \to S$ be the map such that $\phi(\partial I^n) = 0$, and define $\psi : I^n \times I \to S$ by $\psi(x_1, \ldots, x_n, r) = \phi(x_1, \ldots, x_n)\phi(x_1 - x_1 r, \ldots, x_n - x_n r)$. Then $\psi(x_1, \ldots, x_n, 0) = [\phi(x_1, \ldots, x_n)]^2 = \phi(x_1, \ldots, x_n)$ and we also have that $\psi(x_1, \ldots, x_n, 1) = \phi(x_1, \ldots, x_n)\phi(0, \ldots, 0) = 0$. ∎

The following pair of theorems were proved by Brown for the n-cell.

5.18   Theorem   Let S be a semilattice on an n-cell and let e be a maximal element of S. Then $e \in \partial S$.

Proof: From 2.23 and 5.17 we have that $S \backslash \{e\}$ is a homotopically trivial subsemilattice, and hence $e \notin S \backslash \partial S$.   ∎

5.19   Theorem   Let S be a semilattice on an n-cell with an identity 1, and let T be an arc chain from 0 to 1 in S. Then $S = (\partial S)T$.

Proof: Now $\partial S \subseteq (\partial S)T$, so it is sufficient to show that $(\partial S)T$ is contractible.   Define $\phi:(\partial S)T \times T \to (\partial S)T$ by $\phi(bt,r) = btr$. Then $\phi(bt,1) = bt$, and $\phi(bt,0) = 0$. The result follows from the fact that ϕ is continuous.   ∎

5.20   Lemma   Let S be a topological semilattice such that $\uparrow x$ is connected for each $x \in S$ and let $\phi:S \to T$ be a continuous homomorphism of S onto a topological semilattice T. Then ϕ is monotone and $\uparrow y$ is connected for each $y \in T$.

Proof: It is immediate that ϕ is monotone. Let $y \in T$, $z \in \uparrow y$, $y = \phi(a)$, and let $z = \phi(b)$. Then $y = yz = \phi(a)\phi(b) = \phi(ab)$. Let C be an arch chain in S from b to ab. Then $\phi(C)$ is an arc chain from z to y in T.   ∎

5.21   Lemma.   Let S be a two-cell and let C and D be arcwise connected subsets of S such that $S = C \cup D$, $C \cap D = \square$, and $\partial S \cap C \neq \square \neq \partial S \cap D$. Then $\partial S \cap C$ and $\partial S \cap D$ are connected sets.

Proof: Suppose that $\partial S \cap C$ is not connected. Then $\partial S \cap D$ is not connected. Let a and b be in different components of $\partial S \cap C$ and let T be an arc in C from a to b. Let d and e be in different components of $\partial S \cap D$ so that $\{a,b\}$ separates d and e in ∂S, and let

J be an arc in D from d to e. Then J and T cannot be disjoint, which contradicts $C \cap D = \square$. ∎

5.22   Corollary   Let S be a semilattice on the two-cell and let $a,b \in \partial S$ such that $\uparrow (ab)$ is connected. Let P and Q be arcs in ∂S such that $\partial S = P \cup Q$ and $P \cap Q = \{a,b\}$. Then either $P \subseteq \uparrow (ab)$ or $Q \subseteq \uparrow (ab)$.

Proof: Now $\uparrow (ab)$ is arcwise connected from 2.23. On the other hand, if $x \in S \backslash \uparrow (ab)$, then there exists an arc chain T in S from 0 to S. Clearly $T \cap \uparrow (ab) = \square$, and hence $S \backslash \uparrow (ab)$ is arcwise connected. From 5.21, $\uparrow (ab) \cap \partial S$ is connected, and the result follows. ∎

5.23   Lemma   Let S be a semilattice on the two-cell such that $\uparrow x$ is connected for each $x \in S$ and $0 \in \partial S$. Then $(\partial S)^2 = S$.

Proof: We first show that $(\partial S)^3 \subseteq (\partial S)^2$. Let $a,b,c \in (\partial S)^3$. In order to prove that $abc \in (\partial S)^2$, it is sufficient to assume that a,b, and c are all distinct and nonzero. Assume also that these points are named so that 0 and b are in different components of $\partial S \backslash \{a,c\}$. From 5.22, one component of $\partial S \backslash \{a,c\}$ lies in $\uparrow (ac)$. Since $0 \notin \uparrow (ac)$, it follows that $b \in \uparrow (ac)$, and hence $abc = ac$ and $(\partial S)^3 \subseteq (\partial S)^2$. Hence $(\partial S)^4 = (\partial S)^3(\partial S) \subseteq (\partial S)^2(\partial S) \subseteq (\partial S)^2$. Since $(\partial S)^2$ is a compact connected semilattice and $\partial S \subseteq (\partial S)^2$, it follows from 2.23 and 5.17 that $(\partial S)^2 = S$. ∎

We remark that 5.23 holds even in the case that $0 \notin \partial S$, as was proved by Brown. However, we will not need this case here.

Recall that $I_m = [0,1]$ under the min multiplication. Let $T = \{(x,y) \in I_m \times I_m : x + y \leq 1\}$. Then T is a subsemilattice of $I_m \times I_m$.

5.24   Theorem   Let S be a semilattice on the two-cell such that $0 \in \partial S$ and $\uparrow x$ is connected for each $x \in S$. Then S is a continous homomorphic image of T.

Proof: Let $R = (I_m \times \{0\}) \cup (\{0\} \times I_m)$. Then R is a closed congruence on T. Let $N = T/R$, and let D be the boundary circle of N. Note that each nonzero element of N has a unique representation as a product of two not necessarily distinct elements of D, and that $ab = 0$ implies that $a = 0$ or $b = 0$. Let $\alpha : D \to \partial S$ homeomorphically with $\alpha(0) = 0$. Extend α to N by defining ϕ: $N \to S$ by $\phi(c) = \alpha(a)\alpha(b)$, where $a, b \in D$. Then ϕ is well defined, and the diagram

$$
\begin{array}{ccc}
N & \xrightarrow{\ \ \phi\ \ } & S \\[2mm]
\uparrow & & \uparrow \\[2mm]
D \times D & \xrightarrow{\ \alpha \times \alpha\ } & \partial S \times \partial S
\end{array}
$$

commutes. Vertical arrows represent the respective multiplication functions of N and S. Since these functions are continuous and α is continuous, it follows that ϕ is continuous. From 5.23, we see that ϕ is surjective.

It remains to see that ϕ is a homomorphism. For this purpose, let $c = ab$, $a = pq$, $b = rs$, with p, q, r, s distinct nonzero elements of D. Some unique pair of p, q, r, s separates the remaining pair from 0 on D. Without loss of generality, we assume that p, r, and 0 lie in different components of $D \setminus \{q, s\}$. By 5.22, we have $\{p, r\} \subseteq \uparrow (qs)$. Hence $ab = pqrs = qs$, and $\phi(c) = \phi(ab) = \alpha(q)\alpha(s)$. On the other hand, since α is a homeomorphism on D, it follows that $\{\alpha(p), \alpha(r)\}$ and $\{\alpha(0) = 0\}$ lie in different components of $\partial S \setminus \{\alpha(q), \alpha(s)\}$. Hence $\{\alpha(p), \alpha(r)\} \subseteq \uparrow (\alpha(q)\alpha(s))$ and therefore $\alpha(q)\alpha(s) = \alpha(p)\alpha(q)\alpha(r)\alpha(s) = \phi(pq)\phi(rs) = \phi(a)\phi(b)$. ∎

Brown proved a converse of 5.24 and an analogous result in the case that $0 \notin \partial S$.

We consider now some of the results in Hildebrant [1967] on uniquely divisible semigroups on the two-cell. First note that if S is a uniquely divisible semigroup on the two-cell and $x \in S \setminus E(S)$, then the unithetic subsemigroup of S generated by x (denoted $[x]$) is topologically isomorphic to I_u since the nondegenerate groups are solenoidal and hence cannot lie in the two-cell (see Bing [1951] and Carruth, Hildebrant, and Koch [1983]). Observe also in this case that for $x,y \in S$, if $(S \backslash E(S)) \cap [x] \cap [y] \neq \square$, then either $[x] \subseteq [y]$ or $[y] \subseteq [x]$. Otherwise, $p \in (S \backslash E(S)) \cap [x] \cap [y]$ would have different rth roots in $[x]$ and $[y]$ for some rational number r, which cannot happen in a uniquely divisible semigroup.

We use 0 to denote a zero for a semigroup and 1 to denote an identity.

5.25 Lemma Let S be a uniquely divisible semigroup on the two-cell such that $E(S) = \{0,1\}$. Then $0 \in \partial S$.

Proof: Suppose that $0 \notin \partial S$, and let $x \in \partial S \backslash E(S)$. Then $\partial S \backslash [x] \neq \square$. Let $p \in \partial S \backslash [x]$. Since $[x] \cap \partial S$ is closed, there exists a point y in the arc from p to x on ∂S which does not contain 1 (we know from 1.7 that $1 \in \partial S$). Then $[y]$ must meet $[p]$ or $[x]$ in a point not in $E(S)$. This contradiction yields the result. ∎

The next lemma employs a technique used in Brown [1965].

5.26 Lemma Let S be a uniquely divisible semigroup on the two-cell with identity 1 and zero 0 such that $0 \in \partial S$, and let A and B denote the arcs on ∂S with endpoints 0 and 1. If A and B are I-semigroups, then $S = AB = BA$.

Proof: Now $1 \in A \cap B$ and hence $\partial S \subseteq AB$. Define $\phi : AB \times B \to S$ by $\phi(ab,c) = abc$. Then ϕ is continuous, $\phi(ab,0) = 0$, and $\phi(ab,1) = ab$. We see that AB is contractible, and conclude that $S = AB$. ∎

5.27 Lemma Let S be a uniquely divisible semigroup on the two-cell with identity 1 and zero 0 such that $0 \in \partial S$, and let A and B be the arcs in ∂S with endpoints 0 and 1. If each point of S lies on an I-semigroup from 0 to 1, then each of A and B is an I-semigroup.

Proof: Let x and y be distinct points of $A \backslash \{0,1\}$ such that y

separates x from 1 on A. Suppose that $[x] \neq [y]$. Let T_1 and T_2 denote the I-semigroups from 0 to 1 in S containing x and y, respectively. Then, since y separates x from 1 on A, $T_1 \cap T_2$ contains an idempotent f such that $xf = x$ and $fy = f$. Hence $xy = (xf)y = x(fy) = xf = x$. Thus, if y separates x from 1 on A and $[x] \neq [y]$, then $xy = x$.

If $A \backslash E(S) = \square$, then the fact that A is an I-semigroup follows from the preceding paragraph. Suppose $A \backslash E(S) \neq \square$, and let $z \in A \backslash E(S)$. Then there is an I-semigroup I in S such that $z \in I$. Let a be the zero of I and let b be the identity of I. Let N be the component of $I \cap A$ containing z, $h = \inf N$, and $g = \sup N$ in the cut-point ordering $<$ of A from 0 to 1. Since $h = \inf N$, there exists a sequence h_n of points of $A \backslash I$ such that $h_n < h$ for each $n \in \mathbf{N}$ and $h_n \to h$. Thus, by the preceding paragraph, $h_n h = h_n$ for each $n \in \mathbf{N}$. From the continuity of multiplication on S we have that $h_n h \to h^2$, so that $h = h^2$. Since $h \in I$, we have $a = h$. Similarly, $g = b$, and hence $I \subseteq A$. We conclude that A is an I-semigroup and similarly B is an I-semigroup. ∎

• If S is a uniquely divisible abelian semigroup on the two-cell, then $M(S)$ is a uniquely divisible abelian group. Since these groups are solenoidal, we must have that $M(S)$ is degenerate. Thus each uniquely divisible abelian semigroup on the two-cell has a zero 0.

Recall that $I_u = [0,1]$ under the usual multiplication and topology. Let $T = (I_u \times I_u)/J$, where $J = \{(x,y): x = 0 \text{ or } y = 0\}$. Then T is a uniquely divisible semigroup on the two-cell.

5.28 Theorem Let S be a uniquely divisible abelian semigroup on the two-cell with $E(S) = \{0,1\}$. Then S is topologically isomorphic to T.

Proof: It is clear that if x is not 0 or 1, then $[x]$ is a usual semigroup (topologically isomorphic to I_u) with endpoints 0 and 1, and that S is ruled by these, i.e., distinct unithetic semigroups meet only in $\{0,1\}$.

From 5.25, we have that $0 \in \partial S$, and hence from 5.27, each of the arcs A and B in ∂S with endpoints 0 and 1 are usual semigroups. From 5.26, we have that $S = AB$. Define $\phi : A \times B \to S$ by $\phi(a,b) = ab$. Then ϕ is a continuous surmorphism whose kernel congruence is $\{(a,0): a \in A\} \cup \{(0,b): b \in B\}$. The result follows. ∎

The property of a semigroup on the two-cell having boundary arcs which are I-semigroups (as in 5.28) was studied extensively in DeVun [1970], Borrego, Cohen, and DeVun [1971], and in DeVun [1972b]. In DeVun [1972a] the equivalence of uniquely divisible and uniquely representable semigroups on the two-cell was established. These concepts were considered again in DeVun [1976] and DeVun [1980]. Idempotents monoids S with boundary I-semigroups A and B such that $1 \in A \cap B$ and $S = AB$ were studied in Cohen and Koch [1981] and again in Cohen and Koch [1982].

An interesting result related to those above appears in Hinman [1974]. This theorem states that if A and B are I-semigroups in a topological semigroup S, then AB is either degenerate, an arc, or contains a two-cell.

Let $I = [0,1]$ with the usual (lattice) ordering. It was established in Clark and Eberhart [1968] that each topological lattice on the two-cell is topologically isomorphic to a sublattice of the product lattice $I \times I$.

6
Semigroup Categories

Up to this point in this treatise and in Carruth, Hildebrant, and Koch, [1983], we have taken the traditional approach and used traditional terminology in treating the various topics. An attempt will be made in this chapter to pull together many of these concepts under the umbrella of category theory.

Notable among the topics which lend themselves to a categorical treatment are those dealing with "free" or "universal" objects (see Chapter 2 of Carruth, Hildebrant, and Koch [1983]). Among the best reasons for approaching topics with a categorical slant are: (i) one is naturally let to ask questions which might not otherwise be asked; (ii) the categorical treatment often ties together seemingly unrelated topics; and (iii) the language is a highly convenient one.

Our first concern will be the setting apart and labeling of certain categories of semigroups which arise often enough to make the endeavor worth while. This labeling process will be presented in Table 1 and Table 2 after recalling some definitions of some types of semigroups. The reason for using two tables will be evident later.

Recall that an element x of a semigroup S is a *regular element* provided $x \in xSx$. If each element of S is a regular element, then S is called a *regular semigroup*.

Elements x and y of a semigroup S are *generalized inverses* of each other provided $x = xyx$ and $y = yxy$. If S is a [topological] semigroup in which each element x possesses a unique generalized inverse x^{-1} [and the function $x \mapsto x^{-1}$ is continuous], then S is a [*topological*] *inverse semigroup*. Observe that $x \in S$ is regular if and only if x admits at least one generalized inverse in S. To see this, note that if $x = xyx$, then yxy is a generalized inverse of x.

In each category of [topological] semigroups in Tables 1 and 2, morphisms are simply [continuous] homomorphisms, except that in the monoid categories morphisms are required to be identity preserving. The rule of composition in each category is ordinary composition of functions.

Observe that each nontopological [topological] category of Table 1 is a full subcategory of S [$\mathcal{TS}$].

Table 1

	Discrete	Topological	Compact
Semigroups	$\mathcal{S}$	$\mathcal{TS}$	$\mathcal{CS}$
Abelian semigroups	$\mathcal{AS}$	$\mathcal{TAS}$	$\mathcal{CAS}$
Groups	$\mathcal{G}$	$\mathcal{TG}$	$\mathcal{CG}$
Abelian groups	$\mathcal{AG}$	$\mathcal{TAG}$	$\mathcal{CAG}$
Bands	$\mathcal{B}$	$\mathcal{TB}$	$\mathcal{CB}$
Semilattices	$\mathcal{X}$	$\mathcal{TX}$	$\mathcal{CX}$
Lawson semilattices		$\mathcal{TL}$	$\mathcal{CL}$
Inverse semigroups	$\mathcal{J}$	$\mathcal{TJ}$	$\mathcal{CJ}$

Table 2

	Discrete	Topological	Compact
Monoids	$\mathcal{M}$	$\mathcal{TM}$	$\mathcal{CM}$
Regular semigroups	$\mathcal{R}$	$\mathcal{TR}$	$\mathcal{CR}$
Divisible semigroups	$\mathcal{D}$	$\mathcal{TD}$	$\mathcal{CD}$
Uniquely divisible semigroups	$\mathcal{UD}$	$\mathcal{TUD}$	$\mathcal{CUD}$
Locally compact abelian groups		$\mathcal{LCAG}$	

Our program now is to specialize the categorical concepts of Appendix C to the categories of Tables 1 and 2 and to certain other categories of semigroups.

Notation   Throughout the remainder of this chapter, unless otherwise stated, $\mathcal{C}$ will represent any one of the categories of Table 1 or 2. Also, since it will occasionally be helpful to "isolate by columns" Tables 1 and 2:

$\mathcal{H}$ will represent a category from column 1 (discrete).
$\mathcal{TH}$ will represent a category from column 2 (topological).
$\mathcal{CH}$ will represent a category from column 3 (compact).

First, and rather obviously, if S is a $\mathcal{C}$-object, then the $\mathcal{C}$-identity morphism for S is the identity function from S into itself (usually denoted 1_S). That $hom_\mathcal{C} (S, T)$ is a set for each pair of $\mathcal{C}$-objects S and T follows from the fact that $hom_\mathcal{C} (S, T) \subseteq T^S$ (actually $\mathcal{C}$ is a concrete category, but we do not choose to dwell on this fact). It is a simple matter to show that $\mathcal{C}$ is not a small category. Following the observation preceding the tables, we remark that the monoid categories $\mathcal{M}$ [$\mathcal{TM}$, $\mathcal{CM}$] are the only categories in either table which fail to be full subcategories of $\mathcal{S}$ [$\mathcal{TS}$].

Let (S,m) be a semigroup. The *dual* of (S,m) is the semigroup (S,n), where $n(xy) = m(y,x)$ for all $(x,y) \in S \times S$. When no confusion is likely we use $\tilde{S}$ to denote the dual semigroup of S. The *dual functor* from $\mathcal{C}$ to $\mathcal{C}$ is defined by $D(S) = \tilde{S}$ and if $\phi:S \to T$, then $D (\phi) = f:\tilde{S} \to \tilde{T}$.

It is trivial to show that the dual functor $D:\mathcal{C} \to \mathcal{C}$ defined above is a (self-inversive) isomorphism. Many theorems have hypothesis and/or conclusions dealing with left or right identities, zeros, ideals, etc. for which the proof for "left" is exactly the same as that for "right" except that analogous terms are written on the other side. A good example is 1.30 of Carruth, Hildebrant, and Koch [1983] which contains the assertion that if S is a semigroup and $e \in E(S)$, then the following are equivalent:
(a) Se is a minimal left ideal.
(b) eSe is a group.

(c) *eS* is a minimal right ideal.

We proved that (a) $\Rightarrow$ (b) $\Rightarrow$ (c) and remarked that (c) $\Rightarrow$ (b) $\Rightarrow$ (a) had similar proofs. Using the dual functor $D: S \rightarrow S$ we observe that $A \subseteq S$ is a minimal left ideal [group] in S if and only if A is a minimal right ideal [group] in $D(S) = \tilde{S}$. It follows immediately that (c) $\Rightarrow$ (b) $\Rightarrow$ (a) by applying the result (a) $\Rightarrow$ (b) $\Rightarrow$ (c) to the semigroup $\tilde{S}$. Thus, when the remaining assertions of a propostion follow by applying the results already obtained to the dual semigroup, we have stated that the remaining assertions *are dual*.

The fact that the dual functor $D: \mathscr{C} \rightarrow \mathscr{C}$ is covariant sets it apart from the functor $op: \mathscr{C} \rightarrow \mathscr{C}^{op}$ defined by $op(A) = A$ and $op(A \xrightarrow{f} B) = B \xrightarrow{f} A$. By going through some painful contortions one can realize S as a pseudocategorical dual of S. The problem which presents an obstruction to making this an easy task is simply that semigroups need not have identities whereas categories must. We end the discussion of dual semigroups by indicating how one achieves this realization. If S is a monoid, then S may be identified with the category $\mathscr{F}$ whose single object is S and whose morphisms are the elements of S. That is, $Ob(\mathscr{F}) = \{S\}$ and $Mor\ \mathscr{F} = S$. For $x, y \in Mor\ \mathscr{F}$, $x \circ y = xy$. Conversely, if $\mathscr{F}$ is a category with exactly one object A, then $Mor\ \mathscr{F}$ is a monoid relative to composition. With this notation, if S is identified with $\mathscr{F}$, then $\tilde{S}$ is identified with $\mathscr{F}^{op}$. The transition to semigroups which are not necessarily monoids may be fairly easily made by moving as follows:

$$S \rightarrow S^1 \rightarrow \mathscr{F}_{S_1} \rightarrow (\mathscr{F}_{S_1})^{op} \rightarrow \tilde{S}^1 \rightarrow \tilde{S}$$

The observation should be made that for each $\mathscr{C}$-object S, S^1 is again a $\mathscr{C}$-object. This would fail to be true for some categories of semigroups (e.g., connected semigroups).

A number of the results in the remainder of this chapter appear in Crawley [1976].

SECTIONS   The $\mathscr{C}$-sections are precisely those $\mathscr{C}$-morphisms $\phi: S \rightarrow T$ such that ϕ is a [topological] isomorphism onto $\phi(S)$ and $\phi(S)$ is a homomorphic retract of T; that is, there exists a $\mathscr{C}$-morphism $\gamma: T \rightarrow T$ such that $\gamma \circ \gamma = \gamma$ and $\gamma(T) = \phi(T)$.

RETRACTIONS The $\mathcal{C}$-retractions are precisely those $\mathcal{C}$-morphisms $\phi: S \to T$ such that there exists a homomorphic retraction $\gamma: S \to S$ (again $\gamma \circ \gamma = \gamma$) and a $\mathcal{C}$-isomorphism $\delta: \gamma(S) \to T$ such that $\phi = \delta \circ \gamma$. Hence, the $\mathcal{C}$-retractions are, up to $\mathcal{C}$-isomorphisms, homomorphic retractions.

ISOMORPHISMS For each nontopological category $\mathcal{C}$, the $\mathcal{C}$-isomorphisms are precisely the algebraic isomorphisms (i.e., bijections which preserve multiplication). For each topological category $\mathcal{C}$, the $\mathcal{C}$-isomorphisms are precisely the topological isomorphims (i.e., homeomorphisms which preserve multiplication).

MONOMORPHISMS In Hofmann and Mostert [1966], it was established that the compact semigroup monomorphisms (i.e., the $\mathcal{CS}$-monomorphisms) are precisely the injective continuous homomorphisms. We will show now, using essentially the same device, that if $\mathcal{C}$ is any Table 1 category, then the $\mathcal{C}$-morphisms are precisely the injective $\mathcal{C}$-morphisms. The technique is to find a universal $\mathcal{C}$-object generated by **N** (see also 3.8 of Carruth, Hildebrant, and Koch [1983]), that is, a $\mathcal{C}$-object $F(\mathbf{N})$ and a homomorphism $\phi: \mathbf{N} \to F(\mathbf{N})$ (not necessarily a $\mathcal{C}$-morphism, as **N** need not be a $\mathcal{C}$-object) such that for any $\mathcal{C}$-object S and any homomorphism $\gamma: \mathbf{N} \to S$, there exists a unique $\mathcal{C}$-morphism $\delta: F(\mathbf{N}) \to S$ such that the triangle:

commutes. Once this is accomplished, if $\psi: S \to T$ is a noninjective $\mathcal{C}$-morphism and $\psi(x) = \psi(y)$ with $x \neq y$, then one obtains γ_y from **N** into S by letting $\gamma_x(n) = x^n$ and $\gamma_y(n) = y^n$ for all $n \in \mathbf{N}$, δ_1 and δ_2 from the properties of $(F(\mathbf{N}), \delta)$, $\psi \circ \delta_1 = \psi \circ \delta_2$, and $\delta_1 \neq \delta_2$.

Hence ψ is not a $\mathscr{C}$-monomorphism. It is clear that each injective $\mathscr{C}$-morphism is a $\mathscr{C}$-monomorphism. Slight modifications of this technique yield that the $\mathscr{C}$-monomorphisms are precisely the injective $\mathscr{C}$-morphisms if $\mathscr{C} \in \{\mathcal{M}, \mathcal{TM}, \mathcal{CM}, \mathcal{LCAG}\}$. The result also holds for $\mathcal{R}, \mathcal{TR}, \mathcal{CR}, \mathcal{UD}, \mathcal{TUD}, \mathcal{CUD}$, and the category of finite semigroups, but the techniques of proof are different (see Crawley [1976]). Then result fails to hold for $\mathcal{D}, \mathcal{TD}$, and $\mathcal{CD}$, Then natural map $\phi:\mathbf{R/Z} \to \mathbf{R/Z}/\{-1, 1\}$ is a $\mathscr{C}$-monomorphism in each of these categories as well as in the categories of connected [abelian] semigroups, compact connected [abelian] semigroups, and compact connected [abelian] monoids.

EPIMORPHISMS   In the nontopological and compact categories any surjective $\mathscr{C}$-morphism is a $\mathscr{C}$-epimorphism and in the topological categories (using Hausdorffness) any dense $\mathscr{C}$-morphism is a $\mathscr{C}$-epimorphism. The converses do not generally hold, however, and we proceed to investigate the question of when the converses do and do not hold.

(a) Let S be the semigroup of nonnegative integers under addition and let $\phi:S \to \mathbf{Z}$ be the inclusion homomorphism. Then clearly ϕ is not dense and it is easy to see that ϕ is a $\mathscr{C}$-epimorphism if $\mathscr{C} \in \{\mathcal{S}, \mathcal{TS}, \mathcal{AS}, \mathcal{TAS}, \mathcal{M}, \mathcal{TM}\}$.

(b) It is a standard exercise to show that $\mathcal{AG}$-epimorphisms are surjective and it is somewhat trickier to establish the fact that $\mathcal{G}$-epimorphisms are surjective (see Herrlich and Strecker [1973] or Rotmann [1973]).

(c) Now from Chapter 2, we have that $\mathscr{C}$-epimorphisms are surjective if $\mathscr{C} \in \{\mathcal{X}, \mathcal{CL}\}$. For $\mathscr{C} = \mathcal{X}$ the result is rather straightforward; however for $\mathscr{C} = \mathcal{L}$ the result was obtained in Hofmann and Mislove [1975]. The introduction to this paper gives an excellent discussion of the epimorphism question.

(d) If $\mathscr{C} \in \{\mathcal{TAG}, \mathcal{LCAG}\}$, then each $\mathscr{C}$-epimorphism is dense. These results follow from the general theory of topological groups (see Husain [1966]). That $\mathcal{CAG}$-epimorphisms are surjective follows from the results of Section 5 of Chapter 1 in Carruth, Hildebrant, and Koch [1983] and the technique for showing that $[\mathcal{AG}, \mathcal{TAG}, \mathcal{LCAG}]$-epimorphisms are dense.

(e) In Hofmann and Mostert [1966] an example was given of a $\mathscr{CS}$-epimorphism which was not surjective. For completeness we discuss the example here, as it shows that epimorphisms need not be surjective in several categories. Let S be the semigroup $[X,S,Y]\sigma/(X \times \{0\} \times Y)$, where $X = \{a,b\} = Y, S = \{0,1\}$ under multiplication, and σ is given by the table

σ	a	b
a	1	0
b	0	1

If we let $e = (a,1,a), x = (a,1,b), y = (b,1,a), f = (b,1,b)$, and $0 = X \times \{0\} \times Y$, then multiplication for S is given by

	e	f	x	y	0
e	e	0	x	0	0
f	0	f	0	y	0
x	0	x	0	e	0
y	y	0	f	0	0
0	0	0	0	0	0

Let $S' = \{e,f,x,0\}$ and let $\phi:S' \to S$ be the inclusion map. Then S' is a subsemigroup of S and ϕ is a homomorphism. Suppose that θ and ψ are homomorphisms from S into a semigroup T such that $\theta \circ \phi = \psi \circ \phi$ (i.e., θ and ψ agree in S'). Then $\psi(y) = \psi(ye) = \psi(y)\psi(e) = \psi(y)\theta(e) = \psi(y)\theta(xy) = \psi(y)\theta(x)\theta(y) = \psi(y)\psi(x)\theta(y) = \psi(yx)\theta(y) = \psi(f)\theta(y) = \theta(f)\theta(y) = \theta(fy) = \theta(y)$ and so $\psi = \theta$. Hence ϕ is a $\mathscr{CS}$-epimorphism which is not surjective. By simply adding identities to S and S' and appropriately extending ϕ one obtains that $\mathscr{CM}$-epimorphisms need not be surjective. By using cones one sees that epimorphisms need not be surjective in the categories of connected semigroups, compact connected semigroups, connected monoids, and compact connected monoids.

(f) It was shown in Poguntke [1970] that $\mathscr{C}\mathscr{G}$-epimorphisms are not surjective.

(g) It was shown in LaMartin [1975] that epimorphisms in the category of Hausdorff [abelian] k-groups need not be dense.

(h) To the authors' knowledge the question remains unanswered for $\mathscr{C}\mathscr{A}\mathscr{S}$, $\mathscr{T}\mathscr{G}$, $\mathscr{B}$, $\mathscr{T}\mathscr{B}$, $\mathscr{C}\mathscr{B}$, $\mathscr{T}\mathscr{X}$, $\mathscr{T}\mathscr{L}$, $\mathscr{I}$, $\mathscr{T}\mathscr{I}$, $\mathscr{C}\mathscr{I}$, $\mathscr{R}$, $\mathscr{T}\mathscr{R}$, $\mathscr{C}\mathscr{R}$, $\mathscr{D}$, $\mathscr{T}\mathscr{D}$, $\mathscr{C}\mathscr{D}$, $\mathscr{U}\mathscr{D}$, $\mathscr{T}\mathscr{U}\mathscr{D}$, $\mathscr{C}\mathscr{U}\mathscr{D}$. Solutions for some of these may lie near the surface. However, at least for $\mathscr{T}\mathscr{G}$ and $\mathscr{C}\mathscr{X}$, the problem appears to be rather difficult (see LaMartin [1975] and Hofmann and Mislove [1973]).

BIMORPHISMS In view of the vacuum of knowledge of monomorphisms and epimorphisms, any attempt at a systematic discussion of bimorphisms seems futile at this time.

INITIAL, TERMINAL, AND ZERO OBJECTS The trivial semigroup (containing a single element) is a $\mathscr{C}$-terminal object for all $\mathscr{C}$. It is a $\mathscr{C}$-initial object only for the monoid and group categories. Hence, the trivial semigroup is a $\mathscr{C}$-zero object if $\mathscr{C} \in \{\mathscr{M}, \mathscr{T}\mathscr{M}, \mathscr{C}\mathscr{M}, \mathscr{G}, \mathscr{T}\mathscr{G}, \mathscr{C}\mathscr{G}, \mathscr{A}\mathscr{G}, \mathscr{T}\mathscr{A}\mathscr{G}, \mathscr{C}\mathscr{A}\mathscr{G}, \mathscr{L}\mathscr{C}\mathscr{A}\mathscr{G}\}$.

FUNCTORS We have already mentioned the dual functor D: $\mathscr{C} \to \mathscr{C}$ which assigns to each semigroup S its dual semigroup $\tilde{S}$. In Chapter 2 of Carruth, Hildebrant, and Koch [1983], for each abelian topological group T, a functor $Hom(-, T)$ was obtained from the category $\mathscr{L}\mathscr{C}\mathscr{S}$ of locally compact semigroups into $\mathscr{T}\mathscr{A}\mathscr{G}$. For $T = \mathbf{R}/\mathbf{Z}$ the restriction (and corestriction) of this functor to $\mathscr{L}\mathscr{C}\mathscr{A}\mathscr{G}$ was treated in that chapter and is called the Pontryagin duality functor. This functor is a dual equivalence from $\mathscr{L}\mathscr{C}\mathscr{A}\mathscr{G}$ onto itself and has many useful properties. The Bohr compactification (see page 99 of Carruth, Hildebrant, and Koch [1983]) is a functor from $\mathscr{T}\mathscr{S}$ into $\mathscr{C}\mathscr{S}$. It is, in fact, a left adjoint to the inclusion functor from $\mathscr{C}\mathscr{S}$ into $\mathscr{T}\mathscr{S}$. This will be discussed further at a later point in this chapter. The free topological semigroup generated by a space is a functor from the category $\mathscr{T}$ of topological spaces into

$\mathcal{TG}$. Again, this functor will be discussed more in a later part of this chapter. Also mentioned in Chapter 2 of Carruth, Hildebrant, and Koch [1983] was the free topological group generated by a Hausdorff space. This is also a functor.

EQUALIZERS   In the literature and in this text, semigroups are required to have nonvoid underlying sets. As a consequence, among the categories in Tables 1 and 2 and other categories of semigroups, only the monoids and group categories have any chance of having equalizers. The equalizer of two $\mathcal{C}$-morphisms $\alpha,\beta:S \rightarrow T$ is the inclusion of $\{x \in S: \alpha(x) = \beta(x)\}$ into S whenever $\mathcal{C} \in \{\mathcal{G}, \mathcal{TG}, \mathcal{CG}, \mathcal{AG}, \mathcal{TAG}, \mathcal{CAG}, \mathcal{M}, \mathcal{TM}, \mathcal{CM}, \mathcal{LCAG}\}$. We hasten to point out, however, that the above description of equalizers does not hold for all group categories. For example, in the category of compact divisible groups, the inclusion of the trivial group into **R/Z** is an equalizer for the identity map and the inversion map [Crawley, 1976]. One could strain a bit and obtain the category $\mathcal{C}_\square$ by adjoining "the empty semigroup" to $\mathcal{C}$ or the category $\mathcal{C}^1$ by adjoining an identity to $\mathcal{C}$-objects, whether or not they had identities to begin with. However, it is unclear that either $\mathcal{C}_\square$ or $\mathcal{C}^1$ would have equalizers for all choices of $\mathcal{C}$ (e.g., $\mathcal{C} = \mathcal{D}$). An aesthetic objection to using $\mathcal{C}^1$ would be the treatment of categories of connected semigroups. At any rate, we will not attempt to modify our categories in order to make them have equalizers and hence most of the categories we will deal with will not be complete.

COEQUALIZERS   If $\alpha,\beta:S \rightarrow T$ are $\mathcal{K}$ [$\mathcal{CK}$] -morphisms, then the natural map from T to T/R is a $\mathcal{K}$ [$\mathcal{CK}$]-coequalizer of α and β, where R is the smallest [closed] congruence on T containing $\{(\alpha(x),\beta(x)):x \in S\}$.

PRODUCTS   It is not a difficult exercise to show that $(\Pi\{S_i\}_{i \in I}, \{\pi_i\}_{i \in I})$ is a $\mathcal{C}$-product of the family $\{A_i\}_{i \in I}$ of $\mathcal{C}$-objects. Hence each category in Tables 1 and 2 has products. The remarks in the section of Chapter 2 of Carruth, Hildebrant, and Koch [1983] may be rephrased by say that $\mathcal{AS}$ [$\mathcal{TAS}$, $\mathcal{CAS}$, $\mathcal{G}$, $\mathcal{TG}$, $\mathcal{CG}$] is closed under products in $\mathcal{S}$[$\mathcal{CS}$, $\mathcal{S}$, $\mathcal{TS}$, $\mathcal{CS}$].

COPRODUCTS   We will show later in this chapter that each of the categories of Table 1 has coproducts. This has been deferred to that point because the technique developed there yields a particularly nice proof.

PROJECTIVE AND INJECTIVE LIMITS   The categorical notation of projective and injective limits are treated in [Herrlich and Strecker, 1973] and they are special cases of general limites in categories. Suffice it to say that:

(a) $\varprojlim S_\alpha$, $\{p_\alpha\}_{\alpha \in D}$) is a projective limit of the family $\{S_\alpha\}_{\alpha \in D}$ of $\mathcal{CS}$-objects, in the categorical sense, where p_β is the restriction of projection $\pi_\alpha : \Pi\{S_\alpha\}_{\alpha \in D} \to S_\beta$ to $\varprojlim S_\alpha$ for each $\beta \in D$.

(b) ($\{p_\alpha\}_{\alpha \in D}$, $\varprojlim S_\alpha$) is an injective limit of the family $\{S_\alpha\}_{\alpha \in D}$ of $\mathcal{S}$-objects, in the categorical sense, where $p_\beta : S_\beta \to \varinjlim S_\alpha$ is defined by $P_\beta(x) = \pi((\beta,x))$ for each $\beta \in D$ and each $x \in S_\beta$ (see 2.31 of Carruth, Hildebrant, and Koch [1983]).

We now introduce two categories $\mathcal{P}$ and $\mathcal{TP}$, the first of which contains each category $\mathcal{H}$ as a (full, in the nonmonoid case) subcategory and the second of which contains each category $\mathcal{TH}$ and $\mathcal{CH}$ as a (full, in the nonmonoid case) subcategory. We will show that each category $\mathcal{H}$[$\mathcal{TH}$, $\mathcal{CH}$] in Table 1 is a reflective subcategory of $\mathcal{P}$[$\mathcal{TP}$] and use these facts to show that each of these categories had coproducts. We will also obtain the existence and uniqueness of Bohr compactifications, free topological semigroups, and a host of other universal mappings as corollaries.

The objects of $\mathcal{P}$[$\mathcal{TP}$] are triples (P,A,m) where P is a set [topological space], A is a subset [subspace] of $P \times P$, and $m:A \to P$ is a [continuous] function. These objects will be called [*topological*] *partial groupoids*. If (P,A,m) and (Q,B,n) are $\mathcal{P}$[$\mathcal{TP}$]-objects, the $\mathcal{P}$[$\mathcal{TP}$]-morphisms from (P,A,m) to (Q,B,n)

are those [continuous] functions $\phi: P \to Q$ such that $(\phi \times \phi)(A) \subseteq B$ and the square

commutes. The category $\mathcal{P}[\mathcal{TP}]$ will be called the *category of [topological] partial groupoids*.

Throughout the text we have taken care to separate topological from nontopological considerations. Some workers in the area have felt that this was unnecessary, since an "algebraic" semigroup can be considered as a topological semigroup with the discrete topology. This device may be viewed as an inclusion of $\mathcal{S}$ into $\mathcal{TS}$ obtained by mapping (S,m) to $(S,m,2^S)$. The problem here is that, under this inclusion, $\mathcal{S}$ is not closed under products in $\mathcal{TS}$. To see this, let $\{S_i\}_{i \in I}$ be an infinite family of nontrivial $\mathcal{S}$-objects. Then $\{S_i\}_{i \in I}$ has a $\mathcal{TS}$-product $(S, \{\pi_i\}_{i \in I})$ where $\mathcal{S}$ is not discrete, and so $\mathcal{S}$ is not an $\mathcal{S}$-object. Because of this difficulty, we will continue to consider nontopological categories separately from topological categories. Note also that we avoid the terminology "discrete categories," since the phrase has a standard categorical meaning. The remarks indicate that one cannot consider algebraic semigroups as discrete topological semigroups when studying categorical properties of the two types of semigroups.

6.1 Theorem Let $\mathcal{K}[\mathcal{TK}, \mathcal{CK}]$ denote one of the categories of Table 1. Then each $\mathcal{P}[\mathcal{TP}]$-object (P, A, m) has a $\mathcal{K}[\mathcal{TK}, \mathcal{CK}]$-universal map (u_p, S_p). Hence, $\mathcal{K}[\mathcal{TK}, \mathcal{CK}]$ is a reflective subcategory of $\mathcal{P}[\mathcal{TP}]$.

Proof: Clearly $\mathcal{K}[\mathcal{TK},\mathcal{CK}]$ is a full subcategory of $\mathcal{P}[\mathcal{TP}]$. For a family $\{(P_i, A_i, m_i)\}_{i \in I}$ of $\mathcal{P}[\mathcal{TP}]$-objects, the pair $((P,A,m),$ $\{\pi_i\}_{i \in I})$ is a $\mathcal{P}[\mathcal{TP}]$-product, where $(P,\{\pi_i\}_{i \in I})$ is the product of $\{P_i\}_{i \in I}$ in the category of sets [topological spaces], $A = \{(f,g) \in P \times P : (f(i),g(i)) \in A_i$ for all $i \in I\}$, and $m:A \to P$ is defined by $m((f,g))(i) = m_i((f(i),g(i)))$ for all $i \in I$. Hence $\mathcal{P}[\mathcal{TP}]$ has products. Observe that a [topological] partial groupoid (Q,B,n) is a [topological] semigroup if and only if Q is Hausdorff, $B = Q \times Q$, and n is associative. It follows immediately that $\mathcal{K}[\mathcal{TK},\mathcal{CK}]$ is closed under $\mathcal{P}[\mathcal{TP}]$-products.

Next we show that each $\mathcal{P}[\mathcal{TP}]$-object (P,A,m) has a $\mathcal{K}[\mathcal{TK},\mathcal{CK}]$-solution set. Let X denote the union of all n-fold products of $P \times \{0,1\}$ with itself in the category of sets (i.e., $X = \cup \{(P \times \{0,1\})^n : n \in \mathbf{N}\})$ and let $Y = 2^{2^X}$. Then, a straightforward set theoretic argument yields that the class $\mathcal{F}$ of all pairs (f,S), where S is a $\mathcal{K}[\mathcal{TK},\mathcal{CK}]$-object whose underlying set is a subset of Y and f is a $\mathcal{P}[\mathcal{TP}]$-morphism from (P,A,m) into S, is a set. We proceed to show that $\mathcal{F}$ is the desired solution set. Let g be a $\mathcal{P}[\mathcal{TP}]$-morphism from (P,A,m) into a $\mathcal{K}[\mathcal{TK},\mathcal{CK}]$-object T.

(a) The categories with no inverses. For

$$\mathcal{K} \in \{\mathcal{S},\mathcal{AS},\mathcal{B},\mathcal{X}\}$$
$$\mathcal{TK} \in \{\mathcal{TS},\mathcal{TAS},\mathcal{TB},\mathcal{TX},\mathcal{TL}\}$$
$$\mathcal{CK} \in \{\mathcal{CS},\mathcal{CAS},\mathcal{CB},\mathcal{CX},\mathcal{CL}\}$$

$\Gamma((g(P))$ is a $\mathcal{K}[\mathcal{TK},\mathcal{CK}]$-object [where $\Gamma(g(P))$ is taken to be $\theta(g(P))$ for $\mathcal{K}$]. Define a mapping $h:P \times \{0,1\} \to T$ by $h((x,0)) = h((x,1)) = g(x)$ for all $x \in P$ and extend h to a surjection $\bar{h}:X \to \theta(g(P))$ in the obvious fashion (if $\theta:\{1,\ldots,n\} \to P \times \{0,1\}$, then $\bar{h}(\phi) = h(\phi(1))\cdots h(\phi(n)))$. Thus $\#(\theta(g(P))) \le \#X$ and hence, $\#(\Gamma(g(P))) \le \#Y$, where $\#$ denotes cardinal number (see 2.42 of Carruth, Hildebrant, and Koch [1983]). Therefore, there is a subset S of Y such that $\#S = \#(\Gamma(g(P)))$. If we transfer the topology and algebraic structure of $\Gamma(g(P))$ to S by means of a bijection $\phi:S \to \Gamma(g(P))$ and define $f:(P,A,m) \to S$ by $f = \phi^{-1} \circ g$, then $(f,S) \in \mathscr{F}$. Moreover, ϕ is a $\mathscr{K}$ $[\mathscr{T}\mathscr{K},\mathscr{C}\mathscr{K}]$-morphism and the triangle

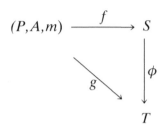

commutes, Hence, $\mathscr{G}$ is a $\mathscr{K}[\mathscr{T}\mathscr{K},\mathscr{C}\mathscr{K}]$-solution set for (P,A,m).

(b)The categories with inverses. For

$$\mathscr{K} \in \{\mathscr{G},\mathscr{A}\mathscr{G},\mathscr{I}\}$$
$$\mathscr{T}\mathscr{K} \in \{\mathscr{T}\mathscr{G},\mathscr{T}\mathscr{A}\mathscr{G},\mathscr{T}\mathscr{I}\}$$
$$\mathscr{C}\mathscr{K} \in \{\mathscr{C}\mathscr{G},\mathscr{C}\mathscr{A}\mathscr{G},\mathscr{C}\mathscr{I}\}$$

$\Gamma(g(P) \cup g(P)^{-1})$ is a $\mathscr{K}$ $[\mathscr{T}\mathscr{K},\mathscr{C}\mathscr{K}]$-object, where $g(P)^{-1}$ denotes $\{g(x)^{-1}:x \in P\}$ (again, $\Gamma = \theta$ for $\mathscr{K}$). Define $h:P \times \{0,1\} \to T$ by $h((x,0)) = g(x)$ and $h((x,1)) = g(x)^{-1}$ for all $x \in P$ and extend h to a surjection $\bar{h}:X \to \theta(g(P) \cup g(P)^{-1}))$. Again, $\#(\theta(g(P) \cup g(P)^{-1})) \leq \#X$ and so $\#(\Gamma(g(P) \cup g(P)^{-1})) \leq \#Y$. The remainder of the argument goes exactly as in part (a).

The proof that the final hypothesis of appendix C.1 holds is similar to (a) and (b) above.

Let $f:(P,A,m) \to S$ be a $\mathscr{P}[\mathscr{T}\mathscr{P}]$-morphism, where S is a $\mathscr{K}[\mathscr{T}\mathscr{K},\mathscr{C}\mathscr{K}]$-object.

(i) The non-topological and topological categories with no inverses. For

$$\mathscr{K} \in \{\mathscr{P},\mathscr{A}\mathscr{P},\mathscr{B},\mathscr{X}\}$$
$$\mathscr{T}\mathscr{K} \in \{\mathscr{T}\mathscr{P},\mathscr{T}\mathscr{A}\mathscr{P},\mathscr{T}\mathscr{B},\mathscr{T}\mathscr{X},\mathscr{T}\mathscr{L}\}$$

we let $T = \theta(f(P))$ and $g:(P,A,m) \to T$ be the corestriction of f. Then, T is a $\mathscr{K}[\mathscr{T}\mathscr{K}]$-object, g is a $\mathscr{P}[\mathscr{T}\mathscr{P}]$-morphism, the triangle

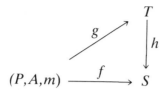

commutes, where h is inclusion, and it is an easy exercise to show that g $\mathcal{K}[\mathcal{JK}]$-generates T.

(ii) The compact categories with no inverses. For

$$\mathcal{CK} \in \{\mathcal{CS}, \mathcal{CAS}, \mathcal{CB}, \mathcal{CX}, \mathcal{CL}\}$$

we let $T = \Gamma(f(P))$ and $g:(P,A,m) \to T$ be the corestriction of f.

(iii) The nontopological and topological categories with inverses. For

$$\mathcal{K} \in \{\mathcal{G}, \mathcal{AG}, \mathcal{TG}\}$$
$$\mathcal{JK} \in \{\mathcal{TG}, \mathcal{TAG}, \mathcal{TI}\}$$

we let $T = \theta(f(P) \cup f(P)^{-1})$ and $g:(P,A,m) \to T$ be the corestriction of f.

(iv) The compact categories with inverses. For

$$\mathcal{CK} \in \{\mathcal{CG}, \mathcal{CAG}, \mathcal{CI}\}$$

we let $T = \Gamma(f(P) \cup f(P)^{-1})$ and $g:(P,A,m) \to T$ be the corestriction of f.

Now applying Appendix C.1 and C.2, the conclusion of the theorem is achieved. Very briefly, the remainder of the proof with the use of C.1 would simply be to map (P,A,m) into the product of $\mathcal{K}[\mathcal{JK},\mathcal{CK}]$ objects in a $\mathcal{K}[\mathcal{JK},\mathcal{CK}]$ subobject of the product generated by $u(P)$, and let $u_p:(P,A,m) \to S_p$ be the corestriction of u. One could readily show that (u_p, A_p) is a $\mathcal{K}[\mathcal{JK},\mathcal{CK}]$-universal map for (P,A,m). The main purpose for developing C.1 in Appendix C is that it illustrates precisely what ideas go into the proof of this theorem. Moreover, it is an adjoint functor theorem which has completeness as a hypothesis neither for the domain nor for the codomain of the functor. ∎

A semigroup S on A Hausdorff space is a *semitopological semigroup* if λ_x and ρ_x are continuous for each $x \in S$. A triple (P,A,m) is a *semitopological partial groupoid* if P is a nonempty Hausdorff space, $A \subseteq P \times P$, and $m{:}A \to P$ is separately continuous; that is, $m \mid (\{x\} \times S) \cap A$ and $m \mid (S \times \{x\}) \cap A$ are continuous for each $x \in S$. The proof of 6.1. can be slightly modified to obtain analogous results for the appropriate categories of semitopological semigroups (from Table 1) and the category of semitopological partial groupoids (and continuous partial homomorphisms).

6.2 Uniqueness   The uniqueness of Bohr compactifications and free topological semigroups were established in Chapter 2 of Carruth, Hildebrant, and Koch [1983]. In view of C.2, all of the universal maps alluded to in 6.1 are unique up to isomorphisms in the individual categories. That is, if $\mathcal{A}$ is one of the categories in Table 1, $\mathcal{B}$ is the appropriate category among $\mathcal{P}$ and $\mathcal{TP}$, (P,A,m) is a $\mathcal{B}$-object, and (u_1,S_1) and (u_2,S_2) are $\mathcal{A}$-universal maps for (P,A,m), then there is a (unique) $\mathcal{A}$-isomorphism $f{:}S_1 \to S_2$ such that the triangle

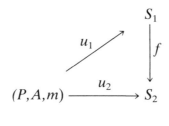

commutes.

By applying 6.1 and 6.2 we obtain the following:
(a) The Bohr compactification of a topological semigroup S:, Let $\mathscr{CK} = \mathscr{CS}$ and let $(P,A,m) = (S, S \times S, m)$

(b) The free topological semigroup generated be the topological space X: Let $\mathcal{TH} = \mathcal{TS}$ and $(P,A,m) = (X,\square,\square)$.

(c) The free topological group generated by a Hausdorff space X: Let $\mathcal{TH} = \mathcal{TG}$ and let $(P,A,m) = (X,\square,\square)$.

(d) The group compactification of a topological semigroup S: Let $\mathcal{CH} = \mathcal{CG}$ and let $(P,A,m) = (S,S \times S,m)$.

(e) The free semigroup [group] generated by the set of X: Let $\mathcal{H} = S$ [$\mathcal{G}$] and let $(P,A,m) = (X,\square,\square)$.

(f) The free compact inverse semigroup generated by the compact semigroup S: Let $\mathcal{CH} = \mathcal{CJ}$ and let $(P,A,m) = (S,S \times S,m)$.

Only the existence and uniqueness of certain universal maps are obtained in 6.1 and 6.2. The more delicate questions relating structure and properties of "universal objects" remain important ones.

Consider the inclusion functor $G:\mathcal{CS} \to \mathcal{TP}$. Then 6.1 yields a left adjoint $F:\mathcal{TP} \to \mathcal{CS}$ for G and (hence) a natural transformation $u = \{u_P\}_{P \in \mathrm{Ob}(\mathcal{TP})}$ from $1_{\mathcal{TP}}$ to $G \circ F$. Now the "Bohr compactification functor" is obtained by restricting F to $\mathcal{TS}$ (and appropriately restricting the natural transformation u). Hence, we have actually obtained Bohr compactifications for a much wider class of topological algebraic objects. Similar remarks can be made about other free [topological] semigroups generated by various sets [spaces] or [topological] semigroups.

We consider two types of structures which lie somewhere between sets [spaces] with no multiplication whatever ($A = \square$) and [topological] semigroups ($A = S \times S$).

Let $\mathcal{A}$ be chosen from Table 1. Recall that an $\mathcal{A}$-coproduct of a family $\{S_i\}_{i \in I}$ of $\mathcal{A}$-objects is a pair $(\{f_i\}_{i \in I}, S)$ satisfying:

(1) S is an $\mathcal{A}$-object.

(2) For each $i \in I$, $f_i:S_i \to S$ is an $\mathcal{A}$-morphism.

(3) For each pair $(\{g_i\}_{i \in I}, T)$, (where T is an $\mathcal{A}$-object and for each $i \in I$, $g_i:S_i \to T$ is an $\mathcal{A}$-morphism) there is a unique $\mathcal{A}$-morphism $h:S \to T$ such that for each $i \in I$, we have $h \circ f_i = g_i$.

We proceed to show, using 6.1, that $\mathcal{A}$ has coproducts. Let $\{(S_i,m_i)\}_{i \in I}$ be a family of $\mathcal{A}$-objects and assume, without loss of generality, that the family $\{S_i\}_{i\in I}$ is pairwise disjoint. Let $P = \bigcup\{S_i : i \in I\}$ (with the disjoint union topology if appropriate), $A = \bigcup\{(S_i \times S_i : i \in I\}$, and $m((s_i, t_i)) = m_i((s_i, t_i))$ for all $(s_i, t_i) \in A$. Then (P, A, m) is readily seen to be a $\mathscr{P}[\mathscr{T}\mathscr{P}]$-object. Using 6.1, let (u, S) be an $\mathscr{A}$-universal map for (P, A, m). It is a straightforward but interesting exercise to verify that $(\{u \circ p_i\}_{i\in I}, S)$ is an $\mathscr{A}$-coproduct of the family $\{(S_i, m_i)\}_{i\in I}$, if $p_i : S_i \to P$ is the obvious inclusion for each $i \in I$. In fact, $(\{p_i\}_{i\in I}, (P, A, m))$ can be shown to be a $\mathscr{P}[\mathscr{T}\mathscr{P}]$-coproduct of the family $\{S_i\}_{i\in I}$ and then one can use the fact that a functor with a right adjoint preserves coproducts.

A [topological] partial groupoid (P, A, m) is a [topological] *partial semigroup* if [P is Hausdorff and] m satisfies the partial associativity condition: For all $x, y, z \in P$ such that $\{(x, y), (y, z), (m(x, y), z), (x, m(y, z))\} \subseteq A$ we have $m(m(x, y), z) = m(x, m(y, z))$. Examples of [topological] partial semigroups (P, A, n) may be obtained by letting (S, m) be a [topological] semigroup, P be any subset of S, $A = \{(x, y) \in P \times P : m(x, y) \in P\}$, and $n = m|A$. For example, let (S, m) be a semigroup with zero and let $P = S \backslash \{0\}$. Another interesting way to obtain topological partial semigroups is as follows: let (S, m) and (T, m) be monoids and let $P = (S \times \{1\}) \cup (\{1\} \times T)$ contained in $S \times T$. Let $A = [(S \times \{1\}) \times (S \times \{1\})] \cup [(\{1\} \times T) \times (\{1\} \times T)]$; that is, the only products defined "between S and T" are those for which one member is the identity. If $(S, m) = \mathbf{R}/\mathbf{Z}$ and $(T, n) = I_u$, then the Bohr compactification (u, B) of P, as above, is the image of the $\mathscr{C}\mathscr{S}$-coproduct of $\mathbf{R}/\mathbf{Z}$ with I_u (this follows from the defining properties of the coproduct and the fact that there are natural $\mathscr{C}\mathscr{S}$-morphisms from $\mathbf{R}/\mathbf{Z}$ and I_u into B). One could conceiveably discover more about the structure of B than that of the coproduct. However, to the authors' knowledge, it is unknown (e.g.) whether $u(\mathbf{R}/\mathbf{Z}) \times \{1\} = H_B(1)$.

7
Manifold Semigroups

In this chapter we discuss the theory of affine semigroups and Lie semigroups. Our intention here is not to present an exhaustive development of these topics, but to present an introduction with references, so that the interested reader may investigate these areas further.

AFFINE SEMIGROUPS

In this section we discuss the first of the topics considered in this chapter. Affine semigroups were studied in Cohen and Collins [1959], Friedberg [1966a, 1966b], Brown and Friedberg [1970]. Most of the results of this section are versions of results which appear in Cohen and Collins [1959].

We will assume in this section that the reader is familiar with the basic notions of a topological vector space, but will recall some of the definitions dealing with convexity.

Throughout this section we use X and Y to denote real topological vector spaces.

A subset C of X is said to be *convex* if $x, y \in C$ and $0 \le \alpha \le 1$, $\alpha \in \mathbf{R}$, implies that $\alpha x + (1 - \alpha)y \in C$.

Observe that the intersection of any family of [closed] convex sets is [closed] convex. If $D \subseteq X$, then the intersection of all [closed] convex subsets of X containing D is called the [*closed*] *convex hull* of D. We use *con D* to denote the closed convex hull of D.

If A is a convex subset of X and B is a convex subset of Y, then a function $\phi:A \to B$ is called an *affine map* if $x,y \in S, 0 \leq \alpha \leq 1$, implies that $\phi(\alpha x + (1 - \alpha)y) = \alpha \phi(x) + (1 - \alpha)\phi(y)$.

Observe that an affine map $\phi:A \to B$ preserves more general affine combinations. If $x_1, x_2, \ldots, x_n \in A, 0 \leq \alpha_1, \alpha_2, \ldots, \alpha_n, \Sigma_{i=1}^n \alpha_i = 1$, and $\Sigma_{i=1}^n \alpha_i x_i \in A$, then $\phi(\Sigma_{i=1}^n \alpha_i x_i) = \Sigma_{i=1}^n \alpha_i \phi(x_i)$.

Recall that for a semigroup S, if $a \in S$, then we define $\lambda_a:S \to S$ by $\lambda_a(x) = ax$ for each $x \in S$, and $\rho_a:S \to S$ by $\rho_a(x) = xa$ for each $x \in S$.

Let S be a convex subset of X and $m:S \times S \to S$ a continuous associative multiplication of S in the relative topology of X such that λ_a and ρ_a are the affine maps of S into itself for each $a \in S$. Then (S,m) is called an *affine semigroup*.

We say that the space X is *locally convex* if each point of X has a basis of open convex sets.

If A is a convex subset of X, then $x \in A$ is called an *extreme point* of A provided that x is interior to no line segment in A, i.e., if $x = \alpha y + (1 - \alpha)z, 0 < \alpha < 1, y,z \in A$, then $x = y = z$. We use *ext A* to denote the set of extreme points of A.

We display (without proof) an old and well-known result in extreme point theory. It first appeared in Krein and Milman [1940].

7.1 The Krein-Milman Theorem   Let X be locally convex and let A be a compact convex subset of X. The A is the closed convex hull of the set of extreme points of A.

In our notation, the Krein-Milman theorem states that if X is locally convex and A is a compact convex subset of X, then $A = con$ (*ext A*).

The following result due to J. G. Wendel (unpublished by Wendel) appears in Cohen and Collins [1959].

7.2 Theorem   Let S be a compact affine monoid in a locally convex space X. Then $H(1) \subseteq ext S$.

Proof: Let $1 = \alpha x + (1 - \alpha)y$, with $0 < \alpha < 1$, and $x, y \in S$. If $q \in ext\ S$, then $q = q1 = \alpha qx + (1 - \alpha)qy$, so that $q = qx = qy$. We obtain that $qx = qy$ for each $q \in ext\ S$. Now let p be in the convex hull of S. Then $p = \Sigma_{i=1}^{n} \alpha_i q_i$, where $q_1, q_2, \ldots, q_n \in ext\ S, 0 < \alpha_1, \ldots, \alpha_n$, and $\Sigma_{i=1}^{n} \alpha_i = 1$. We have $px = \Sigma_{i=1}^{n} \alpha_i q_i x = \Sigma_{i=1}^{n} \alpha_i q_i y = py$. Now, according to 7.1, there exists a net p_δ in the convex hull of $ext\ S$ such that $p_\delta \to 1$. Thus $p_\delta x \to 1 \cdot x = x, p_\delta y \to 1 \cdot y = y$, and since $p_\delta x = p_\delta y$ for each δ, we obtain that $x = y$. We see that $1 \in ext\ S$.

If $t \in H(1)$, and $t = \alpha x + (1 - \alpha)y$ for $x, y \in S, 0 < \alpha < 1$, then $1 = tt^{-1} = \alpha t^{-1}x + (1 - \alpha)t^{-1}y$, so that $t^{-1}x = t^{-1}y$, and $x = y$. It follows that $t \in ext\ S$. ∎

If A is a compact convex subset of a locally convex space X and $\phi : A \to A$ is continuous, then according to a well-known result of Tychonov [1935] there exists $p \in A$ such that $\phi(p) = p$, i.e., p is a fixed point of ϕ. A simple proof in the case that ϕ is affine appears in Nikaido [1955].

7.3 Lemma If A is a compact subset of X, then con A is the convex hull of A and is compact.

Proof: We need only show that the convex hull of A is compact. For this purpose, let x_δ be a net in the convex hull of A. We will show that x_δ clusters to some x in the convex hull of A. Since each x_δ is in the convex hull of A, there exists for each $\delta, 0 \leq \alpha_\delta \leq 1$ and $a_\delta, b_\delta \in A$ such that $x_\delta = \alpha_\delta a_\delta + (1 - \alpha_\delta)b_\delta$. Now, considering that A and $[0,1]$ are compact and using subnets, we can assume that $a_\delta \to a, b_\delta \to b$, and $\alpha_\delta \to \alpha$ for some $a, b \in A$ and $0 \leq \alpha \leq 1$. Let $x = \alpha a + (1 - \alpha)b$. Then x is in the convex hull of A and $x_\delta \xrightarrow{f} x$. It follows that the convex hull of A is compact. ∎

Let X^* denote the space of continuous linear functions from X into **R**. For $a \in \mathbf{R}^n$ with $n \in \mathbf{N}$, we let $\| a \|$ denote the standard norm of a.

7.4 Theorem Let X be locally convex, let S be a compact affine monoid in X, and let G be a closed subgroup of S. Then there exist $x \in con\ G$ and $p \in G$ such that $x(con\ G)p = \{xp\}$.

   Proof: Let $A = \{a_1, a_2, \ldots, a_m\}$ be a finite subset of G, and let $B = \{f_1, f_2, \ldots, f_n\}$ be a finite subset of X^*. Define $F: X \to \mathbf{R}^n$ by $F(x) = (f_1(x), f_2(x), \ldots, f_n(x))$. Then F is continuous and linear. Now the map $s \mapsto (1/m)\ \Sigma_{i=1}^m sa_i$ of $con\ G$ into itself is affine and continuous, so by Nikaido's theorem, there exists $t \in con\ G$ such that $t = (1/m)\ \Sigma_{i=1}^m ta_i$ and hence $tg = (1/m)\ \Sigma_{i=1}^m ta_ig$ for all $g \in G$. We have that $F(tg) = (1/m)\ \Sigma_{i=1}^m F(ta_ig)$ for all $g \in G$, and since G is compact, there exists $g_0 \in G$ such that $\| F(tg_0) \| = max\{\|F(tg)\|: g \in G\}$. Then $\| F(tg_0) \| = \| (1/m)\ \Sigma_{i=1}^m F(ta_ig_0) \| \le (1/m)\ \Sigma_{i=1}^m \| F(ta_ig_0) \|$, and $\| F(tg_0) \| \ge \| F(ta_ig_0) \|$ for all i, since $a_ig_0 \in G$, and from the choice of g_0. We obtain that $\| F(tg_0) \| = \| F(ta_ig_0) \|$, $i = 1, 2, \ldots, m$. Now $F(tg_0) = (1/m)\ \Sigma_{i=1}^m F(ta_ig_0)$, so that $F(tg_0) = F(ta_ig_0)$ for $i = 1, 2, \ldots, m$. Let $N(A, G) = \{(s, g) \in con\ G \times G: f(sg) = f(sag)$ for all $a \in A$ and $f \in B\}$. Then for finite sets $A_1, A_2 \in G$ and $B_1, B_2 \in X^*$, if $A_1 \subseteq A_2$ and $B_1 \subseteq B_2$, then $N(A_2, B_2) \subseteq N(A_1, B_1)$. Thus $\{N(A, B): A$ finite $\subseteq G, B$ finite $\subseteq G, B$ finite $\subseteq X^*\}$ is a descending family of closed subsets (since X^* consists of continuous functions) of the compact set $con\ G \times G$ ($con\ G$ is compact from 7.3). Let $(x, p) \in \cap \{N((A, B): A$ finite $\subseteq G, B$ finite $\subseteq X^*\}$. Then $f(xp) = f(xap)$ for all $g \in G$ and all $f \in X^*$. Now X^* separates points of X, so that $xp = xap$ for all $a \in G$, i.e., $xGp = \{xp\}$. In particular, $x(con\ G)p = \{xp\}$.   ∎

   An affine semigroup S is said to be *group-extremal* if *ext S* is a group.
   If X is locally convex and S is a compact affine monoid which is group extremal, then in view of 7.2, we see that $H(1) = ext\ S$.

7.5   Corollary.   If X is locally convex and S is a compact group extremal affine semigroup in X, then S has a zero.

   Proof: Let $G = H(1)$, and let $x \in con\ G$ and $p \in G$ such that $x(con\ G)p = \{xp\}$. From the Krein–Milman theorem (7.1), $S = con\ G$, so that $xSp = \{xp\}$. Let p^{-1} be the inverse of p in G. Then

$xS = xSpp^{-1} = \{xpp^{-1}\} = \{x \cdot 1\} = x$. We obtain that x is a left zero for S. From the dual of 7.4, we obtain a right zero $y \in S$, and finally yx is a zero for S. ∎

We investigate the ideal structure of a compact affine semigroup in a locally convex space.

7.6 Theorem Let X be locally convex and let S be a compact affine semigroup in X. Then:
(a) Each minimal left ideal and each minimal right ideal of S is convex.
(b) $M(S) \subseteq E(S)$.
(c) If $e \in M(S)$, then $eSe = \{e\}$.

Proof: To prove (a), let L be a minimal left ideal of S and let $a \in L$. Then $L = Sa$, since L is minimal. The map ρ_a of S onto L is affine, and hence L is convex, since S is convex.

To prove (b) and (c), let $x \in M(S)$. Then there exists a unique minimal left ideal L and a unique minimal right ideal R such that $x \in L \cap R = eS \cap Se = eSe$ for some $e \in M(S) \cap E(S)$ and e is the identity of the group eSe (see 3.17 and 3.18 of Carruth, Hildebrant, and Koch [1983]). Now $y \mapsto eye$ is an affine map of S onto eSe, so that eSe is convex. Thus eSe is a compact affine group. From 7.2, $eSe = \{e\}$. The conclusions of (b) and (c) now follow. ∎

A subset M of X is called a *linear manifold* or simply a *manifold* if there exists a subspace N of X such that $M = a + N$ for some $a \in X$. Observe that $a \in M$, since $0 \in N$, and that $N + x = M$ for all $x \in M$.

If A is a nonempty subset of X, then the intersection A_M of all manifolds containing A is called the *manifold generated* by A.

7.7 Lemma If A is a nonempty subset of X, then A_M is a manifold, and for each $a \in A$, $A_M = \{x \in X : x = \Sigma_{i=1}^n \alpha_i x_i + (1 - \Sigma_{i=1}^n \alpha_i)a$, where $n \in \mathbf{N}$, $\alpha_1, \ldots, \alpha_n \in \mathbf{R}$, and $x_1, \ldots, x_n \in A\}$.

Proof: The proof is straightforward. ∎

7.8 Theorem If S is a compact affine semigroup and $L[R]$ is a minimal left [right] ideal of S, then $L_M \cap S = L$ $[R_M \cap S = R]$.

Proof: Clearly, $L \subseteq L_M \cap S$. Fix $e \in L \cap E(S)$, and let $x \in L_M \cap S$. Then there exist $n \in \mathbf{N}$, $x_1, \ldots, x_n \in L$, and $\alpha_1, \ldots, \alpha_n \in \mathbf{R}$ such that $x = \Sigma_{i=1}^n \alpha_i x_i + (1 - \Sigma_{i=1}^n \alpha_i)e$. Now $L = Se$, so that $xe = \Sigma_{i=1}^n \alpha_i x_i e + (1 - \Sigma_{i=1}^n \alpha_i)e^2 = \Sigma_{i=1}^n \alpha_i x_i + (1 - \Sigma_{i=1}^n \alpha_i)e = x$. It follows that $x = xe \in Se = L$, and $L_M \cap S \subseteq L$. ∎

Recall that if $S \subseteq X$, then $\partial S = \tilde{S} \cap \overline{(X \setminus S)}$ is called the *boundary* of S.

7.9 Theorem Let S be a compact affine semigroup. Then $H(e) \subseteq \partial S$ for each $e \in E(S) \setminus M(S)$.

Proof: Let $e \in E(S) \setminus M(S)$ and fix $f \in M(S)$. Then $efe \in M(S)$, so that $efe \in E(S)$ from 7.6 and $efe \neq e$. Let A be the manifold generated by e and efe. The line segment $T = A \cap S$ is a compact affine semigroup.

We show that e is an endpoint of T. Otherwise, there exists $a \in S$ and $\alpha > 1$ such that $a = \alpha e + (1 - \alpha)efe$, and it follows that $a^n = \alpha^n e + (1 - \alpha^n)efe$ for all $n \in \mathbf{N}$. Since $e \neq efe$, there exists $F \in X^*$ such that $F(e) \neq F(efe)$. Now if $F(efe) = 0$, then $F(a^n) = \alpha^n F(e)$ for each $n \in \mathbf{N}$, and $\{F(a^n):n \in \mathbf{N}\}$ is unbounded. If $F(efe) \neq 0$, let $r = F(efe)$ and define $G:S \to \mathbf{R}$ by $G(x) = (1/r) \cdot F(x)$ for $x \in S$. Then $G(a^n) = \alpha^n(G(e) - 1) + 1$ for each $n \in \mathbf{N}$, and $\{G(a^n):n \in \mathbf{N}\}$ is unbounded. Since F and G are continuous functions from S into $\mathbf{R}$ and S is compact, $F(S)$ and $G(S)$ must be compact and hence bounded. This contradiction proves that e is an endpoint of T.

We claim that $e \in \partial S$. Otherwise, $e \in S^\circ$ (interior of S), and there exist $x, y \in T$ and $0 < \alpha < 1$ such that $e = \alpha x + (1 - \alpha)y$, contradicting that e is an endpoint of T. It follows that $e \in \partial S$.

If $H(e) = \{e\}$, then $H(e) \subseteq \partial S$ and the proof is complete. We can assume then that $H(e) \neq \{e\}$. Let $T = con\ H(e)$. Then T is a compact affine subsemigroup of S with $ext\ T = H(e)$. It follows from 7.5 that T has a zero z and $z \notin H(e)$.

Now let $x \in H(e)$. We first claim that x is an endpoint of the manifold generated by x and z. Otherwise, there are $a \in S$ and $\alpha > 1$ such that $a = \alpha x + (1 - \alpha)z$ and hence $ax^{-1} = \alpha e + (1 - \alpha)z$. As above, since e is the identity of $\{e,z\}_M$ and z is its zero, e is an endpoint of S in $\{e,z\}_M$, so $\alpha \leq 1$. This contradiction proves that e is an endpoint of $\{x,z\}_M$ and hence $x \in \partial S$. We conclude that $H(e) \subseteq \partial S$. ∎

The result of 7.2, that $H(1) \subseteq ext\ S$ for a compact affine monoid S, is not unexpected in view of the fact that the group of units of any compact monoid S is contained in *edge S*. However, the result of 7.9 gives a compact affine semigroup a very unique character. It can, for example, be used to immediately determine that certain compact subsemigroups of X are not affine.

Example   Let $[0,2]$ be an *I*-semigroup such that each of $[0,1]$ and $[1,2]$ is isomorphic to I_u and for $a \in [0,1]$ and $b \in [1,2]$, $ab = ba = min\{a,b\}$. Let $T = [0,2] \times \mathbf{R}/\mathbf{Z}$. Then the minimal ideal of T is $M(T) = \{0\} \times \mathbf{R}/\mathbf{Z}$. Let $S = T/M(T)$. Then S is a compact convex semigroup in $\mathbf{R}^2$:

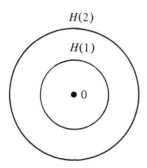

$H(2)$

$H(1)$

• 0

with $E(S) = \{0,1,2\}$ (where 1 and 2 are identified with their image in S). Since $M(S) = \{0\}$, it is clear from 7.9 that S is not affine.

Example   The semigroup $S = (I_u \times \mathbf{R}/\mathbf{Z})/(\{0\} \times \mathbf{R}/\mathbf{Z})$ is a compact affine group-extremal monoid. Observe that $ext\ S = \partial S \overset{\tau}{\approx} \mathbf{R}/\mathbf{Z}$.

Our next example illustrates that it is not always the case that
ext S = ∂*S*.

Example   Consider the preceding example S as the unit complex
disk in the plane. Let T be the convex hull of the three cube roots of
unity on ∂S. Then T is a compact affine group–extremal
subsemigroup of S and ∂S is a triangle with *ext S* as its set of
vertices.

Let A be a convex subset of X and consider the manifold A_M
generated by A. Then there exists a unique subspace N of X such
that $A_M = N + a$ for each $a \in A$. The *dimension* of A is defined to be
the linear dimension of N as a vector subspace of X.

If S is an n-dimensional affine semigroup, then if $x \in S_M$, then
x is uniquely expressible as $x = \Sigma_{i=1}^n \alpha_i x_i + (1 - \Sigma_{i=1}^n \alpha_i)a$ for any
fixed set $\{x_1, x_2, \ldots, x_n, a\} \subseteq S$ for which $\{x_1 - a, \ldots, x_n - 1\}$ is
linearly independent. Such a set $\{x_1, x_2, \ldots, x_n, a\} \subseteq S$ is called an
affine basis for S_M.

It is established in Cohen and Collins [1959] that each finite
dimensional affine semigroup S with a left identity is isomorphic to
a semigroup (under composition) of affine transformations of S_M,
i.e., S can be algebraically represented by a semigroup of real $n \times n$
matrices. In addition to a characterization of the multiplications on
a one-dimensional affine semigroup, they prove that if S is a
compact affine semigroup of dimension ≤ 2, or S is a compact
affine monoid of dimension 3, then $M(S)$ is convex. We present
their example of a three dimensional compact affine semigroup S
in which $M(S)$ is not convex.

Example   Let S be the unit cube in $\mathbf{R}^3$, i.e., $S = \{(x,y,z): 0 \leq x \leq 1,$
$0 \leq y \leq 1, 0 \leq z \leq 1\}$, with multiplication defined by $(a,b,c) \circ$
$(x,y,z) = (a,y,ay)$. Then S is a compact affine semigroup with no
identity. If we represent (x,y,z) as the matrix

$$\begin{pmatrix} 1 & y & 0 \\ 0 & 0 & 0 \\ x & z & 0 \end{pmatrix}$$

then multiplication is matrix multiplication. Now $M(S) = \{(x,y,z):z = xy\}$, which is a hyperbolic paraboloid and hence is not convex.

The theory of representations of affine semigroups was developed in Friedberg [1966a, 1966b]. The following is an interesting and important result which we offer without proof:

7.10 Theorem Let S be a compact group-extremal affine semigroup. Then S is a projective limit of finite-dimensional compact group-extremal affine semigroups.

LIE SEMIGROUPS

Lie semigroups have been studied in Hofmann and Lawson [1981a, 1981b, 1983a, 1983b, 1984] and Hilgert and Hofmann [1984a, 1984b, 1985]. Related material can be found in Langlands [1960], Houston [1973], Poguntke [1977], and Graham [1981]. An excellent treatise on the foundations of Lie semigroup theory appears in Hofmann and Lawson [1981].

A *Lie algebra* over **R** is a vector space L over **R** with a Lie bracket $[\cdot,\cdot]:L \times L \to L$ such that for $r,s \in$ **R** and $a,b,c \in L$;

(1) $[a,rb + sc] = r[a,b] + s[a,c]$ (bilinear)
(2) $[a,b] + [b,a] = 0$ (anticommutative)
(3) $[a,[b,c]] + [c,[a,b]] + [b,[c,a]] = 0$ (Jacobi identity)

A *Dynkin algebra* over **R** is a Lie algebra L which has a complete norm $\| \cdot \| :L \to [0,\infty)$ such that $\| [a,b] \| \le \| a \| \cdot \| b \|$ for all $a,b \in L$ and $[\cdot,\cdot]:L \times L \to L$ is continuous. We will hereafter in this section assume that L is a Dynkin algebra.

We define formally the series needed to define the Cambell-Hausdorff multiplication on L. Let x and y be noncommuting variables. Define

$$\exp(x) = 1 + x^2 + \frac{x^2}{2} + \cdots$$

and define

$$\ln(1 + x) = x - \frac{x^2}{2} + \frac{x^3}{3} - \frac{x^4}{4} + \cdots$$

Define

$$H(x,y) = \ln(\exp(x) \cdot \exp(y)) = \ln((1 + x + \frac{x^2}{2} + \cdots)(1 + y$$
$$+ \frac{y^2}{2} + \cdots)) = \ln(1 + x + y + \frac{x^2}{2} + xy + \frac{y^2}{2} + \cdots)$$

Define $H:L \times L \to \mathbf{R}$ formally by $H(x,y) = x + y + (\frac{1}{2})[x,y]$ $+ (\frac{1}{12})[x,[x,y]] + (\frac{1}{12})[y[y,x]] + \cdots$. It is known that if $\| x \| +$ $\| y \| < \ln 2$, then $H(x,y)$ converges. If $K = \{(x,y) \in L \times L : H(x,y)$ converges$\}$. then we define the *Cambell–Hausdorff* multiplication by $x * y = H(x,y)$ for $(x,y) \in K$. A neighborhood B of 0 in L such that $B \subseteq K$ is called a *CH-neighborhood* of 0.

A *Lie group* is a triple $(G,L, \exp)$, where G is a topological group, L is finite dimensional over $\mathbf{R}$ and $\exp:L \to G$ is a function such that:

(1) exp is a homeomorphism on some neighborhood U of 0.
(2) for $x,y \in U$, $\exp(x * y) = \exp(x) \cdot \exp(y)$.
(3) $\exp \mid \mathbf{R}x$ is a one-parameter group for each $x \in G$.

If no confusion seems likely, we use simply G to denote a Lie group.

Let B be an ϵ ball for $\epsilon > 0$ centered at 0 and contained in a CH-neighborhood of 0 in L. A subset S of B is called a *local semigroup* [*group*] with respect to B if $0 \in S$ and $x,y \in S$, and $x * y \in B$ implies that $x * y \in S$ [and $S = -S$]. If there exists a CH-neighborhood of 0 in L such that S is a local semigroup [group] with respect to B, then S is called a *local semigroup* [*group*].

The condition that S be a local semigroup (with respect to B) can be restated as $0 \in S$ and $(S * S) \cap B \subseteq S$.

For a local semigroup S the modifier "with respect to B" is frequently assumed and therefore omitted. We define $S' = \bar{S} \cap B$.

If S is a local semigroup, we let $H(S) = -S \cap S$.

7.11 Theorem If S is a local semigroup, then $H(S)$ is the maximal local subgroup of S.

Proof: Let $x, y \in H(S)$. Then $x * y \in B$ implies $x * y \in S$, since S is a local semigroup. Now $-(x * y)(-y) * (-x)$ is in B, since $B = -B$ and thus in S since $-y, -x \in S$. Thus $x * y \in H(S)$, and hence $H(S)$ is a local semigroup.

Now $H(S) = -H(S)$, so that $H(S)$ is a local group. If G is a local group contained in S, then $G = -G \cap G \subseteq -S \cap S = H(S)$. ∎

7.12 Theorem Let S be a local semigroup. Then S' is also a local semigroup.

Proof: Let $x, y \in S'$. Then there exists x_n and y_n in S such that $x_n \to x$ and $y_n \to y$. Then $x_n * y_n \to x * y$. Now if $x * y \in B$, then $x_n * y_n \in^e B$ and thus $x_n * y_n \in^e S$ and it follows that $x * y \in S'$. We conclude that S' is a local semigroup. ∎

Let $X \subseteq L$. An element $b \in B$ is said to be *X-generated* if $b \in \cup_{n \in \mathbf{N}} X^n$, where X^n is defined recursively by $X^1 = (B \cap X) \cup \{0\}$, and $X^n = (X^{n-1} * X^{n-1}) \cap B$. Let $\langle X \rangle_B$ [or $\langle X \rangle$ if B is understood] be the set of all elements of B which are X-generated with respect to B.

7.13 Theorem The set $\langle X \rangle$ is the smallest local semigroup in B containing $X \cap B$.

Proof: Let $a \in X^m$ and $b \in X^n$, where $m \leq n$. Since $0 \in X^k$ for all $k \in \mathbf{N}$, we have $a \in X^n$. Now if $a * b \in B$, then $a * b \in X^{n+1}$ and $\langle X \rangle$ is a local semigroup.

If S is a local semigroup containing $X \cap B$, then $X^n \subseteq S$ for all $n \in \mathbf{N}$, and thus $\langle X \rangle$ is the smallest local semigroup containing $X \cap B$. ∎

For a local semigroup S, we let $G(S) = \langle S \cup -S \rangle$.

7.14 Corollary If S is a local semigroup, then $G(S)$ is the smallest local group containing S.

Proof: Any local group containing S must contain $\langle S \cup -S \rangle$. Since $B = -B$, it is straightforward to show that $(S \cup -S)^n$ is closed under $-$ for all $n \in \mathbf{N}$. Hence $\langle S \cup -S \rangle$ is a local group. ∎

Recall that $\mathbf{H} = [0, \infty)$ in $\mathbf{R}$ under addition. The following lemma is important to subsequent definitions.

7.15 Lemma Let S be a local semigroup. Then $\{x \in L : x = \lim nx_n, x_n \in S\} = \{x \in L : \mathbf{H}x \cap \bar{B} \subseteq \bar{S}\} = \{x \in L : \mathbf{H}x \cap B \subseteq S'\}$. Moreover, if $x = \lim nx_n$ then $\lim x_n = 0$.

Proof: Suppose first that $x = \lim nx_n$ for $x_n \in S$. Let $r > 0$ such that $rx \in B$, and let $m_n = [rn]$, the greatest integer less than or equal to rn. Then $rx = \lim rnx_n = \lim ([rn]x_n + \epsilon_n x_n)$, where $0 \leq \epsilon_n < 1$. Now $x = \lim nx_n$ implies $\|x\| = \lim n\|x_n\|$, and thus $\lim \|x_n\| = 0$, so that $\lim x_n = 0$. We obtain that $\lim \epsilon_n x_n = 0$, and conclude that $rx = \lim [rn]x_n$. Since $rx \in B$, $[rn]x_n \in^e B$ and hence $x_n, 2x_n, \ldots, [rn]x_n \in B$, since B is an ϵ-ball. Since S is a local semigroup and $x_n \in S$, $[rn]x_n \in S$. Thus $rx \in \bar{S} \cap B = S'$, and hence the first set is contained in the third.

Suppose x is in the third set and $rx \in \bar{B}$. Then $rx = \lim (r - 1/n)x$ and each $(r - 1/n)x \in B$ for $1/n < r$. Thus $(r - 1/n)x \in^e \bar{S}$, and hence $rx \in \bar{S}$. We conclude that the third set is contained in the second.

To see that the second set is contained in the first, suppose that $\mathbf{H}x \cap \bar{B} \subseteq \bar{S}$. For sufficiently large $n \in \mathbf{N}$, let $x_n \in S$ such that $\|(1/n)x - x_n\| < 1/n^2$ (let $x_n = 0$ for smaller n). Then $\|x - nx_n\| = n\|(1/n)x - x_n\|$, and $n\|(1/n)x - x_n\| < n(1/n^2) = 1/n$. Thus $x = \lim nx_n$, and the proof is complete. ∎

Let S be a local semigroup. We define the *set of tangent vectors* to S at 0 by $L(S) = \{x \in L : x = \lim nx_n, x_n \in S, \lim x_n = 0\} = \{x \in L : \mathbf{H}x \cap B \subseteq S'\}$.

Observe that if $x \in L(S) \cap B$, then $x = 1 \cdot x \in \mathbf{H}x \cap B \subseteq S'$. Hence, $L(S) \cap B \subseteq S'$ and from 7.13, we have $\langle L(S) \cap B \rangle \subseteq S'$.

A nonempty closed subset K of a vector space V which is closed under vector addition and multiplication by nonnegative scalars is called a *wedge*, i.e., $K + K \subseteq K$ and for each $r \in \mathbf{H}$, $rK \subseteq K$. If K is a wedge satisfying $K \cap -K = \{0\}$, then K is called a *cone*. We say that the wedge K *generates* V if $V = K - K$ (we also use the terminology that K is *generating*), i.e., V is the smallest subspace containing K.

In addition to the results of 7.15, another useful characterization of $L(S)$ for a local semigroup S is $L(S) = \{x \in L : x = \lim m_n x_n,$ for $x_n \in S$ and m_n an increasing sequence in $\mathbf{N}\}$. The proof is similar to the first part of 7.15.

7.16 Theorem   Let S be a local semigroup. Then:
(1) $L(S)$ is a wedge.
(2) $L(S) = L(S')$.
(3) $L(H(S)) \subseteq L(S) \cap (-L(S))$.
(4) If $L(S) \cap B \subseteq S$ (which is the case for $S = S'$), then $L(H(S)) = L(S) \cap (-L(S)) = L(S') \cap (-L(S')) = L(H(S'))$.

Proof: (1) Let $x,y \in L(S)$. Then $x = \lim nx_n$ and $y = \lim ny_n$, where $x_n \to 0$ and $y_n \to 0$ in S. We obtain that $x + y = \lim n(x_n * y_n)$ and $x_n * y_n \in^e B$ and hence in S. It follows that $x + y \in L(S)$. To see that $L(S)$ is closed, we use the results of the remark preceding 7.16. Let $tx \in B$, $0 < t$, where B is the ϵ-ball contained in a CH-neighborhood of 0 in L with respect to which S is a local semigroup. Then, from 7.15, $x = \lim nx_n$ and $x_n \to 0$. Thus $tx = \lim tnx_n = \lim [tn]x_n$ (from the remark) $= \lim (tm_n x_n - \epsilon_n)x_n$ (where $0 \le \epsilon_n < 1) = \lim tm_n x_n - \lim \epsilon_n x_n = \lim tm_n x_n - 0 = tx$. Thus for large n, $[tm_n]x_n \in B$, $x_n \in S$, $x_n, 2x_n, \ldots, [tm_n]x_n \in B$, and we have that $tx \in \bar{S}$.

(2) Now $L(S) \subseteq L(S')$. Let $x = \lim nx_n$, where $x_n \in S'$, and let $y_n \in S$ such that $\|x_n - y_n\| < 1/n^2$. Then $x = \lim ny_n$, so that $x \in L(S)$.

(3) Now $-L(S) = L(-S)$ and $H(S) = S \cap -S$, so that $L(H(S)) \subseteq L(S) \cap L(-S) = L(S) \cap (-L(S))$.

(4) Let $x \in L(S) \cap (-L(S))$. Then $\mathbf{H}x \cap B \subseteq S'$ and $\mathbf{H}(-x) \cap$

$B \subseteq S'$. Since from our hypothesis, $L(S) \cap B \subseteq S$, if $rx \in B$, then $rx \in L(S) \cap B \subseteq S$. Also $rx \in B$ implies that $r(-x) \in B$, and thus $r(-x)B \cap L(S) \subseteq S$. Since $-rx = r(-x)$, we have $rx \in H(S)$ if $rx \in B$. It follows that $\mathbf{H}x \cap B \subseteq H(S)$ and $x \in L(H(S))$. From (3) we have $L(H(S)) = L(S) \cap (-L(S))$. Replacing S by S' the rest follows. ∎

A subset K of L is called a *Lie wedge* if there exists a local semigroup S with respect to some open ϵ-ball B such that $K = L(S)$. From 7.16, we see that K is closed under vector addition and scalar multiplication by scalars in $\mathbf{H}$ and that K is a closed subset of L. It follows that a Lie wedge is a wedge.

A Lie wedge K is called a *Lie semialgebra* if there exists an open ϵ-ball B such that $K \cap B$ is a local semigroup with respect to B.

A local semigroup S with respect to B is called a *local analytic semigroup* if $S = L(S) \cap B$. If, in addition, S is closed in B, then S is called a *local Lie semigroup* (with respect to B).

7.17 Theorem Let W be a Lie wedge in L. Then there is an open ϵ-ball B and a local semigroup S with respect to B such that $W = L(S)$. Let C be any open ball containing 0 in B and let $T = \langle W \cap C \rangle_C$.

(1) T is a local analytic semigroup in C and $L(T) = W$.

(2) $L(S \cap C) = W$.

(3) If S is a local analytic semigroup in B with $L(S) = W$, then for any C as above, the set $S \cap C$ is a local subsemigroup of C with $L(S \cap C) = W$. For the local analytic semigroup $T = \langle W \cap C \rangle_C$ of C we have (i) $L(T) = W$, (ii) $T \subseteq S \cap C$, and (iii) $\langle T \rangle_B = S$.

Proof: (1) Now $W \cap C \subseteq L(T)$, since W is a wedge and $W \cap C \subseteq T$. Thus $W \subseteq L(T)$ is also a wedge. From the remark preceding 7.16, we have that $W \cap B \subseteq S'$, so that $T = \langle W \cap C \rangle \subseteq \langle W \cap C \rangle_B \subseteq S'$, since S' is a local subsemigroup of B. Thus $L(T) \subseteq L(S') = L(S)$ by 7.16. It follows that $L(T) = W$, and $T = \langle L(T) \cap C \rangle_C$. We conclude that T is a local analytic semigroup.

(2) Now from 7.16 (2) and the remark preceding it, we conclude $W = L(\langle W \cap C \rangle_C) \subseteq L((S \cap C)') \subseteq L(S \cap C) \subseteq L(S) = W$.

(3) To prove (i) observe that from (2), we have $L(S \cap C) = W$. We want to show that $S \cap C \supset \langle W \cap C \rangle_C$. From the hypothesis on S, we have $S = \langle W \cap B \rangle_B$. Thus $\langle W \cap C \rangle_C \subseteq \langle W \cap B \rangle_B = S$, and $\langle W \cap C \rangle_C \subseteq S \cap C$.

To prove (ii), observe that since $T = \langle W \cap C \rangle_C$, we have $T \subseteq \langle W \cap B \rangle_B = S$.

To prove (iii) note that $\langle T \rangle_B \subseteq \langle S \cap C \rangle_B$ which from (ii) is contained in $S = \langle W \cap B \rangle_B$. Since W is a wedge, $\langle W \cap C \rangle_B \supset W \cap B$. It follows that $\langle W \cap B \rangle_B = \langle W \cap C \rangle_B \subseteq \langle T \rangle_B$. ∎

We now turn from the local theory in the Dynkin algebra L to the global theory in a Lie group G. We will hereafter in this section assume that G is a Lie group whose Lie algebra is L.

A subsemigroup S of G is called a *wedge subsemigroup* if there exists a Lie wedge W in L such that S is the smallest subsemigroup of G containing $\exp(W)$. A topological semigroup is called a *wedge semigroup* if it is topologically isomorphic to a wedge subsemigroup of a Lie group.

Recall that a *one-parameter semigroup [group]* in G is a continuous homomorphism $\sigma: \mathbf{H} \to G$ $[\sigma: \mathbf{R} \to G]$. Observe that each one-paramenter semigroup $\sigma: \mathbf{H} \to G$ can be extended to a one-parameter group $\sigma^*: \mathbf{R} \to G$ by defining $\sigma^*(-t) = \sigma(t)^{-1}$ (inverse in G) for each $t > 0$ in $\mathbf{R}$.

A subsemigroup S of G is called a *ray subsemigroup* if S is generated by the union of the ranges of the one-parameter semigroups which it contains. A topological semigroup which is topologically isomorphic to a ray subsemigroup of a Lie group is called a *ray semigroup*. A *Lie subsemigroup* of G is the closure of a ray subsemigroup. A topological semigroup is called a *Lie semigroup* if it is topologically isomorphic to a Lie subsemigroup of a Lie group.

Observe that a wedge semigroup is a ray semigroup. However, if S is the interior of the first quadrant in $\mathbf{R}^2$ together with 0, then S is a ray semigroup which is not a wedge semigroup.

A nice example of a ray semigroup (which in this example is closed and therefore is a Lie semigroup) is the Heisenberg group example formulated in Hofmann and Lawson [1981a].

Example   Let G be the group on $\mathbf{R}^3$ with multiplication defined by $(a,b,c)\circ(x,y,z) = (a + x, b + y, c + z + ay)$. Then G is topologically isomorphic to a group of 3×3 matrices matching (a,b,c) with

$$\begin{pmatrix} 1 & a & c \\ 0 & 1 & b \\ 0 & 0 & 1 \end{pmatrix}$$

Let $S = \{(a,b,c): 0 \le a,b; 0 \le c \le ab\}$. Then S is a subsemigroup of G. In $\mathbf{R}^3$ the space of S in the region in the first octant bounded by the surface $z = xy$ and the xy-plane.

To see that S is a ray semigroup, define $\sigma: H \to S$ by $\sigma(t) = (t,0,0)$ and define $\tau: H \to S$ by $\tau(t) = (0,t,0)$. Now if $(a,b,c) \in S$ and $b > 0$, then $(a,b,c) = \sigma(a/b)\, \tau(b)\, \sigma(a - c/b)$. If $b = 0$, then $(a,b,c) = \sigma(a)$. In any case S is a three dimensional closed ray subsemigroup of $\mathbf{R}^3$ generated by $\sigma(\mathbf{H}) \cup \tau(\mathbf{H})$.

For $A \subseteq G$, we use $\langle A \rangle$ to denote the subsemigroup of G generated by A.

7.18   Theorem   A subsemigroup S of G is a wedge subsemigroup if and only if there exists a local analytic subsemigroup T of L such that $S = \langle \exp(T) \rangle$.

Proof: Suppose first that S is a wedge subsemigroup of G with $S = \langle \exp(W) \rangle$ for some Lie wedge W in L. According to 7.17, there exists an open ϵ-ball B such that if T is the local semigroup with respect to B generated by $W \cap B$, then T is a local analytic semigroup and $L(T) = W$. By 7.17, we can assume that B is sufficiently small so that exp is injective on B and satisfies $\exp(a) \exp(b) = \exp(a * b)$ for all $a,b \in B$. Then $W \cap B \subseteq \exp^{-1}(S) \cap B$ (this is a local semigroup with respect to B). Thus $T \subseteq \exp^{-1}(S) \cap$

B. Thus we have $S = \langle \exp(W) \rangle = \langle (W \cap B) \rangle$ (since W is a wedge) $\subseteq \langle \exp(T) \rangle \subseteq \langle \exp(\exp^{-1}(S)) \rangle \subseteq \langle S \rangle = S$. We conclude that $S = \langle \exp(T) \rangle$.

Conversely suppose that $S = \langle \exp(T) \rangle$ where T is a local analytic semigroup. Then T is locally generated by $L(T)$. It thus follows that $S = \langle \exp L(T) \rangle$. ∎

Let S be a subsemigroup of G and denote by S_R the ray semigroup generated by the union of the images of all one-parameter semigroups lying entirely in S, and let $G(S_R)$ be the subgroup of G generated by S_R. Let S^* be the closure of S_R in the unique topology of $G(S_R)$ making it a Lie group. Define

$$P(S) = \{x \in L : \exp(tx) \in S^* \text{ for all } t \in \mathbf{H}\}$$

Note that $P(S) = \cap_{r>0} r \exp^{-1} S^*$. We call $P(S)$ the *wedge associated* to S.

Note that for a closed subsemigroup S of G we have $P(S) = \cap_{r>0} r \exp^{-1} S$ and that this set is the set of tangent vectors of $\exp^{-1}(S)$ at 0, i.e., in this case $P(S) = L(\exp^{-1} S)$.

7.19   Theorem   If S is a subsemigroup of G, then $P(S)$ is a Lie wedge.

Proof: Now $P(S) = P(S_R)$, and so we can assume without loss of generality that $S = S_R$. Let B be an open ϵ-ball in L such that the $*$ multiplication is defined on B and $\exp|B$ is a homeomorphism. Since $G(S)$ is an analytic subgroup, there is a Lie subalgebra L_S of L such that the exponential function of $G(S)$ [denoted $\exp_{G(S)}$] is the restriction of the exponential function of G to L_S. Now S^* is closed in the Lie group topology of $G(S)$. Hence $\exp_{G(S)}^{-1}(S^*)$ is closed in L_S, and thus $T = B \cap \exp_{G(S)}^{-1}(S^*)$ is closed in B. Also, T is a local semigroup with respect to B since S^* is a semigroup in G.

Since T is closed in B, we have that $x \in L(T)$ if and only if $\mathbf{H}x \cap B \subseteq T$. Now $tx \in T$ for small positive t if and only if $\exp(tx) \in$

S^*, since S is a subsemigroup of G. It follows that $x \in P(S)$. Thus $P(S) = L(T)$. Since $L(T)$ is a Lie wedge, the proof is complete. ∎

7.20 Theorem Let S be an analytic subsemigroup of a Lie group G. Then S is a wedge subsemigroup and hence a ray subsemigroup.

Proof: From 7.19, $P(S)$ is a Lie wedge. Thus $S = \langle \exp P(S) \rangle$ implies that S is a wedge semigroup. ∎

7.21 Theorem Let S be a closed subsemigroup of a Lie group G. Then these are equivalent:
  (1) S is a ray semigroup.
  (2) S is a wedge semigroup.
  (3) S is analytic.
and these conditions imply that S is a Lie semigroup.

Proof: If S is a closed ray semigroup, then $S = S_R = S^*$. Hence $\exp(P(S))$ is the union of the image of all one-parameter semigroups contained in S. Since S is a ray semigroup, this set generates S, i.e., S is analytic. This shows that (1) implies (3). The other implications are clear. ∎

If W is a wedge in the Dynkin algebra L then $W \cap -W$ is sometimes called *the edge of the wedge*. The so called "edge of the wedge problem" has received a great deal of attention in the literature. It inquires whether a Lie wedge and a compatible wedge (defined below) must be the same. Significant partial solutions were obtained in Hofmann and Lawson [1983b, 1984] and a complete solution was found in Hofmann and Hilgert [1984b]. We state the problem and display one of the implications established in Hofmann and Lawson [1981].

For $x \in L$, define $ad\, x : L \to L$ by $ad\, x(y) = [x,y]$. Then $ad\, x$ is a linear transformation on L for each $x \in L$. For a linear transformation $A : L \to L$, define

$$e^A = I + A + \frac{1}{2} A^2 + \cdots + \frac{1}{n} A^n + \cdots$$

Then the series $e^A(x)$ converges in L for each $x \in L$.

A wedge W in L is said to be *compatible* provided that for each $x \in W \cap -W$, we have $e^{ad x}W = W$.

7.22 Theorem Each Lie wedge is a compatible wedge.

Proof: Let W be a Lie wedge, and let B be CH-neighborhood of 0 in L and S a relatively closed local subsemigroup in B such that $W = L(S)$. Then $x \in W$ if and only if $\mathbf{H}x \cap B \subseteq S$. Let $H = W \cap -W$. Then $H \cap B$ is a local subgroup of B.

Let $x \in H$ and $y \in W$. Then $sy \in S$ for sufficiently small $s \geq 0$ and $tx \in S$ for sufficiently small $t \in \mathbf{R}$. Thus for s, t sufficiently small with $s \geq 0$, we have $tx * sy * -tx$ is well defined and contained in S. Now $tx * sy * -tx = e^{t \cdot ad\, x}sy$. The left-hand side of this equation is linear in s, so that $tx * sy * -tx = n(tx * (s/n)y * -tx)$. This element is therefore in $W = L(S)$, because $tx * (s/n)y * -tx$ is in S since $(s/n)y \in S$ for all large n. It follows that $e^{t \cdot ad\, x}xy \in W$ for all sufficiently small $s \in H$ and all sufficiently small $t \in \mathbf{R}$. Since W is a wedge, this holds for all s and sufficiently small t. In particular, this holds for $s = 1$. Thus $e^{t \cdot ad\, x}W = W$ for sufficiently small t. Since the Lie group of all vector space automorphisms g with $gW = W$ contains $e^{t \cdot ad\, x}$ for all sufficiently small t, and hence for all t, we obtain that $e^{ad x}W = W$. ∎

There are a number of additional interesting results which appear in the works cited at the beginning of this section. Of particular interest to one studying divisible semigroups is the following result appearing in Hofmann and Lawson [1983], which we offer without proof.

7.23 Theorem Let S be a closed subsemigroup of a connected Lie group G. Then S is divisible if and only if $S = \exp P(S)$.

We conclude with a euclidean example which appears in Hofmann and Lawson [1981].

Example   Consider the unit vectors in $\mathbf{R}^3$ along each corrdinate axis: $a = (1,0,0)$, $b = (0,1,0)$, and $c = (0,0,1)$. Let $W = con\{a + tb + (t^2/2)c : t \in \mathbf{R}\}$. Then W is a closed cone spanned by $a + c$, and with the vectors a and c on its boundary. Let $T : \mathbf{R}^3 \to \mathbf{R}^3$ be the linear transformation such that $Ta = b$, $Tb = c$, and $Tc = (0,0,0)$. Define for $x, y \in \mathbf{R}^2$, $[x,y] = Ty$. Then $(\mathbf{R}^3, [\cdot,\cdot])$ is a Lie algebra, and for each $x \in \mathbf{R}^3$, we have $ad\ x = T$. Moreover, $e^{tT} W = W$ for all $t \in \mathbf{R}$, so that W is a compatible wedge, and hence is a Lie wedge.

8
Problems

In this chapter we discuss some of the outstanding problems in topological semigroup theory. We mention some of the results which are partial solutions to these problems. These problems come from a variety of sources including Wallace [1961c], Hofmann and Mostert [1969], and Brown and Stralka [1973]. We do not include problems on semitopological semigroups, but refer the reader to Ruppert [1984] for a list of problems on this topic. Our presentation is somewhat chronological, but we will occasionally modify this pattern where similar problems are involved.

WALLACE'S PROBLEMS

In this section we discuss problems posed by A.D. Wallace from early unpublished problems lists and from Wallace [1961c, 1962]. Remarks from Mostert [1963] regarding some of these problems are also considered.

8.1 Problem Does the n-cell S for $n \geq 2$ admit the structure of a compact semigroup such that $\partial S = E(S)$?

This is the "skin problem" which for $n = 2$ was answered in the negative in Ferguson [1967] (see the section on semigroups on the 2-cell in Chapter 5).

8.2 Problem Does an n-sphere S admit the structure of a compact semigroup such that $S^2 = S$ and S has a zero?

As indicated by Wallace, the answer is negative in the case that $n = 1$ [Koch and Wallace, 1958]. From Mostert and Shields [1956], if S is a two-sphere semigroup with a nontrivial connected subgroup, then $S^2 \neq S$. Other contributions to this problem appear in Cohen and Koch [1965] and McCharen [1969] (see the remarks at the end of the section on admissibility in Chapter 5).

8.3 Problem Suppose S is a monoid on $\mathbf{R}^n$. Can a compact connected subgroup of $H(1)$ be self-linked?

It was proved in Curtis [1959] that if S is a semigroup on $\mathbf{R}^3$ and G is a compact subgroup of S, then G is not self-linked. As indicated in Mostert [1963b], it was established in Mostert [1963a] that if S is a contractible semigroup and G is a subgroup of S, then G is not self-linked.

8.4 Problem If S is a compact connected locally connected one-dimensional metric monoid, then it is known that S is either a dendrite or contains exactly one simple closed curve which coincides with $M(S)$. Is there an analogous proposition for higher dimensions?

8.5 Problem If S is a compact connected semilattice with identity, does S have the fixed point property?

A compact connected monoid without the fixed point property was constructed in Cohen [1960], and a compact connected semilattice (without an identity) without the fixed point property was constructed in Cohen [1974].

8.6 Problem What conditions on a compact connected semigroup S with $S = ESE$ will insure that S and $M(S)$ have the same cohomology?

This is always true if S has dimension 0 or 1. This follows from the theorem that if S is a compact connected semigroup such that $S = ESE$, then $H^1(S) = H^1(M(S))$ [Cohen and Koch, 1965]. As we hve seen, if S is a compact connected semigroup with a left (or right) identity, then S and $M(S)$ have the same cohomology (see 1.2). An example was constructed in Hudson [1963] of a semigroup S on a 2-sphere with four stickers at the zero of S such that $S = ESE$.

8.7 Problem Let S be a semigroup and let ∂S denote the boundary of S in some suitable sense.
(a) If every element of S has a square root, does every element of ∂S have a square root in ∂S? (Problem of H. H. Corson.)
(b) Under some interpretations of "boundary" it is known that if S has an identity, then it lies in ∂S. Are there other useful interpretations of "boundary" for which this is so?
(c) If one assumes that multiplication on ∂S is commutative, are there agreeable conditions under which S is commutative?

Useful notions of boundary have appeared in Hofmann and Mostert [1966] and Lawson and Madison [1970]. These were discussed in Chapter 1. For each of the concepts of ∂S, it was established that $H(1) \subseteq \partial S$. For an affine monoid S, as it was proved in Cohen and Collins [1959], we have seen in Chapter 7 that $H(1) \subseteq ext S \subseteq \partial S$. It was proved in Faucett [1955] that if S is a tree such that the endpoints of S commute, then S is abelian.

We consider now the problems listed in [Wallace, 1962].

8.8 Problem If S is a nondegenerate finite dimensional compact connected monoid such that no retract of S cuts S, is S topologically an n-sphere, $n = 1$ or 3?

It is known that such an S must be a group if it is homogeneous. [Hudson and Mostert, 1963] (see 1.10).

An element x of a semigroup S is said to be *periodic* if for some $n \in \mathbb{N}$ we have $x^{n+1} = x$. The least such n is called the *period* of x and is denoted as $p(x)$ in the next problem. A semigroup S is said to be *pointwise periodic* is each element of S is periodic.

8.9   Problem   Let S be a pointwise periodic semigroup on an n-cell. Can it be that $S\backslash E(S) \neq \square$ and that $p(x) > 2$ for each $x \in S\backslash E(S)$ and that p is constant on $S\backslash E(S)$?

8.10   Problem   If S is a compact semigroup, under what conditions on S will there exist a regular measure μ on the Borel sets of S and a function $g:S \to \mathbb{R}$ such that $\mu(xA) = g(x)\mu(A)$ for each $x \in S$ and each Borel set A?

Measures on semigroups were studied in Pym [1962], Rosen [1956], Rosenblatt [1960] and Paalman-De-Miranda [1970].

THE PROBLEMS OF HOFMANN AND MOSTERT

The problems in this section are selected from Hofmann and Mostert [1969]. The reader is referred to Carruth, Hofmann, and Mislove [1973] for additional remarks concerning the original Hofmann and Mostert problem list.

8.11   The Centralizer Conjecture   Let S be a compact connected monoid with zero and let G be a compact connected subgroup of $H(1)$. Then the centralizer $Z(G)$ of G in S is connected.

There were some equivalent formulations of this conjecture and some special cases considered by Hofmann and Mostert. One of these cases is presented in 8.12.

Some progress has been made on this conjecture in Castellano [1983] and Hunter [1973] (see also Hofmann and Hunter [1973]). We summarize Hunter's result:

Let S be a compact connected monoid and let G be a compact subgroup of $H(1)$. If either

(1) $cd\ S/G \leq 2$; or

(2) S/G is embeddable in a 3-manifold,

then S satisfies then centralizer conjecture with respect to G.

8.12 Problem Let S be a compact connected semigroup, with $E(S) = \{0,1\}$. Is there a one parameter semigroup in the centralizer of $H(1)$? Is there one at least in the centralizer of the identity component of $H(1)$?

If S is a compact connected monoid, then there is a natural automorphism action of $H(1)$ on S defined by $\psi:H(1) \times S \to S$, where $\psi(h,x) = h^{-1}xh$ for each $(h,x) \in H(1) \times S$. We say that $T \subseteq S$ is *invariant* provided $\psi(H(1) \times T) = T$. A subsemigroup W of S is called a *wedge* provided $W \cap H(1) = \{1\}$ and $W \cap M(S) \neq \square$.

8.13 The Invariant Wedge Problem Let S be a compact connected semigroup. Does there exist an invariant wedge T in S?

The following is a modified version of a Hofmann and Mostert problem which appears in Carruth and Clark [1972].

8.14 Problem Let S be a compact connected monoid. Is there a closed connected subsemigroup T of S such that $H(1) \subseteq T, M(S) \subseteq T$, and if D is a regular $\mathcal{D}$-class in S and $T \cap D \neq \square$, then $D \subseteq T$ and $T/\mathcal{D}_T$ is totally ordered?

As observed by Hofmann and Mostert, if $\mathcal{D}$ is a congruence on S, then the answer is yes.

8.15 Problem Let S be a compact connected semigroup with identity. Let T be the smallest closed subsemigroup containing all irreducible semigroups. Can one somehow characterize T?

8.16 Problem Let S and T be compact monoids and let $S \sqcup T$ denote the coproduct of S and T in the category of compact monoids and identity preserving continuous homomorphisms. There is a natural morphism $\psi : H_S(1) \sqcup H_T(1) \to H_{S \sqcup T}(1)$ from the property of the coproduct.

(1) Is ψ surjective?

(2) Is ψ an isomorphism?

(3) Is ψ surjective if S is a group and $T = I_u$?

(4) Let $\pi : S \sqcup T \to T$ be the natural map defined via the coproduct property by the *map* $S \to T$ defined by $x \mapsto 1$ and the identity map $T \to T$. If S is a group and $H_T(1) = \{1\}$, is $\pi^{-1}(1) = H_{S \sqcup T}(1)$?

(4a) Is the answer to (4) positive if $T = I_u$?

As it was indicated in Hofmann and Mostert [1969] a positive answer to (1) would settle the wedge problem (8.13) (which in turn has the potential of leading to a solution of the centralizer conjecture).

The following is still unsolved to our knowledge.

8.17 Problem Determine the structure of $\mathbf{R/Z} \sqcup I_u$ in the category of compact monoids and identity preserving continuous homomorphisms?

8.18 Problem (Jane Day) Let S be a compact connected monoid with $E(S) = \{0,1\}$ such that $H(1)$ is connected and each element of S has a square root (i.e., S is 2-divisible). Is the union of one parameter semigroups dense in S? If $H(1)$ is arcwise connected, does every element lie on a one parameter semigroup?

If $H(1)$ is normal (in particular if S is abelian), then according to Hofmann and Mostert, the answer is yes on both counts. If S is divisible, then the answer to the first question is yes.

8.19 Problem Which classes of compact monoids are characterized by the property that the representations by semigroups of linear contractions on some Hilbert space separate points?

8.20 Problem Describe all linear representations of cylindrical semigroups.

8.21 Problem Let S be a compact connected monoid. Determine the automorphism group of S; in particular if: (1) S is a cylindrical semigroup; (2) S is an I-semigroup; (3) S is an irreducible semigroup; or (4) S is a paragroup.

8.22 Problem If S is a compact connected abelian monoid with $E(S) = \{1,0\}$, does $S \to S/\mathcal{H}$ allow a cross-section morphism?

A cross section in this case would be a compact connected subsemigroup T of S such that T meets each $\mathcal{H}$-class of S in one point.

In the case that $S/\mathcal{H}$ is finite dimensional, as indicated by Hofmann and Mostert, the answer is positive (see Brown and Friedberg [1968]).

THE COMPACT SEMILATTICE PROBLEMS OF BROWN AND STRALKA

In this section we discuss the problems listed in Brown and Stralka [1973]. Credit for contributing some of these problems to this list is attributed by Brown and Stralka to J. D. Lawson, K. H. Hofmann, A. Lau, J. W. Stepp, and A. D. Wallace.

Recall from Chapter 6 that $\mathcal{CX}$ denotes the category of compact semilattices and continuous homomorphisms and $\mathcal{CL}$ denotes the subcategory of compact Lawson semilattices. Let $\mathcal{CX}_f$ denote the subcategory of $\mathcal{CX}$ of finite dimensional compact semilattices and let $\mathcal{CL}_f$ the subcategory of finite dimensional copact Lawson semilattices. If $n \in \mathbf{N}$, then $\mathcal{CX}_n$ denotes the subcategory of n-dimensional compact semilattices and $\mathcal{CL}_n$

denotes the subcategory of compact n-dimensional Lawson semilattices.

8.23   Problem.   Let $S \in \mathcal{C}L_f$ (or $\mathcal{C}\mathcal{L}$). Can S be represented as a strict projective limit of locally connected members of $\mathcal{C}\mathcal{L}_f$ (or $\mathcal{C}\mathcal{L}$)?

In Lau [1972b] it was shown that S can be represented as an inverse limit of locally connected objects of $\mathcal{C}\mathcal{L}_f$, but this system need not be strict. It was demonstrated in Hofmann and Stralka [1973] that there exists an object T in $\mathcal{C}\mathcal{L}_1$ which could be represented as a strict projective limit of locally connected objects of $\mathcal{C}\mathcal{L}_f$, but in any such limit system the dimensions of the factors must be unbounded.

An object $S \in \mathcal{C}\mathcal{X}$ is called *polyhedral* if its underlying space is homeomorphic to the geometric realization of a finite simplicial complex.

8.24   Problem   If S is a locally connected, connected object in $\mathcal{C}\mathcal{L}_n$, is S a strict projective limit of polyhedral semilattices in $\mathcal{C}\mathcal{L}_n$ (or $\mathcal{C}\mathcal{L}_f$)?

8.25   Problem   Is the class of objects of $\mathcal{C}\mathcal{L}$ which are constructible from I_m by the operations of finite products, quotients, and subsemilattices precisely the subclass of objects of $\mathcal{C}\mathcal{L}$ which have finite breadth?

8.26   Problem   Do compact semilattices of finite breadth have the congruence extension property? (See Stralka [1971].) Does the class of objects defined in the previous problem have this property?

Compact distributive lattices of finite breadth do have this property, but not every object of $\mathcal{C}\mathcal{L}$ does (see Stralka [1971]).

Some results have been obtained toward a solution of this problem in Crawley [1973].

8.27 Problem Let S be a connected object of $\mathscr{CX}_1$ and suppose the endpoints of S is compact. Is $S \in \mathscr{CL}_1$?

8.28 Problem Let $S \in \mathscr{CL}$ and let $\mathscr{U}$ be an open cover of S. Does there exist a closed congruence ρ on S such that the ρ congruence classes refine $\mathscr{U}$ and S/ρ is locally connected and finite dimensional?

Let $\phi: X \to Y$ be a map of a space X into a metric space (Y, d). A point $y \in \phi(X)$ is said to be *unstable* if for each $\delta > 0$, there exists a map $\theta: X \to Y$ such that:
(1) $d(\phi(x), \theta(x)) < \delta$ for each $x \in X$; and
(2) $\theta(X) \subseteq Y \setminus \{y\}$.
Otherwise y is called a *stable* value of ϕ.

8.29 Problem Suppose that $S \in \mathscr{CX}_k$ and $\phi: S \to I^n_m$ is a $\mathscr{CX}$-morphism with $k < n$. Must every element of $\phi(S)$ be stable in I^n_m?

8.30 Problem Let S be an object in $\mathscr{CX}_f$ *(or $\mathscr{CL}_f$)*. Does there exist $x \in S$ such that $dim\ xS = dim\ S$? Suppose that $S \in \mathscr{CX}$ (or $\mathscr{CL}$) such that the dimension of each point of S is infinite. Is there $x \in S$ such that $dim\ xS = \infty$?

The first question was answered in the positive if S is locally connected and $cd\ S$ is finite [Lawson, 1972]. In the event that S is metric and x is a 0-middle point such that the upper end generated by x has a nonempty interior, the answer is positive [Lau, 1971].

8.31 Problem Let A be a compact pospace such that $dim\ A = 0$. Is there a continuous isotone map of A into an object of $\mathscr{CX}$?

8.32 Problem No connected object of $\mathscr{CX}$ of finite codimension is homogeneous (see Lawson and Madison [1970]). Must every connected homogeneous metric object in $\mathscr{CX}$ be homeomorphic to the Hilbert cube?

PROBLEMS OF KOCH

In this section we present a list of problems from Koch [1969].

8.33 Problem If S is a locally compact monothetic semigroup and S has an identity, must S be compact?

It is known from Koch [1957a] that if S is compact, then it must be a group. From that paper it is also known that if S contains a minimal ideal or if S is locally compact and totally disconnected, then the answer is affirmative. A related question was successfully considered in Horne [1964]. This paper gives an example of a locally compact monoid in which $H(1)$ is a copy of $[0,\infty)$ under multiplication, and is dense in S.

8.34 Problem If S is a compact connected semigroup with zero such that $S^2 = S$, and if e is a maximal idempotent in S, can e have a euclidean neighborhood? If $S = ESE$, does each maximal idempotent lie on the edge?

The best results to our knowledge which are related to this problem appear in McCharen [1971]. We have seen in Chapter 2, that if S is a monoid and 1 has a euclidean neighborhood, then S is a group.

8.35 Problem If S is an absolute retract with an edge point, does S admit the structure of a monoid?

It is well known that a retract of a 1-cell does admit the structure of a monoid. An answer to this question was given in the affirmative for a retract of a 2-cell in Williams [1975]. A retract of a 3-cell does not always admit the structure of a monoid (see Koch [1970]). Bing's house of 2-rooms provides an example of a continuum with no edge points and hence, in view of 1.7, does not admit the structure of a monoid.

8.36 Problem If S is a locally compact connected locally connected semilattice with zero 0 and identity 1, is there an arc chain from 1 to 0 in S?

If S is compact, then the answer is affirmative [Koch, 1959] (see also Appendix B.8 and 2.22).

Small arc-chains exist near 1, but it is not clear that they can be continued to 0. This problem illustrates the difficulty of controlling one-parameter semigroups in the large. This question has also been raised by L. E. Ward, Jr., and D. R. Brown.

8.37 Problem Does each metric generalized tree admit the structure of a semigroup S with $E(S) = \{0,1\}$?

In the nonmetric case a counterexample appears in Eberhart [1966].

8.38 Problem Do the members of the class of ruled spaces of Koch and McAuley have the fixed point property?

PROBLEMS ON DIVISIBLE SEMIGROUPS

In this section we list some problems pertaining to divisibility in compact semigroups. The algebraic counterparts of these questions have for the most part been resolved.

8.39 Problem Determine the structure of a compact divisible (abelian) semigroup.

The local structure of a compact divisible semigroup was determined in Hildebrant [1969]. Significant contributions toward the global theory appear in Brown and Friedberg [1968] and Keimel [1967]. The algebraic structure of uniquely divisible abelian semigroups was determined in Brown and LaTorre [1966].

8.40 The Compact Divisible Embedding Conjecture   Each compact semigroup can be embedded in a compact divisible semigroup.

This problem was posed by R. J. Koch in 1967 and appears first in print in Brown and Friedberg [1968]. The algebraic analog of the problem was resolved for abelian semigroups in Hancock [1960]. Partial solutions for compact abelian semigroups were obtained in Hildebrant and Lawson [1972] and in Hildebrant [1976] (see 4.18 for an alternate proof of the Hildebrant–Lawson theorem as it appears in Hildebrant, Lawson, and Yeager [1976]).

The next pair of problems arise from the conjecture of 8.41.

8.41 Problem   If S is a compact power-cancellative (abelian) semigroup T, can we obtain from T a compact uniquely divisible (abelian) semigroup D and an embedding $\phi : S \to D$?

The uniquely divisible reflection (see Carruth, Hildebrant, and Koch [1983]) does not provide an answer here in general.

8.42 Problem   Can a topological semigroup S be embedded into a compact uniquely divisible abelian semigroup if S is a union of subsemigroups, each of which satisfies the conditions of 4.18?

Carol Collins has discovered a partial solution of this problem (unpublished).

A subsemigroup S of a Lie group G is said to be *locally divisible* provided there exists a neighborhood V of 1 in G such that $(S \cap V, V)$ is a divisible local semigroup.

The following problem is due to K. H. Hofmann and J. D. Lawson.

8.43 Problem   Let S be a closed divisible subsemigroup of a Lie group. Must S be locally divisible?

8.44 Problem Let S be a compact uniquely divisible semigroup such that $E(S) = \{0,1\}$. Is $S \setminus \{0\}$ a cancellative subsemigroup of S?

It is known that $S \setminus \{0\}$ is a subsemigroup [Brown and Friedberg, 1968]. Moreover, the answer is affirmative if S is abelian.

TRANSLATIONAL HULL PROBLEMS

8.45 Problem Is there a structure theorem analogous to 4.22 for compact reductive abelian semigroups?

8.46 Problem Let S be a compact abelian semigroup. Compare the structure of $\Omega(S)$ with that of $\Omega(ES)$. In particular, if S is a finite semigroup, under what conditions is $\#\Omega(S) = \#\Omega(ES)$?

The structure of $\Omega(ES)$ has been determined in Hildebrant, Lawson, and Yeager [1976] (see 4.22).

8.47 Problem Let S be a locally compact reductive (abelian) semigroup and let $\beta:S \to B$ denote the Bohr compactification of S. How does $\Omega(B)$ compare with the Bohr compactification of $\Omega(S)$?

PROBLEMS OF CARRUTH AND CLARK

The problems in this section are derived from Carruth and Clark [1972]. The first two problems are modifications of problems of Hofmann and Mostert.

8.48 Problem If S is a compact connected monoid, is there a hormos T contained in S such that $1 \in T$, $T \cap M(S) \neq \square$, and T contains each subgroup of S which it meets?

8.49   Problem   If S is a compact connected monoid, is there a hormos T contained in S such that $H(1) \subseteq T$ and $T \cap M(S) \neq \square$?

8.50   Problem   If S is a compact connected monoid, does there exist a compact connected submonoid T containing $H(1)$, meeting $M(S)$, and on which $\mathcal{H}_T$ is a congruence?

8.51   Problem   If S is a compact semigroup on which $\mathcal{H}_S$ is a congruence and T is a closed subsemigroup such that T contains each subgroup ($\mathcal{H}$-class) which it meets, must $\mathcal{H}_T$ be a congruence?

8.52   Problem   If S is a compact connected monoid, $\mathcal{H}_S$ is a congruence, and I is an I-semigroup in $S/\mathcal{H}_S$ from its zero to its identity, must $\mathcal{H}_{\eta^{-1}(I)}$ be a congruence?

8.53   Problem   If S is a compact connected monoid and $\mathcal{H}_S$ is a congruence, is there an I-semigroup I in $S/\mathcal{H}_S$ from its zero to its identity such that $\mathcal{H}_{\eta^{-1}(I)}$ is a congruence?

An affirmative answer to 8.51 would yield an affirmative answer to 8.52, and an affirmative answer to 8.52 would yield an affirmative answer to 8.53. If any of these three problems were to be answered in the affirmative, then the equivalence of 8.48 and 8.49 would follow.

APPENDIX A
Cohomology

We present the fundamentals of Alexander–Wallace–Spanier (AWS) cohomology theory. The seven axioms of Eilenberg and Steenrod [1952] for a cohomology theory are identified. In addition to these, the AWS theory also satisfies the extension and reduction axioms which together are equivalent to the continuity axiom of Eilenberg and Steenrod.

Throughout this appendix we use X to denote a topological space, and p is a nonnegative integer; X^{p+1} denotes the $(p + 1)$-fold cartesian product of X with itself, and G denotes an additive abelian group.

Let $C^p(X) = \{\phi:X^{p+1} \to G\}$ (the set of all functions from X^{p+1} into G), and define, for $\phi, \psi \in C^p(X)$, $(\phi + \psi)(x_0,x_1,\ldots,x_p) = \phi(x_0,x_1,\ldots,x_p) + \psi(x_0,x_1,\ldots,x_p)$, and $0(x_0,x_1,\ldots,x_p) = 0$. Then $C^p(X)$ is an abelian group.

Define $\bar{\delta}_p:C^p(X) \to C^{p+1}(X)$ by

$$(\bar{\delta}_p\phi)(x_0,x_1,\ldots,x_{p+1}) = \sum_{i=0}^{p+1} (-1)^i\phi(x_0,\ldots,x_{i-1},x_{i+1},\ldots,x_{p+1})$$

where $\phi \in C^p(X)$. Then $\bar{\delta}_p$ is a homomorphism and $\bar{\delta}_{p+1}\bar{\delta}_p = 0$.

If $\phi \in C^p(X)$ and $A \subseteq X$, then ϕ is said to be *locally zero* on A provided that for each $a \in A$, there exists U which is open in the relative topology of A, $a \in U \subseteq A$, and $\phi(x_0,x_1,\ldots,x_p) = 0$ if $(x_0,x_1,\ldots,x_p) \in U^{p+1}$.

If $A \subseteq X$, then we use $C^p(X,A)$ to denote the elements of $C^p(X)$ which are locally zero on A. Observe that if $B \subseteq A \subseteq X$, then $C(X,A)$ is a subgroup of $C^p(X,B)$ and $\bar{\delta}_p C^p(X,A) \subseteq C^{p+1}(X,A)$. Note that $C^p(X,\square) = C^p(X)$.

Define $Z^p(X,A) = C^p(X,A) \cap \bar{\delta}_p^{-1} C^{p+1}(X,X)$ (the group of p-cocycles of X mod A), $B^0(X,A) = \{0\}$, and $B^p(X,A) = \bar{\delta}_{p-1} C^{p-1}(X,A) + C^p(X,X)$ for $p > 0$ (the group of cobounding p-cocycles of X and A). Observe that $B^p(X,A)$ is a subgroup of $Z^p(X,A)$ for each p.

The *pth cohomology group of X mod A* is defined:

$$H^p(X,A) = Z^p(X,A)/B^p(X,A).$$

Considering the restriction of $\bar{\delta}_p$ to $C^p(X,A)$, the *p*th cohomology group can be constructed in an alternate fashion by declaring that $Z^p(X,A)$ is the kernel of $\bar{\delta}_p | C^p(X,A)$ and that $B^p(X,A)$ is the image of $\bar{\delta}_{p-1} C^{p-1}(X,A)$. This approach is employed in Spanier [1966].

If X and Y are topological spaces, $A \subseteq X$, and $B \subseteq Y$, then $f:(X,A) \to (Y,B)$ means that $f:X \to Y$ is a function such that $f(A) \subseteq B$.

If $f:X \to Y$, we define $f^\#:C^p(Y) \to C^p(X)$ by

$$(f^\# \phi)(x_0,x_1,\ldots,x_p) = \phi(f(x_0),f(x_1),\ldots,f(x_p)).$$

Note that:
(1) $f^\#:C^p(Y) \to C^p(X)$ is a homomorphism.
(2) $f^\# \bar{\delta} = \bar{\delta} f^\#$.
(3) If $f:(X,A) \to (Y,B)$ is continuous, then $f^\# C^p(Y,B) \subseteq C^p(X,A)$, $f^\# Z^p(Y,B) \subseteq Z^p(X,A)$, and $f^\# B^p(Y,B) \subseteq B^p(X,A)$.

Hence there is an induced homomorphism $f^*:H^p(Y,B) \to H^p(X,A)$.

A.1   Theorem (Axiom 1C)   If $f:(X,A) \to (X,A)$ is the identity map, then $f^*:H^p(X,A) \to H^p(X,A)$ is the identity homomorphism.

A.2   Theorem (Axiom 2C)   If $(X,A) \xrightarrow{f} (Y,B) \xrightarrow{g} (T,C)$ and f and g are continuous, then $(gf)^* = f^* g^*$.

Observe that $H^p(\square) = 0$ for all p; and $H^0(\text{point}) = G$ and $H^p(\text{point}) = 0$ if $p > 0$. Let $E^n = \{x : |x| \le 1\}$ denote the closed n-cell in euclidean n-space, $S^{n-1} = \{x \in E^n : |x| = 1\}$ the $n-1$ sphere, and let $S^{-1} = \square$. Then $H^0(E^n) = G$ and $H^p(E^n) = 0$ if $p > 0$, and $H^0(S^n) = H^n(S^n) = G$ and $H^p(S^n) = 0$ otherwise.

If X is a topological space and $B \subseteq A \subseteq X$, then the following diagram indicates the construction of a homomorphism $\delta : H^p(A,B) \to H^{p+1}(X,A)$:

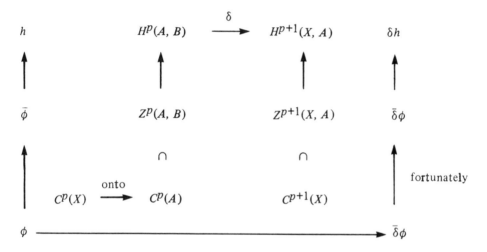

Let X and X' be spaces, $B \subseteq A \subseteq X$, $B' \subseteq A' \subseteq X'$, and $f : (X,A,B) \to (X',A',B')$ continuous. Let $f_3 : (A,B) \to (A',B')$ and $f_1 : (X,A) \to (X',A')$ have the same rule of correspondence as f.

A.3 Theorem (Axiom 3C) The following diagram commutes:

$$H^p(A,B) \stackrel{\delta}{\to} H^{p+1}(X,A)$$
$$\uparrow f_3^* \qquad\qquad \uparrow f_1^*$$
$$H^p(A',B') \underset{\delta}{\to} H^{p+1}(X',A')$$

Let $j : (X,B) \hookrightarrow (X,A)$ and $i : (A,B) \hookrightarrow (X,B)$ be inclusions, where $B \subseteq A \subseteq X$.

A.4 Theorem (Axiom 4C)   The sequence

$$H^0(X,A) \xrightarrow{j^*} H^0(X,B) \xrightarrow{i^*} H^0(A,B)$$

$$\xrightarrow{\delta}$$

$$H^1(X,A) \xrightarrow{j^*} H^1(X,B) \xrightarrow{i^*} H^1(A,B)$$

$$\xrightarrow{\delta}$$

$$H^2(X,A) \xrightarrow{j^*}$$

is exact in the sense that $j^*:H^0(X,A) \to H^0(X,B)$ is an injective isomorphism and the image of each homomorphism is the kernel of the next one.

A.5 Theorem   If X and Y are homeomorphic spaces, then $H^*(X)$ is isomorphic to $H^*(Y)$.

A.6 Theorem.   If X is a connected space, then $H^0(X)$ is isomorphic to G.

A.7 Theorem.   If X is a space and A is a retract of X, $X \xrightarrow{r} A \xhookrightarrow{i} X$, then r^* is injective, i^* is surjective, and $H^*(X)$ is isomorphic to $H^*(A) \oplus H^*(H,A)$.

If $\pi:T \times (X,A) \to (Y,B)$ is continuous and $t \in T$, we define $\hat{t}:(X,A) \to (Y,B)$ by $\hat{t}(x) = \pi(t,x)$.

A.8 Theorem.   Let X be compact, $h \in H^p(Y,B)$, and let $t \in T$. Then there exists an open set M in T with $t \in M$ such that $\hat{s}^*(h) = \hat{t}^*(h$ for each $s \in M$. Thus, if T is connected, then $\hat{s}^* = \hat{t}^*$ for each t, $s \in T$.

A.9 Generalized Homotopy Theorem (Axiom 5C).   Let T be a connected space, let X be a compact space, and let $F:(X \times T, A \times T) \to (Y,B)$ be a continuous function. If f and g are continuous functions from (X,A) to (Y,B) and there exist $s,t \in T$ such that $F(x,s) = f(x)$ and $F(x,t) = g(x)$ for all $x \in X$, then $f^* = g^*$.

Observe that in the hypothesis of A.9, if $T = [0,1]$, then f and g are homotopic.

If X is a compact Hausdorff space and $A \subseteq X$, then A is a *deformation retract* of X provided there is a retraction $r: X \to A$ such that $ir: X \to X$ is homotopic to 1_X (the identity map on X), where $i: A \to X$ is inclusion. Note that, in this case, $H^*(A) \approx H^*(X)$.

A.10   Weak Excision Axiom (Axiom 6C).   Let U be an open subset of a space X such that $\bar{U} \subseteq A^\circ \subseteq X$. If $k: (X\backslash U, A\backslash U) \to (X,A)$ is inclusion, then $k^* H^p(X,A) \to H^p(X\backslash U, A\backslash U)$ is an isomorphism for each nonnegative integer p.

A.11   Dimension Axiom (Axiom 7C).   If card $X = 1$, then $H^0(X) = G$ and $H^p(X) = 0$ for $p > 0$.

For a space X and $A \subseteq X$, let $f: (X,A) \to (0,0)$, $g: X \to 0$, and let $h: A \to 0$. Define $\tilde{H}^0(X,A) = H^0(H,A)/Im\ f^*$, $\tilde{H}^0(X) = H^0(X)/Im\ g^*$, and $\tilde{H}^0(A) = H^0(A)/Im\ h^*$. The groups $\tilde{H}^0(X,A)$, $\tilde{H}^0(X)$, and $\tilde{H}^0(A)$ are called the *reduced cohomology groups* in dimension 0. There are induced homomorphisms $\tilde{j}$, $\tilde{i}$, and $\tilde{\delta}$ in A.4 so that the sequence there remains exact with reduced groups in the top row.

A.12   Theorem.   If X is a space and $g: X \to 0$, then these are equivalent:
(a) X is connected.
(b) g^* is an isomorphism.
(c) $\tilde{H}^0(X) = 0$.

We will hereafter use $H^0(X,A)$, $H^0(X)$, $H^0(A)$,...to denote $\tilde{H}^0(X,A)$, $\tilde{H}^0(X)$, $\tilde{H}^0(A)$,..., respectively.

A.13 Map Excision Theorem. Let (X,A) and (Y,B) be compact Hausdorff pairs, and let $f: (X,A) \to (X,B)$ be continuous such that f takes $X \backslash A$ homeomorphically onto $Y \backslash B$. Then $f^*: H^*(Y,B) \to H^*(X,A)$ is an isomorphism.

We remark that A.13 holds in X and Y are fully normal spaces and f is a closed map.

A.14 Strong Excision Theorem. Let X be a compact Hausdorff space and A and B closed subsets of X such that $X = A \cup B$, and let $j: (B, A \cap B) \hookrightarrow (X,A)$. Then $j^*: H^*(X,A) \to H^*(B, A \cap B)$ is an isomorphism.

If X is a space, $A \subseteq X$, and $h \in H^p(X)$, then we denote by $h|A$ the image of h under the natural homomorphism $i^*: H^p(X) \to H^p(A)$ induced by inclusion $i: A \hookrightarrow X$. We say that $k \in H^p(A)$ is *extendable* to X provided that $k \in \text{Im } i^*$.

A.15 Reduction Theorem. Let X be a compact Hausdorff space, A, X_0 closed subsets of X, and let $h \in H^p(X, X_0)$ be such that $h|(A, A \cap X_0) = 0$. Then there exists an open set U in X such that $A \subseteq U$ and $h|(\bar{U}, \bar{U} \cap X_0) = 0$.

Example. As an illustration of the reduction theorem, let X be a space consisting of a sequence C_n of tangent circles with *diam* $C_n \to 0$ clustering to a point p. Let $h \in H^1(X)$ such that $h|\{p\} = 0$. Then there exists $m \in \mathbf{N}$ such that $h|C_i = 0$ for all $i \geq m$.

A.16 Extension Theorem. Let X be a compact Hausdorff space, A, X_0 closed subsets of X, and let $h \in H^p(A, A \cap X_0)$. Then there exists an open set U in X with $A \subseteq U$ and there exists $h_0 \in H^p(\bar{U}, \bar{U} \cap X_0)$ such that $h_0|(A, A \cap X_0) = h$.

Example. As an illustration of the extension theorem, let X be a compact Hausdorff space, $\mathscr{F}$ a filter base of closed subsets of X, and let $A = \bigcap \mathcal{F}$. *If $H^n(F) = 0$ for some $n \in \mathbf{N}$ and some $F \in \mathcal{F}$, then $H^n(A) = 0$.*

The extension and reduction theorems are together equivalent to the continuity axiom: Let (X_α, A_α) be a projective system of compact pairs with $(X,A) = \varprojlim (X_\alpha, A_\alpha)$. Then, in a natural way, $H^*(X,A)$ is isomorphic to $\varprojlim H^*(X_\alpha, A_\alpha)$.

A.17 Mayer-Vietoris Exact Sequence. Let A, B, and C be closed subsets of a compact Hausdorff space X with $X = A \cup B$, let $j_1:(A, A \cap C) \hookrightarrow (X,C), j_2:(B, B \cap C) \hookrightarrow (X,C), i_1:(A \cap B, A \cap B \cap C) \hookrightarrow (A, A \cap C)$, and $i_2:(A \cap B, A \cap B \cap C) \hookrightarrow (B, B \cap C)$. Then the following sequence is exact:

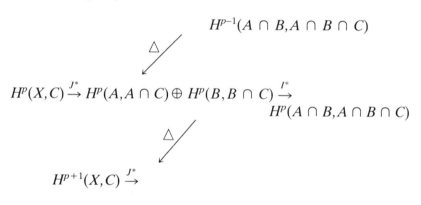

$$H^{p-1}(A \cap B, A \cap B \cap C)$$

$$H^p(X,C) \xrightarrow{J^*} H^p(A, A \cap C) \oplus H^p(B, B \cap C) \xrightarrow{I^*}$$
$$H^p(A \cap B, A \cap B \cap C)$$

$$H^{p+1}(X,C) \xrightarrow{J^*}$$

where $J^*(h) = (j_1^* h, j_2^* h)$ and $I^*(h_1, h_2) = i_1^* h_1 - i_2^* h_2$.

A.18 Existence of Floors. Let X be a compact Hausdorff space, A a closed subset of X, and let $h \in H^p(X,A)$, $h \neq 0$. Then there exists a closed subset F of X such that $h|(F, F \cap A) \neq 0$ but $h|(F', F' \cap A) \neq 0$ if F' is a proper closed subset of F.

A set such as F in A.18 is called a *floor* for h. We remark that an n-manifold M is a floor for each nonzero $h \in H^n(M)$.

A.19 Existence of Roofs. Let X be a compact Hausdorff space,

A a closed subset of X, and let $h \in H^n(A)$ such that h cannot be extended to $H^n(X)$, i.e., $h_0|A = h$ for no $h_0 \in H^n(X)$. Then there exists a closed subset R of X such that h is not extendable to $H^n(R \cup A)$ but h is extendable to $H^n(R_0 \cup A)$ for any closed proper subset R_0 of R.

A set such as R in A.19 is called a *roof* for h. We remark that the n-cell B^n is a roof for each nonzero element in $H^{n-1}(S^{n-1})$. It follows from A.17 that roofs and floors are connected.

We summarize some of the basic facts concerning cohomological dimension. The defintions are in Hurewicz and Wallmann [1941] and are due to Alexandroff. An exposition and development appears in Cohen [1954].

For a compact Hausdorff space X, $cd\, X = -1$ if and only if $X = \square$, and if $X \neq \square$, $cd\, X \leq n$ if and only if $i^*:H^n(X) \to H^n(A)$ is surjective for each closed subset A of X (where $i: A \hookrightarrow X$). For a locally compact Hausdorff space, $cd\, X \leq n$ provided $cd\, K \leq n$ for each compact subset K of X.

A.20 Theorem. If A is a closed subset of a locally compact Hausdorff space X and $cd\, X \leq n$, then $cd\, A \leq n$.

A.21 Sum Theorem. If X is a locally compact Hausdorff space such that $X = \bigcup \{C_i : i \in \mathbf{N}\}$ with each C_i closed, and if $cd\, C_i \leq n$ for each i, then $cd\, X \leq n$.

A.22 Product Theorem. Let X be a compact Hausdorff space. Then $cd\, X = n$ if and only if $cd(X \times [0,1]) = n + 1$.

A.23 Theorem. If X is a compact Hausdorff space, then $cd\, X \leq ind\, X$, where $ind\, X$ denotes the small inductive dimension of X. The converse holds if X is metrizable and has finite codimension.

In A.24 and A.25, (X,A) is a compact Hausdorff pair, Z is a continuum, and $m: Z \times X \to X$ is continuous. For $p \in Z$, let

$f_p : A \to ZA$ be defined by $F_p(x) = m(p,x) = px$. We call ZA the
sweep-out set of A.

A.24 Theorem. If $p,q \in Z$ and $h \in H^{n-1}(qA), h \neq 0$, satisfy
$h|pA \cap qA = 0$ and $f_q^* h \neq 0$, then $cd\ ZA \nleq n - 1$.

   Proof: Suppose that $cd\ ZA \leq n - 1$, and consider the
diagram

$$H^{n-1}(pA \cup qA) \xrightarrow{J^*} H^{n-1}(pA) \oplus H^{n-1}(qA) \xrightarrow{J^*} H^{n-1}(pA \cap qA)$$

$$\uparrow k^*$$

$$H^{n-1}(ZA)$$

where the top row is a portion of the Mayer-Vietoris sequence
A.17, and k^* is induced by injection. Let $(0,h) \in H^{n-1}(pA) \oplus$
$H^{n-1}(qA)$ with $h \neq 0$. Then $I^*(0,h) = 0$, so by exactness, there
exists $h_1 \in H^{n-1}(pA \cup qA)$ such that $J^* h_1 = (0,h)$. Since $cd\ ZA \leq$
$n - 1$, k^* is surjective, and hence there exists $h_2 \in H^{n-1}(ZA)$ such
that $k^* h_2 = h_1$. Thus, $h_2 | pA = 0$ and the diagram commutes, where
the unlisted maps are induced by inclusion, and $\hat{f}_p$ is the
corestriction of f_p. Thus $f_p^* = f_q^* = 0$, and this contradiction yields
the result. ∎

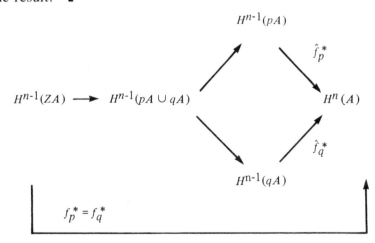

A.25   Theorem.   Let $A \subseteq ZA$, $H^n(X) = 0$, and $cd\, X \leq n$. Let $h \in H^{n-1}(A)$, $h \neq 0$, let R be a roof for h, and suppose that $H^{n-1}(ZA) = 0$. Then $R \subseteq ZA$ and in particular $cd\, ZA \nleq n - 1$.

Proof: Suppose that $R \nsubseteq ZA$. Then $R \cap ZA$ is a closed proper subset of R. Note that $(R \cup A) \cap ZA = A \cup (R \cap ZA)$, and consider the Mayer-Vietoris sequence

$$H^{n-1}(R \cup ZA) \overset{J^*}{\to} H^{n-1}(R \cup A) \oplus H^{n-1}(ZA) \overset{I^*}{\to} H^{n-1}(A \cup (R \cap ZA))$$

$$H^n(R \cup ZA) \to$$

Let h be extended to $h_1 \in H^{n-1}(A \cup (R \cap ZA))$. Since $H^n(X) = 0$ and $cd\, X \leq n$, it follows that $H^n(R \cup ZA) = 0$, so $\triangle(h_1) = 0$. By exactness, there exists $h_2 \in H^{n-1}(R \cup A) \oplus H^{n-1}(ZA)$ with $I^* h_2 = h_1$. Since $H^{n-1}(ZA) = 0$, h_2 is of the form $(\alpha, 0)$ and h is thus extended to $\alpha \in H^{n-1}(R \cup A)$. This contradiction completes the proof.   ∎

A space X is said to be *acyclic* provided $H^*(X) = 0$. If $\leq$ is an order relation on X and $A \subseteq X$, then $\downarrow A = \{x \in X : x \leq y \text{ for some } y \in A\}$.

The following result dealing with acyclicity has numerous applications in topological semigroups.

A.26   Theorem.   Let $\leq$ be a closed quasi-order on a compact Hausdorff space X such that $\downarrow A$ is connected for each closed subset A of X and $H^*(\downarrow p) = 0$ for each $p \in X$. Then $H^*(\downarrow A) = 0$ for each closed subset A of X.

Proof: Let A be a closed subset of X and let $n \in \mathbf{N}$. Suppose that $H^m(\downarrow A) = 0$ for all $m < n$, and that $H^n(\downarrow A) \neq 0$. Let $h \in H^n(\downarrow A)$ such that $h \neq 0$. Since $\leq$ is closed, there exists a closed set

F such that $h| \downarrow F \neq 0$ but $h| \downarrow B = 0$ if B is a proper closed subset of F. If $F = \{p\}$ for some p, then $h| \downarrow p = 0$ is a contradiction. Thus F is not a point, and hence there exist closed proper subsets M and N of F with $F = M \cup N$. Note that $\downarrow F = \downarrow M \cup \downarrow N$. Consider the Mayer-Vietoris sequence

$$H^{n-1}(\downarrow M \cap \downarrow N)$$

$$H^n(\downarrow F) \underset{J^*}{\rightarrow} H^n(\downarrow M) \oplus H^n(\downarrow N) \rightarrow$$

Let $h_1 = h| \downarrow F \neq 0$. Then $h_1| \downarrow N = 0 = h_1| \downarrow M$, so that $J^* h_1 = 0$. By exactness, there exists $h_2 \in H^{n-1}(\downarrow M \cap \downarrow N) = 0$ with $\triangle h_2 = h_1$, so that $h_1 = 0$. This contradiction completes the proof. ∎

A.27 Generalized Homotopy Lemma. Let (X,A) and (Y,B) be compact Hausdorff pairs, T a space, and let $m: T \times (X,A) \rightarrow (Y,B)$ be an action of T on (X,A). Let $h \in H^n(Y,B)$ and $t_0 \in T$. Then there exists an open set U containing t_0 such that for each $t \in U$, the induced homomorphism $\hat{t}^*:H^n(Y,B) \rightarrow H^n(X,A)$ satisfies $\hat{t}^*(h) = \hat{t}_0^*(h)$. Moreover, if T is connected, then $\hat{t}_1^* = \hat{t}_2^*$ for each $t_1, t_2 \in T$.

The following result appears in Cohen and Koch [1965].

A.28 Theorem. Let A be a closed subset of a compact Hausdorff space X. If $cd\, X \leq n$, then $cd(X/A) \leq n$.

Proof: Let $\phi: X \rightarrow X/A$ be the natural map, and let B be a closed subset of X/A. Denote $0 = \phi(A)$ and consider two cases.
    Case 1. Suppose that $A \subseteq \phi^{-1}(B)$. Let $\theta:(X, \phi^{-1}(B)) \rightarrow (X/A, B)$ be determined by ϕ. Then θ is a closed map, and $\theta(X \setminus \phi^{-1}(B))$ is homeomorphic to $(X/A) \setminus B$. By the map excision theorem, θ^* is an isomorphism. Now $H^{n+1}(X, \phi^{-1}(B)) = 0$ so that $H^{n+1}(X/A, B) = 0$, and $cd(X/A) \leq n$ in this case.

Case 2. Suppose that $0 \notin B$. We have in this case $\phi^{-1}(B) \cap A = \square$. Consider the diagram:

Now $H^{n+1}(X/A, B \cup 0) \approx H^{n+1}(X, \phi^{-1}(B) \cup A) = 0$; $H^{n+1}(X/A) \approx H^{n+1}(X, A) = 0$. Let $h \in H^{n+1}(X/A, B)$, then $i^*h = 0$, so there exists $h_1 \in H^n(B)$ such that $\delta h_1 = h$. Now m^* is an isomorphism. Let $h_2 = m^{*-1}(h_1)$. Then $h = \delta m^*(h_2) = k^*(j^*h_2) = k^*(0) = 0$, and so $H^{n+1}(X/A, B) = 0$. This completes the proof. ∎

We conclude this appendix with the Vietoris mapping theorem. A proof appears in Spanier [1966] and a generalization of the result appears in Lawson [1969b].

A.29   The Vietoris-Begel Mapping Theorem.   Let X and Y be paracompact Hausdorff spaces and let $f:X \to Y$ be a continuous map of X onto Y. Suppose that for some $n \geq 0$, $H^q(f^{-1}(y)) = 0$ for all $y \in Y$ and all $q < n$. Then $f^*:H^q(Y) \to H^q(X)$ is an isomorphism for $q < n$ and a monomorphism for $q = n$.

APPENDIX B
Topological Spaces

In this appendix we treat some of the topological concepts needed in the text.

If X is a compact Hausdorff space, let $C(X)$ denote the family of all closed subsets of X. For open sets U and V in X let $K(U,V) = \{T \in C(X): T \subseteq U$ and $T \cap V \neq \square\}$. Then $\{K(U,V): U$ and V open in $X\}$ is a subbasis for a topology on $C(X)$ called the *Vietoris topology*.

To see that the Vietoris topology on $C(X)$ is Hausdorff let A and B be distinct elements of $C(X)$. We can assume that $B \backslash A \neq \square$, and let $p \in B \backslash A$. Let U and V be disjoint open sets in X such that $A \subseteq U$ and $p \in V$. Then $A \in K(U,X)$ and $B \in K(X,V)$; and $K(U,X) \cap K(X,V) = \square$. It follows that $C(X)$ is Hausdorff.

Recall that if A_α is a net of subsets of X, then we define *lim sup* $A_\alpha = \{y \in X:$ if $y \in U$ (open), then $U \cap A_\alpha \neq^f \square\}$ and *lim inf* $A_\alpha = \{y \in X:$ if $y \in U$ (open), then $U \cap A_\alpha \neq^e \square\}$. Observe that *lim inf* $A_\alpha \subseteq$ *lim sup* A_α, and if X is a compact Hausdorff space, then *lim sup* $A_\alpha \neq \square$ for any net A_α of nonempty closed subsets of X. Observe also, in this case, that *lim sup* A_α and *lim inf* A_α are closed. If *lim inf* $A_\alpha =$ *lim sup* A_α, then we define *lim* $A_\alpha =$ *lim sup* $A_\alpha =$ *lim inf* A_α.

If A_α in $C(X)$ and $A =$ *lim* A_α, then for each open set U in X such that $A \subseteq U$, we have $A_\alpha \subseteq^e U$. To see this, suppose that $A_\alpha \cap (X \backslash U) \neq^f \square$. Let $a_\alpha \in A_\alpha \cap (X \backslash U)$ for these α's. Then a_α clusters to some $a \in$ *lim sup* $A_\alpha = A$ and $a \notin U$. This contradiction shows that $A_\alpha \subseteq^e U$.

If $\{A_\alpha : \alpha \in D\}$ in a net of subsets of a space X, it is useful to observe that $\lim \sup A_\alpha = \bigcap_{\alpha \in D} \bigcup_{\alpha \leq \beta} A_\beta$.

B.1   Lemma   Let T_α be a net in $C(X)$. Then $T = \lim T_\alpha$ if and only if $T_\alpha \to T$ in the Vietoris topology on $C(X)$.

Proof: Suppose first that $T = \lim T_\alpha$. Let U and V be open in X and let $T \in K(U,V)$. Then $T \subseteq U$ and $T \cap V \neq \square$. Thus $T_\alpha \subseteq^e U$ and $T_\alpha \cap V \neq^e \square$, so that $T_\alpha \in^e K(U,V)$ and $T_\alpha \to T$.

Suppose, on the other hand, that $T_\alpha \to T$. Let $x \in T$ and let V be an open set such that $x \in V$. Then $T \in K(X,V)$, $T_\alpha \in^e K(X,V)$ and $T_\alpha \cap V \neq^e \square$. Thus $x \in \lim \inf T_\alpha$ and $T \subseteq \lim \inf T_\alpha$. Fix $y \in X \backslash T$ and let P and Q be disjoint open sets with $y \in P$ and $T \subseteq Q$. Now $T \in K(Q,X)$, so that $T_\alpha \in^e K(Q,X)$ and $T_\alpha \subseteq^e Q$. In particular, $T_\alpha \subseteq^e X \backslash P$, and hence $y \in X \backslash \lim \sup T_\alpha$. It follows that $\lim T_\alpha = \lim \sup T_\alpha \subseteq T$, and we obtain that $T = \lim T_\alpha$. ∎

B.2   Theorem   The space $C(X)$ is a compact Hausdorff space.

Proof: We have already seen that $C(X)$ is Hausdorff. To see that $C(X)$ is compact, let T_α be a universal net in $C(X)$ and let $T = \lim \sup T_\alpha$. Observe that for each open subset V of X, $T_\alpha \cap V \neq^f \square$ if and only if $T_\alpha \cap V \neq^e \square$, since T_α is universal. Thus $T = \lim \sup T_\alpha = \lim \inf T_\alpha = \lim T_\alpha$, and from B.1, $T_\alpha \to T$, and we conclude that $C(X)$ is compact. ∎

Observe that if X is a compact Hausdorff space, then the map $x \mapsto \{x\}$ is an embedding (homeomorphism into) of X into $C(X)$.

We present some topological results which are useful in the chapter of the text on irreducible semigroups.

If X is a topological space, we let $\mathcal{U}(X) = \{U : U \text{ is open in } X \times X \text{ and } \triangle(X) \subseteq U\}$. Recall that $\triangle(X)$ denotes the diagonal of $X \times X$, i.e., $\triangle(X) = \{(x,x) : x \in X\}$. For $U \in \mathcal{U}(X)$, $A \subseteq X$ and $a,b \in A$, a U-*chain* from a to b in A is a finite subset $\{x_1, \ldots, x_n\}$ of A such that $a = x_1, x_n = b$, and $(x_i, x_{i+1}) \in U$ for $i = 1, 2, \ldots, n-1$. Recall that A is U-*connected* if each pair of points in A can be joined by a U-chain in A.

For $U, V \in \mathcal{U}(X)$, $U \circ V = \{(a,b) \in X \times X : (a,x) \in U$ and (x,b) $\in V$ for some $x \in X\}$, $U^{-1} = \{(b,a):(a,b) \in U\}$, and U is symmetric provided $U = U^{-1}$. If $U \in \mathcal{U}(X)$, then there exists $V \in \mathcal{U}(X)$ such that V is symmetric and $V \subseteq U$. Let $V = U \cap U^{-1}$.

Now for $U \in \mathcal{U}(X)$ and $x \in X$, let $U[x] = \{y \in X:(x,y) \in U\}$, and for $A \subseteq X$, let $U[A] = \cup\{U[x]:x \in A\}$.

If X is a T_1-space, then for each $a \in X$, $\{U[a]:U \in \mathcal{U}(X)\}$ is an open basis at a. To see this, let W be an open set with $a \in W$, and let $U = (W \times W) \cup ((X \setminus \{a\}) \times X)$. Then $\triangle(X) \subseteq U \subseteq X \times X$, so that $U \in \mathcal{U}(X)$, and $a \in U[a] \subseteq W$. On the other hand, let $U \in \mathcal{U}(X)$, let $a \in X$, and let $b \in U[a]$. Then $(a,b) \in U$. Since U is open in $X \times X$, there exist open sets V_1 and V_2 in X such that $(a,b) \in V_1 \times V_2 \subseteq U$. We obtain that $b \in V_2 \subseteq U[a]$.

Let $x \in X$. We will show that there is an open set W_x containing x and a symmetric neighborhood V_x of $\triangle(X)$ such that for each $y \in W_x$, $V_x[y] \times V_x[y] \subseteq U$. To see this, let T_x be an open set containing x such that $T_x \times T_x \subseteq U$ and let W_x be an open subset of X such that $x \in W_x \subseteq \overline{W}_x \subseteq T_x$. Then, for $p \in X \setminus \overline{W}_x$, let Q_p be an open set containing p such that $Q_p \cap \overline{W}_x = \square$ and $Q_p \times Q_p \subseteq U$. Thus $T_x \cup \{Q_p:p \in X \setminus \overline{W}_x\}$ is an open cover of X. Let $T_x, Q_1, \ldots, Q_n$ be a finite subcover and let $V_x = (T_x \times T_x) \cup \cup_{j=1}^n(Q_j \times Q_j)$. Then V_x is symmetric and if $y \in W_x$, then $V_x[y] = T_x$ and hence $V_x[y] \times V_x[y] \subseteq U$.

If X is a compact Hausdorff space and $U \in \mathcal{U}(X)$, then there exists $V \in \mathcal{U}(X)$ such that V is symmetric and $V \circ V \subseteq U$. To see this, for $x \in X$ let W_x and V_x be as in the preceding paragraph. Now $\{W_x:x \in X\}$ covers X. Let $W_1, \ldots, W_m$ be a finite subcover and let $V_1, \ldots, V_m$ be the corresponding symmetric neighborhoods of $\triangle(X)$. Let $V = \cap_{j=1}^m V_j$. Then V is a symmetric neighborhood of $\triangle(X)$. Now let $t \in X$. Then $t \in W_k$ for some $1 \leq k \leq m$ and $V_k[t] \times V_k[t] \subseteq U$. It follows that $V[t] \times V[t] \subseteq U$ and since V is symmetric, we have $V \circ V = \cup_{t \in X}(V[t] \times V[t]) \subseteq U$.

B.3   Lemma   Let X be a compact Hausdorff space $(T_\alpha, \alpha \in D)$ a net of closed subsets of X, and let $T = \lim T_\alpha$. If for each $U \in \mathcal{U}(X)$, there exists $\alpha_U \in D$ such that T_α is U-connected whenever $\alpha_U \leq \alpha$ in D, then T is connected.

Proof: Suppose that T is not connected. Then $T = A \cup B$, where A and B are disjoint, nonempty, and compact. Let U and V be elements of $\mathcal{U}(X)$ such that $U[A] \cap V[B] = \square$. To see that U and V exist, let W_1 and W_2 be disjoint open sets containing A and B, respectively, and let $U = (W_1 \times W_1) \cup (X \backslash A) \times X$ and $V = W_2 \times W_2 \cup (X \backslash B) \times X$. Now let $W \in \mathcal{U}(X)$ be symmetric such that $W \circ W \circ W \subseteq U \cap V$. Then, since $\lim T_\alpha = T \subseteq W[T] = W[A] \cup W[B]$, $T_\alpha \subseteq^e W[A] \cup W[B]$ and $T_\alpha \cap W[A] \neq^e \square \neq^e T_\alpha \cap W[B]$. Let $\beta \in D$ be such that these conditions hold and such that T_α is W-connected when $\beta \leq \alpha$ in D. Let $a \in T_\beta \cap W[A]$ and $b \in T_\beta \cap W[B]$. Since T_β is W-connected, there exists a W-chain $x_0, x_1, \ldots, x_n$ in T_β such that $x_0 = a$ and $x_n = b$. Fix i, so that $i + 1 = \min\{j : x_j \in W[B]\}$. Then $x_0, \ldots, x_i \in W[A]$ and $x_{i+1} \in W[B]$. There exist $a_1 \in A$ and $b_1 \in B$ such that $(a_1, x_i) \in W$ and $(b_1, x_{i+1}) \in W$. Since $(x_i, x_{i+1}) \in W$, we have $(a_1, b_1) = (a_1, x_i) \circ (x_i, x_{i+1}) \circ (x_{i+1}, b_1) \in W \circ W \circ W \subseteq U \cap V$, so that $b_1 \in U[A] \cap V[B]$. This contradicts that $U[A] \cap V[B] = \square$. ∎

We turn our attention to material that are needed in the text on topological semilattices.

A *partially ordered space* (*pospace*) is a pair $(X, \leq)$ such that X is a Hausdorff space and $\leq$ is a closed partial order on X, i.e., $\leq$ is a closed subset of $X \times X$. We will say that X is a pospace and use $\leq$ to denote the closed partial order on X. For $x \in X$, we write $\uparrow x = \{a \in X : x \leq a\}$ and $\downarrow x = \{b \in X : b \leq x\}$. For $A \subseteq X$, we write $\uparrow A = \cup\{\uparrow x : x \in A\}$ and $\downarrow A = \cup\}\{\downarrow x : x \in A\}$.

Observe that if X is a compact pospace and A is a closed subset of X, then $\uparrow A$ and $\downarrow A$ are closed, and in particular, $\uparrow x$ and $\downarrow x$ are closed for each $x \in X$.

If X is a pospace and $A \subseteq X$, we write $a = \sup A [\inf A]$ provided $x \leq a[a \leq x]$ for all $x \in A$ and if $x \leq b[b \leq x]$ for all $x \in A$, then $a \leq b[b \leq a]$. Observe that if $\sup A[\inf A]$ exists, then it is unique, since $\leq$ is antisymmetric.

A subset D of a pospace X is said to be *up-directed* [*down-directed*] if for each $a, b \in D$, there exists $c \in D$ such that $a \leq c$ and $b \leq c[c \leq a$ and $c \leq b]$. Observe that if D is an up-directed or down-directed subset of a pospace, then D is a net. We write $D \to x$ to denote that D converges to x.

B.4 **Theorem** If X is a compact pospace and D is an up-directed [down-directed] subset of X, then $sup\ D[inf\ D]$ exists, and $D \to sup\ D[D \to inf\ D]$.

Proof: Let a be a cluster point of D. Suppose that $x \not\leq a$ for some $x \in D$. Now $\uparrow x$ is closed, $a \notin \uparrow x$, and $D \xrightarrow{f} a$, so that $D \cap (X \backslash \uparrow x) \neq \square$. Let $b \in D \cap (X \backslash \uparrow x)$. Let $c \in D$ such that $b \leq c$ and $x \leq c$, and let $d \in D$ such that $c \leq d$ and $d \in X \backslash \uparrow x$. Since $x \leq c \leq d$, we have $x \leq d$, and hence $d \in \uparrow x$. This contradiction proves that $x \leq a$ for all $x \in D$.

Now if $x \leq b$ for all $x \in D$ and $a \not\leq b$, then $a \in X \backslash \downarrow b$ and $y \in X \backslash \downarrow b$ for some $y \in D$. We have $y \not\leq b$. This contradiction proves that $a \leq b$, $a = sup\ D$, and $D \to a$ ($sup\ D$ is unique). ∎

B.5 **Lemma** Let X be a compact pospace and $A = \downarrow A$ and $B = \uparrow B$ closed subsets of X such that $A \cap B = \square$. Then there exists open set U and V such that $U = \downarrow U$, $V = \uparrow V$, $A \subseteq U$, $B \subseteq V$, and $U \cap V = \square$.

Proof: Since X is a normal space, there exist open sets P and Q such that $A \subseteq P$, $B \subseteq Q$, and $P \cap Q = \square$. Let $U = X \backslash \uparrow (X \backslash P)$ and let $V = X \backslash \downarrow (X \backslash Q)$. ∎

A subset C of a pospace X is said to be *order convex* or simply *convex* if $a,b \in C$ and $a \leq x \leq b$ implies $x \in C$. We say that X is *locally order convex* or simply *locally convex* if each point of X has a neighborhood base of convex sets. Observe that if $A \subseteq X$ and $A = \downarrow A$ or $A = \uparrow A$, then A is convex. Also notice that if A and B are convex, then $A \cap B$ is convex.

The following important result appears in Nachbin [1965].

B.6 **Theorem** Each compact pospace is locally convex.

Proof: Let X be a compact pospace, let $x \in X$, and let P be an open set with $x \in P$. For each $y \in X \backslash P$ either $y \not\leq x$ or $x \not\leq y$, so that either $\uparrow y \cap \downarrow x = \square$ or $\downarrow y \cap \uparrow x = \square$. In either case, from B.5, there are open convex sets U_y and V_y such that $x \in U_y$, $y \in V_y$, and $U_y \cap V_y = \square$. Now $X \backslash P$ is compact, so a finite number of the V_y's cover $X \backslash P$. Let $V_1, V_1, \ldots, V_n$ cover $X \backslash P$ and let $U_1, U_2, \ldots, U_n$ denote the corresponding U_y's. Set $U = U_1 \cap U_2 \cap \cdots \cap U_n$ and $V = V_1 \cup V_2 \cup \cdots \cup V_n$. Then $x \in U \subseteq P$, since $U \cap V = \square$ and $X \backslash P \subseteq V$. Moreover, U is convex. ∎

For a subset W of a space X we let $\partial W = \overline{W} \cap \overline{(X \backslash W)}$ (the boundary of W in X).

Recall that a *chain* in a pospace X is a totally ordered subset of X.

A subset W of a pospace X is said to *contain no local minimum* if for each $x \in W$ and each open set V such that $x \in V \subseteq W$, there exists $y \in V$ such that $y < x (y \leq x$ and $y \neq x)$.

B.7 Lemma Let X be a compact pospace, W an open subset of X which contains no local minimum, and let C be a component of W. then $\overline{C} \cap \partial W \neq \square$.

Proof: Let V be an open subset of W. We will show that $\partial V \neq \square$. Let M be a maximal chain in $\overline{V}$. Then M is compact and hence has a minimal element $m \in \overline{V}$. If $m \in V$, then M can be extended, contrary to maximality. Thus $m \in \partial V$ and $\partial V \neq \square$.

Suppose that $\overline{C} \cap \partial W = \square$. Then there is an open and closed set N such that $C \subseteq N \subseteq W$. Hence N is an open subset of W with $\partial N = \square$. This contradiction proves the result. ∎

The following result appears in Koch [1959]. It has a number of important consequences in the theory of arc chains in compact semilattices.

B.8 Koch's Arc Theorem Let X be a compact pospace and W an open subset of X which contains no local minimum. Then for each $a \in W$, there exists a compact connected chain C such that $C \cap \partial W \neq \square$ and $a = sup\ C$.

Proof: Let $a \in W$. Then $\overline{W} \cap \downarrow a$ is a compact pospace and contains the relatively open set $W \cap \downarrow a$ which contains no local minimum. Thus we may assume that $X = \downarrow a$ and that W is open in X with $a \in W \subseteq \overline{W} = X$. Let $\mathscr{C} = \{C : C$ is a closed chain in X, $a \in C$, and $C \cap \partial W \neq \square\}$. Now $\partial W \neq \square$ from B.7, and hence if $z \in \partial W$, then $\{a, z\} \in \mathscr{C}$. Thus $\mathscr{C} \neq \square$.

We claim that $\mathscr{C}$ is closed in $C(X)$. We show that $C(X) \backslash \mathscr{C}$ is open. For this purpose, let $A \in C(X) \backslash \mathscr{C}$. If A is not a chain, then there are elements x and y in A with $x \not\leq y$ and $y \not\leq x$. Thus $\downarrow x \cap \uparrow y = \square$ and $\downarrow y \cap \uparrow x = \square$. According to B.5, there are open sets U_1, U_2, V_1, V_2 such that $x \in U_1 = \downarrow U_1, y \in V_1 = \uparrow V_1, U_1 \cap V_1 = \square, x \in U_2 = \uparrow U_2, y \in V_2 = \downarrow V_2$, and $U_2 \cap V_2 = \square$. Let $U = U_1 \cup U_2$ and $V = V_1 \cap V_2$. Then $A \in K(X,U) \cap K(X,V)$ and $K(X,U) \cap K(X,V) \cap \mathscr{C} = \square$. Now if A is a chain but $a \notin A$, then $K(X\backslash a, X\backslash a)$ is an open set containing A and missing $\mathscr{C}$. The case is which $\partial W \cap A = \square$ is similar.

Let $(x,y) = \{z \in X : x < z < y\}$. If δ is an open cover of X, define $M_\delta = \{C \in C(X) : C$ is a closed chain in X, and if $x < y$ in C and $(x,y) \cap C = \square$, then there exists $V \in \delta$ such that $\overline{V} \cap \downarrow x \cap C \neq \square$ and $\overline{V} \cap \uparrow y \cap C \neq \square.\}$

We next claim that $M_\delta \cap \mathscr{C} \neq \square$ for each open cover δ of X. Let δ be an open cover of X, and let $\mathscr{K}' = \{C : C$ is a closed chain in X, $C \subseteq W$, $C \in M_\delta$, and $a \in C\}$. Let $\mathscr{K}$ be a maximal tower in $\mathscr{K}'$ and let $T = \cup\{C : C \in \mathscr{K}\}$. Then T is a chain with $a \in T$, and $\overline{T}$ is a chain such that $\inf T = \inf \overline{T}$. To see that $\overline{T} \in M_\delta$, let $x, y \in \overline{T}$ with $x < y$ and $(x,y) \cap \overline{T} = \square$. Now if $x = \inf T$ and $x \notin T$, then $T \subseteq \uparrow y$ and hence $x \in \overline{T} \subseteq \uparrow y$, which is a contradiction. Thus if $x = \inf T$ and $x \in T$, then $x \in T_1$ for some $T_1 \in \mathscr{K}$. Since $T_1 \in M_\delta$, there exists $V \in \delta$ such that $\overline{V} \cap \downarrow x \cap T_1 \neq \square$ and $\overline{V} \cap \uparrow y \cap T_1 \neq \square$. It follows that $\overline{V} \cap \downarrow x \cap \overline{T} \neq \square$ and $\overline{V} \cap \uparrow y \cap \overline{T} \neq \square$. Thus we have that $\overline{T} \in M_\delta$ if $x = \inf T$. Suppose then that $\inf T < x < y$, and let $t_0 \in T_0 \in \mathscr{K}$ such that $\inf T < t_0 \leq x < y$. Since $T_0 \in M_\delta$, we have $\overline{T} \in M_\delta$. We conclude that $\overline{T} \in M_\delta$ in any case. It remains to show that $\overline{T} \in \mathscr{C}$. Now if $\overline{T} \subseteq W$, then $\overline{T} \in \mathscr{K}'$, so that by maximality, we have $\overline{T} = T$. Hence $\inf T \in T \subseteq W$, and there exists $V \in \delta$ with $\inf T \in V$. There exists $y \in V \cap W$ with $y < x$, and $T \cup y \in M_\delta$, so that $T \cap y \in \mathscr{K}'$, $T \cup y = T$, and $y \in T$. This contradiction proves that $\overline{T} \cap \partial W \neq \square$, and hence $T \in M_\delta \cap \mathscr{C}$.

We will show that $M_\delta \cap \mathscr{C}$ is closed for each finite open cover δ of X. Let δ be a finite open cover of X. We claim that $C(X)\backslash(M_\delta \cap \mathscr{C})$ is open. Let $A \in C(X)\backslash(M_\delta \cap \mathscr{C})$. Then either $A \notin \mathscr{C}$ or $A \in \mathscr{C}$ but $A \notin M_\delta$. If $A \notin \mathscr{C}$, then there exists an open set containing A in $C(X)$ that misses $\mathscr{C}$, since $\mathscr{C}$ is closed in $C(X)$. Suppose then that $A \in \mathscr{C}$ and $A \notin M_\delta$. Then for some $x,y \in A$, we have $(x,y) \cap A = \square$, and for each $V \in \delta$, $\bar{V} \cap \downarrow x \cap A = \square$ or $\bar{V} \cap \uparrow y \cap A = \square$. In view of B.5, there exist open sets U_1 and W_1 in X such that $\downarrow x \cap A \subseteq U_1$, $\uparrow y \cap A \subseteq W_2$, $U_1 = \downarrow U_1$, $W_1 = \uparrow W_1$, and $U_1 \cap W_1 = \square$. Let $U_2 = \cap\{X\backslash\bar{V}:V \in \delta$ and $\bar{V} \cap \downarrow x \cap A = \square\}$ and let $W_2 = \cap\{X\backslash\bar{V}:V \in \delta$ and $\bar{V} \cap \uparrow y \cap A = \square\}$. Then, since δ is finite, U_2 and W_2 are open. Now $\downarrow x \cap A \subseteq U_2$ and $\uparrow y \cap A \subseteq W_2$, and for each $V \in \delta$, $\bar{V} \cap U_2 = \square$ or $\bar{V} \cap W_2 = \square$. Let $U' = U_1 \cap U_2$ and $W' = W_1 \cap W_2$. Then $A \subseteq K(U' \cup W', U' \cup W')$. We show that this open set containing A misses $M_\delta \cap \mathscr{C}$. Suppose that $C \in \mathscr{C} \cap K(U' \cup W', U' \cup W')$. Let $x' = sup(C \cap U')$ and $y' = inf(C \cap W')$. Then $(x',y') \cap C = \square$. Now $\downarrow x' \cap C \subseteq U'$ and $\uparrow y' \cap C \subseteq W'$ and since for each $V \in \delta$, $\bar{V} \cap U' = \square$, or $\bar{V} \cap W' = \square$, we conclude that $C \notin M_\delta$.

For each finite open cover δ of X, let $P_\delta = M_\delta \cap \mathscr{C}$ and let $\mathscr{P} = \{P_\delta\}$. Now $\mathscr{P}$ is a descending family and hence $\cap\{P_\delta:P_\delta \in \mathscr{P}\} \neq \square$. Let $C \in \cap P_\delta:P_\delta \in \mathscr{P}\}$. We show that C is order dense. Let $x < y$ in C. Then $\downarrow x \cap \uparrow y \cap C = \square$, so that by normality there are open sets U and V such that $\downarrow x \cap C \subseteq U$, $\uparrow x \cap C \subseteq V$, and $\bar{U} \cap \bar{V} = \square$.

Let α be the open cover $\{X\backslash\bar{U}, X\backslash\bar{V}\}$. Then $C \in P_\alpha$ and it is false that the closure of each member of α meets both $\downarrow x$ and $\uparrow y$, so that $(x,y) \cap C \neq \square$, and C is order dense. It follows that C is a compact order-dense chain from a to ∂W, and is therefore an arc. ∎

B.9 Corollary Let X be a compact pospace with a unique minimal element 0. If $\downarrow x$ is connected for each $x \in X$, then X is arcwise connected.

Proof: Let $W = X\backslash 0$. Since $\downarrow x$ is connected for each $x \in X$, W has no local minimum. The result now follows from B.8. ∎

APPENDIX C
Category Theory

Our notation and terminology will be, for the most part, that of the excellent text *Category Theory* [Herrlich and Strecker, 1973]. For completeness we include the basic definitions and concepts which we shall need. For our purposes it suffices to use the Gödel–Bernays–von Neumann axioms for set theory. Hence we have classes and sets (classes that are elements of other classes). Classes which are not sets are termed *proper classes*. Occasionally it will be convenient to use the notation $\mathscr{C} \in \{\mathscr{A},\mathscr{B},\dots\}$ where $\mathscr{C},\mathscr{A},\mathscr{B},\dots$ are proper classes. This is an admissible procedure in set theory if one allows an additional "level of objects," called conglomerates. The reader is referred to the above-mentioned text for a more thorough treatment of the foundational aspects of category theory.

A *category* is a quintuple $\mathscr{C} = (\mathcal{O},\mathcal{M},dom,\ cod,\ \circ)$ where:

(1) $\mathcal{O}$ is a class whose members are called $\mathscr{C}$-*objects*.
(2) $\mathcal{M}$ is a class whose members are called $\mathscr{C}$-*morphisms*.
(3) *dom* and *cod* are functions from $\mathcal{M}$ to $\mathcal{O}$ (*dom f* is called the *domain of f* and *cod f* is called the *codomain of f*).
(4) $\circ$ is a function from $D = \{(f,g) : f,g \in \mathcal{M}$ and $dom\ f = cod\ g\}$ into $\mathcal{M}$, called the *composition law* of $\mathscr{C}$ [$\circ$ (f,g) is usually written $f \circ g$, and we say that $f \circ g$ is defined if and only if $(f,g) \in D$] such that the following conditions are satisfied:

> *Matching Condition.* If $f \circ g$ is defined, then $dom(f \circ g) = dom\ g$ and $cod(f \circ g) = cod\ f$.

Associativity Condition. If $f \circ g$ and $h \circ f$ are defined, then $h \circ (f \circ g) = (h \circ f) \circ g$.

Identity Existence Condition. For each $\mathscr{C}$-object A there is a $\mathscr{C}$-morphism e such that $dom\ e = A = cod\ e$ and $f \circ e = f$ whenever $f \circ e$ is defined, and $e \circ g = g$ whenever $e \circ g$ is defined.

Smallness of Morphism Class Condition. For any pair (A,B) of $\mathscr{C}$-objects, the class $hom_{\mathscr{C}}(A,B) = \{f : f \in M,\ dom\ f = A,\ \text{and}\ cod\ f = B\}$ is a set.

NOTATION   For a given category $\mathscr{C}$, the class of $\mathscr{C}$-objects will be denoted $Ob(\mathscr{C})$ and $Mor(\mathscr{C})$ will stand for the class of $\mathscr{C}$-morphisms. Morphisms will usually be denoted by lower-case letters, with upper-case letters being reserved for objects. Also, instead of $hom_{\mathscr{C}}(A,B)$ we often write $hom(A,B)$ when no confusion seems likely. Although $\mathscr{C}$-morphisms need not be functions, we use the notation: $f \in hom(A,B)$, $A \xrightarrow{f} B$, and $f : A \to B$, interchangeably. Likewise, the composition law will usually be denoted by $\circ$ and the statement that the triangle [square]:

commutes means that $h = g \circ f\ [k \circ h = g \circ f]$.

A category $\mathscr{C}$ is said to be *small* is $Ob(\mathscr{C})$ is a set.

A category $\mathscr{B}$ is said to be a *subcategory* of the category $\mathscr{C}$ provided that the following conditions are satisfied:

(1) $Ob(\mathscr{B}) \subseteq Ob(\mathscr{C})$.

(2) $Mor(\mathscr{B}) \subseteq Mor(\mathscr{C})$.

(3) The domain, codomain, and composition functions of $\mathscr{B}$ are restrictions of the corresponding functions of $\mathscr{C}$.

(4) Every $\mathscr{B}$-identity if a $\mathscr{C}$-identity.

A subcategory $\mathcal{B}$ of a category $\mathcal{C}$ is said to be a *full subcategory* of $\mathcal{C}$ provided that for all $A, B \in Ob(\mathcal{B})$, $hom_{\mathcal{B}}(A, B) = hom_{\mathcal{C}}(A, B)$.

For any category $\mathcal{C} = (\mathcal{O}, \mathcal{M}, dom, cod, \circ)$ the *opposite* (or *dual*) *category* of $\mathcal{C}$ is the category $\mathcal{C}^{op} = (\mathcal{O}, \mathcal{M}, cod, dom, *)$, where $*$ is defined by $f * g = g \circ f$.

Observe that a category $\mathcal{C}$ and $\mathcal{C}^{op}$ have the same objects and morphisms, but the domain and codomain functions are switched and the composition laws are the "opposites" of each other.

Each categorical concept, statement, or property P (which we will not attempt to define) has a dual concept, statement, or property, obtained from P by considering P in the opposite category or reversing all arrows, as appropriate. The meaning of this sentence will become clearer as we treat the next several categorical ideas. Of course, the reader is again referred to Herrlich and Strecker [1973] for a more detailed treatment of categorical duality.

Let $\mathcal{C}$ be a category, A and B $\mathcal{C}$-objects, and $f: A \to B$ a $\mathcal{C}$-morphism. Then:

(a) f is called a $\mathcal{C}$-*section* if there exists a $\mathcal{C}$-morphism $g: B \to A$ such that $g \circ f = 1_A$ (i.e., f has a "left inverse" in $\mathcal{C}$).

(b) f is called a $\mathcal{C}$-*retraction* if there exists a $\mathcal{C}$-morphism $g: B \to A$ such that $f \circ g = 1_B$ (i.e., f has a "right inverse" in $\mathcal{C}$).

(c) f is called a $\mathcal{C}$-*isomorphism* if it is both a $\mathcal{C}$-section and a $\mathcal{C}$-retraction (i.e., f has both a "left inverse" and "right inverse" in $\mathcal{C}$).

(d) f is called a $\mathcal{C}$-*monomorphism* provided that for all $\mathcal{C}$-morphisms h and k such that $f \circ h = f \circ k$, it follows that $h = k$ (i.e., f is "left cancellable" with respect to composition in $\mathcal{C}$).

(e) f is called a $\mathcal{C}$-*epimorphism* provided that for all $\mathcal{C}$-morphisms h and k such that $h \circ f = k \circ f$, it follows that $h = k$ (i.e., f is "right cancellable" with respect to composition in $\mathcal{C}$).

(f) f is called a $\mathcal{C}$-*bimorphism* if it is both a $\mathcal{C}$-monomorphism and a $\mathcal{C}$-epimorphism (i.e., f is "cancellable" with respect to composition in $\mathcal{C}$).

Let X be an object in a category $\mathcal{C}$:

(a) X is called a $\mathcal{C}$-*initial object* rovided that for all $\mathcal{C}$-objects B, $hom_{\mathcal{C}}(X, B)$ has exactly one member.

(b) X is called a $\mathscr{C}$-*terminal object* provided that for all $\mathscr{C}$-objects B, $hom_\mathscr{C}(B,X)$ has exactly one member.

(c) X is called a $\mathscr{C}$-*zero object* provided that X is both an initial and a terminal $\mathscr{C}$-object.

As an illustrations of duality, a $\mathscr{C}$-morphism f is a $\mathscr{C}$-section [$\mathscr{C}$-monomorphism] if and only if f is a $\mathscr{C}^{op}$-retraction [$\mathscr{C}^{op}$-epimorphism], and a $\mathscr{C}$-object X is a $\mathscr{C}$-initial if and only if X is $\mathscr{C}^{op}$-terminal.

Let $\mathscr{C}$ and $\mathscr{D}$ be categories. A (*covariant*) *functor* from $\mathscr{C}$ to $\mathscr{D}$ is a triple ($\mathscr{C},F,\mathscr{D}$) where F is a function from the class of morphisms of $\mathscr{C}$ to the class of morphisms of $\mathscr{D}$. (That is, $F:Mor(\mathscr{C}) \to Mor(\mathscr{D})$ satisfying the following conditions:

(1) F preserves identities, i.e. if e is a $\mathscr{C}$-identity, then $F(e)$ is a $\mathscr{D}$-identity.

(2) F preserves composition, i.e., whenever $dom\, f = dom\, g$, then $cod\, F(f) = cod\, F(g)$ and $F(f \circ g) = F(f) \circ F(g)$.

NOTATION   Instead of writing ($\mathscr{C},F,\mathscr{D}$) is a functor, we will write $F:\mathscr{C} \to \mathscr{D}$, or $\mathscr{C} \overset{F}{\to} D$, or F is a functor from $\mathscr{C}$ to $\mathscr{D}$. Also we write F instead of ($\mathscr{C},F,\mathscr{D}$) and say that F has *domain* $\mathscr{C}$ and *codomain* $\mathscr{D}$.

Because for any category there is a one-to-one correspondence ($A \leftrightarrow 1_A$) between objects and identities and because functors preserve identities, each functor $F:\mathscr{C} \to \mathscr{D}$ induces a unique function (also denoted by F) from $Ob(\mathscr{C})$ to $Ob(\mathscr{D})$, such that for each $\mathscr{C}$-object A, $F(1_A) = 1_{F(A)}$. In view of this, we will describe functors by means of their object functions and their "*hom-set*" restrictions ($Mor(\mathscr{C}) = \bigcup\{hom_\mathscr{C}(A,B):A,B \in Ob(\mathscr{C})\}$).

Let $\mathscr{C}$ and $\mathscr{D}$ be categories. A *contravariant functor* from $\mathscr{C}$ to $\mathscr{D}$ is a triple ($\mathscr{C},F,\mathscr{D}$) where F is a function from $Mor(\mathscr{C})$ to $Mor(\mathscr{D})$ which preserves identities and reverse composition, i.e., whenever $dom\, f = cod\, g$, then $cod\, F(f) = dom\, F(g)$ and $F(f \circ g) = F(g) \circ F(f)$. Equivalently, a contravariant functor from $\mathscr{C}$ to $\mathscr{D}$ is a functor from $\mathscr{C}$ to $\mathscr{D}^{op}$.

Let $F:\mathscr{A} \to \mathscr{B}$ and $G:\mathscr{A} \to \mathscr{B}$ be functors. A *natural transformation* from F to G is a triple (F,η,G) where $\eta:Ob(\mathscr{A}) \to$

$Mor(\mathcal{B})$ is a function satisfying the following conditions:
(1) For each $\mathcal{A}$-object A, $\eta(A)$ (usually denoted η_A) is a $\mathcal{B}$-morphism $\eta_A:F(A) \to G(A)$;
(2) For each $\mathcal{A}$-morphism $A \xrightarrow{f} A'$, the diagram

$$
\begin{array}{ccc}
F(A) & \xrightarrow{\eta_A} & G(A) \\
{\scriptstyle F(f)}\downarrow & & \downarrow{\scriptstyle G(f)} \\
F(A') & \xrightarrow[\eta_{A'}]{} & G(A')
\end{array}
$$

commutes.

A natural transformation (F,η,G) is called a *natural isomorphism* provided that for each $\mathcal{A}$-object A, η_A is a $\mathcal{B}$-isomorphism. Finally, F and G are said to be *naturally isomorphic* if there exists a natural isomorphism from F to G. If F and G are naturally isomorphic we write $F \approx G$.

Let $F:\mathcal{A} \to \mathcal{B}$ be a functor. Then F is an *isomorphism* [*equivalence*] if there exists a functor $G:\mathcal{B} \to \mathcal{A}$ such that $F \circ G = 1_{\mathcal{B}}$ and $G \circ F = 1_{\mathcal{A}}$ [$F \circ G \approx 1_{\mathcal{B}}, G \circ F \approx 1_{\mathcal{A}}$] (where $1_{\mathcal{A}}$ and $1_{\mathcal{B}}$ denote the identity functors on $\mathcal{A}$ and $\mathcal{B}$, respectively). Two categories are *isomorphic* [*equivalent*] if there exists an isomorphism [equivalence] from one to the other.

It is observed in Herrlich and Strecker [1973] that, from a categorical point of view, equivalent categories are "essentially the same." The only difference between them lies in the fact that in one of them some objects might be "counted more times" than in the other – in other words, the categories obtained from $\mathcal{A}$ and $\mathcal{B}$ by "counting" each object just once are isomorphic.

Categories $\mathcal{A}$ and $\mathcal{B}$ are *dually equivalent* if there exist contravariant functors $F:\mathcal{A} \to \mathcal{B}$ and $G:\mathcal{B} \to \mathcal{A}$ such that $F \circ G \approx 1_{\mathcal{B}}$ and $G \circ F \approx 1_{\mathcal{A}}$, i.e., if $\mathcal{A}$ and $\mathcal{B}^{op}$ are equivalent.

Let $\mathcal{C}$ be a category and let $f,g:\mathcal{A} \to \mathcal{B}$ be a pair of $\mathcal{C}$-morphisms. A pair (E,e) is an *equalizer* in $\mathcal{C}$ of f and g if the following conditions hold:
(1) $e:E \to A$ is a $\mathcal{C}$-morphism.
(2) $f \circ e = g \circ e$.

(3) For any $\mathscr{C}$-morphism $e': E' \to A$ such that $f \circ e' = g \circ e'$, there exists a unique $\mathscr{C}$-morphism $\bar{e}:E' \to E$ such that the triangle

commutes.

Dually, if $c:B \to C$ is a $\mathscr{C}$-morphism, then (c,C) is a *coequalizer* in $\mathscr{C}$ of a pair $f,g:A \to B$ of $\mathscr{C}$-morphisms if $c \circ f = c \circ g$ and each $\mathscr{C}$-morphism c' with the property that $c' \circ f = c' \circ g$ can be uniquely factored through c. A category $\mathscr{C}$ *has equalizers* [*coequalizers*] provided that every pair of $\mathscr{C}$-morphisms with common domain and common codomain has an equalizer [coequalizer].

If $\mathscr{C}$ is a category, then a $\mathscr{C}$-*product* of a family $\{A_i\}_{i \in I}$ of $\mathscr{C}$-objects is a pair $(A,\{f_i\}_{i \in I})$ satisfying:
(1) A is a $\mathscr{C}$-object.
(2) For each $i \in I$, $f_i:A \to A_i$ is a $\mathscr{C}$-morphism.
(3) For each pair $(B,\{g_i\}_{i \in I})$, (where B is a $\mathscr{C}$-object and for each $i \in I$, $g_i:B \to A_i$ is a $\mathscr{C}$-morphism) there is a unique $\mathscr{C}$-morphism $h:B \to A$ such that for each $i \in I$, the triangle

commutes.

A category $\mathscr{C}$ *has products* provided that for every set I, each family of $\mathscr{C}$-objects indexed by I has a $\mathscr{C}$-product.

Let $\mathscr{C}$ be a full subcategory of a category $\mathscr{D}$. Then $\mathscr{C}$ is *closed under $\mathscr{D}$-products* if whenever $\{A_i\}_{i \in I}$ is a set-indexed family of

$\mathscr{C}$-objects and $(A,\{f_i\}_{i\in I})$ is a $\mathscr{D}$-product of $\{A_i\}_{i\in I}$ we have $A \in Ob(\mathscr{C})$.

In a category $\mathscr{C}$, a $\mathscr{C}$-*coproduct* of a family $\{A_i\}_{i\in I}$ *of* $\mathscr{C}$-objects is a pair $(\{f_i\}_{i\in I},A)$ satisfying:

(1) A is a $\mathscr{C}$-object.

(2) For each $i \in I$, $f_i:A_i \to A$ is a $\mathscr{C}$-morphism.

(3) For each pair $(\{g_i\}_{i\in I}, B)$ (where B is a $\mathscr{C}$-object and for each $i \in I$, $g_i:A_i \to B$ is a $\mathscr{C}$-morphism), there is a unique $\mathscr{C}$-morphism $h:A \to B$ such that for each $i \in I$, the triangle

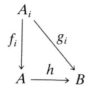

commutes.

The category $\mathscr{C}$ *has coproducts* if for each set I, each family of $\mathscr{C}$-objects indexed by I has a $\mathscr{C}$-coproduct. If $\mathscr{C}$ is a full subcategory of a category $\mathscr{D}$, then $\mathscr{C}$ is *closed under* $\mathscr{D}$-*coproducts* if whenever $\{A_i\}_{i\in I}$ is a set-indexed family of $\mathscr{C}$-objects and $(\{f_i\}_{i\in I},A)$ is a $\mathscr{D}$-coproduct of $\{A_i\}_{i\in I}$ we have $A \in Ob(\mathscr{C})$.

A category $\mathscr{C}$ is said to be *complete* is it has products and equalizers.

The definition of completeness given here is not the standard one. However, it is equivalent to the standard definition and it suffices for our purposes. Again, the reader is referred to Herrlich and Strecker [1973] for a detailed study of limits and completeness in categories.

A category $\mathscr{C}$ is said to be *cocomplete* if it has coproducts and coequalizers.

Let $\mathscr{B}$ be a category and let $\mathscr{A}$ be a subcategory of $\mathscr{B}$. If $B \in Ob(\mathscr{B})$, then a pair (u,A) with $A \in Ob(\mathscr{A})$ and $u:B \to A$ a $\mathscr{B}$-morphism is called an $\mathscr{A}$-*universal map* for $\mathscr{B}$ provided that for each $A' \in Ob(\mathscr{A})$ and each $\mathscr{B}$-morphism $f:B \to A'$ there exists a unique $\mathscr{A}$-morphism $\bar{f}:A \to A'$ such that the triangle

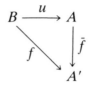

commutes.

Let $\mathcal{B}$ be a category and let $\mathcal{A}$ be a subcategory of $\mathcal{B}$. If $\mathcal{B} \in Ob(\mathcal{B})$, $A \in Ob(\mathcal{A})$ and $f:B \to A$ is a $\mathcal{B}$-morphism, then f is said to $\mathcal{A}$-*generate* A provided that whenever $r,s:A \to A'$ are $\mathcal{A}$-morphisms such that $r \circ f = s \circ f$, then $r = s$ (i.e., f is right cancellable for $\mathcal{A}$-morphisms).

Let $\mathcal{B}$ be a category and let $\mathcal{A}$ be a subcategory of $\mathcal{B}$. If $B \in Ob(\mathcal{B})$, then an $\mathcal{A}$-solution set for B is a set indexed family $\{(u_i, A_i)\}_{i \in I}$, where:
(1) $A_i \in Ob(\mathcal{A})$ for each $i \in I$.
(2) $u_i:B \to A_i$ is a $\mathcal{B}$-morphism for each $i \in I$.
(3) For each $\mathcal{A}$-object $\hat{A}$ and each $\mathcal{B}$-morphism $f:B \to \hat{A}$, there exists some $i \in I$ and some $\mathcal{A}$-morphism $\hat{f}:A_i \to \hat{A}$ such that the triangle

commutes.

C.1   Universal Map Existence Theorem   Let $\mathcal{B}$ be a category with products and let $\mathcal{A}$ be a full subcategory of $\mathcal{B}$ which is closed under $\mathcal{B}$ products and each $\mathcal{B}$-object has an $\mathcal{A}$-solution set. If each $\mathcal{B}$-morphism $f:B \to A$, where $A \in Ob(\mathcal{A})$, admits a factorization such that $A' \in Ob(\mathscr{A})$ and $g:B \to A'$ $\mathscr{A}$-generates A'. Then each $\mathscr{B}$-object has an $\mathscr{A}$ universal map.

Proof: Fix a $\mathscr{B}$-object B and an $\mathscr{A}$-solution set $\{(u_i, A_i)\}_{i \in I}$ for B. Let $(A, \{f_i\}_{i \in I})$ be a $\mathscr{B}$-product of $\{A_i\}_{i \in I}$ and let $f:B \to A$ be the unique $\mathscr{B}$-morphism such that for each $i \in I$, the triangle

commutes. Now, $\mathscr{A}$ is closed under $\mathscr{B}$-products and so $A \in Ob(\mathscr{A})$ and $f_i \in Mor\ \mathscr{A}$ for each $i \in I$. Using the final hypothesis of the theorem, let

be a factorization of $f: B \to A$ such that $A' \in Ob(\mathscr{A})$ and $g:B \to A'$ $\mathscr{A}$-generates A'.

We proceed to show that (g, A') is an $\mathscr{A}$-universal map for B. Let $\hat{A} \in Ob(\mathscr{A})$ and let $k:B \to \hat{A}$ be a $\mathscr{B}$-morphism. Then, since $\{(u_i, A_i)\}_{i \in I}$ is an $\mathscr{A}$-solution set for $\mathscr{B}$, there exists an $i \in I$ and an $\mathscr{A}$-morphism $\hat{k}:A_i \to \hat{A}$ such that the triangle

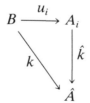

commutes. Now, the commutative diagram

yields at least one $\mathcal{A}$-morphism r (namely, $\hat{k} \circ f_i \circ h$) such that the triangle

commutes. The uniqueness of r follows immediately from the fact that $g:B \rightarrow A'$ $\mathcal{A}$-generates A'. ∎

The result of C.1 on the existence of universal maps is extremely useful. Let $\mathcal{A}$ be a full subcategory of $\mathcal{B}$ which has the property that every $\mathcal{B}$-object B has an $\mathcal{A}$-universal map (u_B, A_B). Denote the inclusion functor from $\mathcal{A}$ into $\mathcal{B}$ by E. Then, we may clearly assume that for $B \in Ob(\mathcal{A})$, $A_B = B$, and $u_B = 1_B$. We define a functor $F:\mathcal{B} \rightarrow \mathcal{A}$ by letting $F(B) = A_B$ and if $f:B \rightarrow B'$ is a $\mathcal{B}$-morphism, then $F(f):A_B \rightarrow A_{B'}$ is the unique $\mathcal{A}$-morphism g making the triangle commute. From the above remarks it follows immediately that $F \circ E = 1_{\mathcal{A}}$. Now, if $f:B \to B'$ is a $\mathcal{B}$-morphism then, by definition, the square

commutes and so $u = \{u_B\}_{B \in Ob(\mathcal{B})}$ is a natural transformation from $1_{\mathcal{B}}$ to $E \circ F$. Hence, $F:B \to \mathcal{A}$ is a functor and u is a natural transformation from $1_{\mathcal{B}}$ to $E \circ F$ such that $F \circ E = 1_{\mathcal{A}}$ and, for each $B \in Ob(\mathcal{B})$, $(u_B, F(B))$ is an $\mathcal{A}$-universal map for B. Herrlich and Strecker would call this (a special type of) an *adjoint situation* and would write $(u,1_{\mathcal{A}}):F \dashv E:(\mathcal{A},\mathcal{B})$. The functor F is called a *left adjoint* of the inclusion functor E. After carefully defining (this special type of) adjoint situation one obtains that if E has a left adjoint F and $(\eta,1_{\mathcal{A}}):F \dashv E:(\mathcal{A},\mathcal{B})$ is an adjoint situation, then for $B \in Ob(\mathcal{B})$, $(\eta_B, F(B))$ is an $\mathcal{A}$-universal map for B.

These observations show that the existence of a left adjoint for the inclusion functor $E:\mathcal{A} \to \mathcal{B}$ is equivalent to the existence of $\mathcal{A}$-universal maps for each $\mathcal{B}$-object. Therefore, we could refer to C.1 as an *adjoint existence theorem* or an *adjoint functor theorem*. We have found that this result is in precisely the form which is most applicable to topological semigroup theory.

Let $\mathcal{B}$ be a category and let $\mathcal{A}$ be a subcategory of $\mathcal{B}$. Then $\mathcal{A}$ is a *reflective subcategory* of $\mathcal{B}$ if the inclusion functor $E:\mathcal{A} \to \mathcal{B}$ has a left adjoint. Equivalently, $\mathcal{A}$ is a reflective subcategory of $\mathcal{B}$ if each $\mathcal{B}$-object B has an $\mathcal{A}$-universal map (u_B, A_B).

C.2 Uniqueness of Universal Maps   Let $\mathcal{B}$ be a category and let $\mathcal{A}$ be a subcategory of $\mathcal{B}$. If $B \in Ob(\mathcal{B})$, and (u_1, A_1) and (u_2, A_2) are $\mathcal{A}$-universal maps for B, then there is a (unique) $\mathcal{A}$-isomorphism $f:A_1 \to A_2$ such that the triangle commutes. Hence $\mathcal{A}$-universal maps are unique up to $\mathcal{A}$-isomorphisms.

Proof: By the defining properties of (u_1, A_1) and (u_2, A_2), there are (unique) $\mathcal{A}$-morphisms f and g such that the diagram

commutes. Hence $h = g \circ f$ is an $\mathcal{A}$-morphism such that the triangle

commutes. Obviously, $h = 1_{A_1}$ is also an $\mathcal{A}$-morphism making this triangle commute. Since (u_1, A_1) is an $\mathcal{A}$-universal map for B, such an $\mathcal{A}$-morphism is unique and we have $g \circ f = 1_{A_1}$. Similarly, $f \circ g = 1_{A_2}$ and so f is an $\mathcal{A}$-isomorphism.   ∎

Bibliography

Anderson, L. W., and R. P. Hunter, Compact semigroups having certain one dimensional hyperspaces, Am J. Math., *XCII* (1970), 894–896.

Anderson, L. W., and R. P. Hunter, A remark on finite dimensional compact connected monoids, Proc. Am. Math. Soc. *42* (1974), 602–606.

Anderson, L. W., and L. E. Ward Jr., One-dimensional topological semilattices, I11. J. Math. (1961), 182–186.

Arens, R., and J. Dugundji, Topologies for function spaces, Pac. J. Math. *1* (1951), 5–31.

Bing, R. H., Snake-like continua, Duke Math. J *18* (1951), 653–663.

Birkhoff, G., *Lattice Theory*. Am. Math. Soc. Colloq., Providence, R.I., 1967.

Borrego, J. T., Continuity of the operation of a semilattice Coll. Math *21* (1970), 49–52.

Borrego, J. T., H. Cohen and E. E. DeVun, Uniquely representable semigroups, Pac. J. Math *39* (1971), 573–579.

Bowman, T. T., The semilattice of left translations of a compact semilattice, Notices Am. Math. Soc. *20* (1973), 670–673.

Bowman, T. T., Analogue of Pontryagin character theory for topological semigroups, Proc. Am. Math. Soc. *48* (1974), 95–105.

Bredon, G. E., *Sheaf Theory*. McGraw-Hill, New York, 1967.

Brown, D. R. On clans of non-negative matrices Proc. Am Math. Soc. *15* (1964), 671–674.

Brown, D. R., Topological semilattices on the 2-cell, Pac. J. Math. *15* (1965), 35–46.

Brown, D. R., Matrix representations of compact simple semigroups, Duke Math J. *33* (1966), 69–74.

Brown, D. R., and M. Friedberg, Representations of topological semigroups Mathematicky Casopis *20* (1970), 304–314.

Brown, D. R., and J. G. LaTorre A characterization of uniquely divisible commutative semigroups, Pac. J. Math. *18* (1966), 57–60.

Brown, D. R., and J. W. Stepp, Inner points and breadth in certain compact semilattices, Proc. Am. Math. Soc. *84* (1982), 581–587.

Brown, D. R., and A. R. Stralka, Problems on compact semilattices, Semigroup Forum *6* (1973), 265–270.

Brown, D. R., and A. R. Stralka, Compact totally instable zero-dimensional semilattices, Gen. Top. and Appl. *7* (1977), 151–159.

Carruth, J. H., *On the Structure of Hyperspace Semigroups* (Master's Thesis) Louisiana State University, 1963a.

Carruth, J. H., A note on partially ordered compacta, Pac. J. Math. *24* (1968), 229–231.

Carruth, J. H., and C. E. Clark, Compact totally H-ordered semigroups Proc. Am. Math. Soc. *27* (1971), 199–204.

Carruth, J. H., and C. E. Clark, Concerning restrictions of Green's $\mathcal{H}$ equivalence, Semigroup Forum *5* (1972), 186–189.

Carruth, J. H., J. A., Hildebrant, and R. J. Koch *The Theory of Topological Semigroups*, Marcel Dekker Inc., New York, 1983.

Carruth, J. H., K. H., Hofmann, and M. W. Mislove, Errors in elements of compact semigroups, Semigroup Forum *5* (1973), 285–322.

Castellano, B. M. The fixed point conjecture and monoids on a manifold with boundary, Semigroup Forum *27* (1983), 237–245.

Christoph, F. T., Jr., Ideal extensions of topological semigroups, Can. J. Math *22* (1970), 1168–1175.

Clark, C. E., and C. Eberhart, A characterization of compact connected planar lattices, Pac. J. Math *24* (1968), 233–240.

Clifford, A. H., and G. B. Preston, *The Algebraic Theory of Semigroups*. Math. Surveys No 7, Am. Math. Soc., Providence R. I., 1961.

Cohen, H, A cohomological definition of dimension for locally compact Hausdorff spaces, Duke Math. J. *21* (1954), 209–224.

Cohen, H., A clan with zero without the fixed point property, Proc. Am. Math. Soc., *11* (1960), 937–939.

Cohen, H., Compact connected semilattices without the fixed point property, Semigroup Forum *7* (1974), 375–379.

Cohen, H. and H. S. Collins Affine semigroups, Trans. Am. Math. Soc. *93* (1959), 97–113.

Cohen, H., and R. J. Koch Acyclic semigroups of multiplications on two-manifolds, Trans. Am. Math. Soc. *118* (1965), 420–427.

Cohen, H, and R. J. Koch, Idempotent semigroups generated by threads I, Semigroup Forum *23* (1981), 247–254.

Cohen, J., and R. J. Koch, Idempotent semigroups generated by threads II, Semigroup Forum *24* (1982), 373–383.

Crawley, J. W., Jr. *A Systematic Study of Certain Categorical Concepts in Various Categories of Topological Semigroups* (Doctoral Dissertation), University of Tennessee, 1973.

Crawley, J. W., Jr., A note on epimorphisms of compact Lawson semilattices, Semigroup Forum *13* (1976), 92–94.

Curtis, M. L., Self-linked subgroups of semigroups, Am. J. Math. *81* (1959), 889–892.

DeVun, E. E., Special semigroups on the two-cell, Pac. J. Math *34* (1970), 639–645.

DeVun, E. E., Uniquely representable semigroups on the two-cell, Pac. J. Math., 38 (1971), 565–569.

DeVun, E. E., The equivalence of uniquely divisible semigroups and uniquely representable semigroups on the two-cell, Semigroup Forum *4* (1972a), 69–72.

DeVun, E. E., Semigroups on the disk with thread boundaries, Kyungpook Math. J. *12* (1972b), 159–169.

DeVun, E. E., Product Semigroups, J. Aust. Math. Soc. *22* (1976), 391–399.

DeVun, E. E., Semigroups with [x][y] = [y][x], Semigroup Forum *20* (1980), 241–253.

Eberhart, C., *Some Classes of Continua Related to Clan Structure* (Doctoral Dissertation) Louisiana State University, 1966.

Faucett, W. M. Topological semigroups and continua with cut points, Proc. Am. Math. Soc. *6* (1955), 357–362.

Ferguson, E. N., 1967 *Semigroups on the Two-Cell with Idempotent Boundary* (Dissertation) University of Oregon, 1967.

Freidberg, M., On representations of certain semigroups Pac. J. Math., 19 (1966a), 269–275.

Freidberg, M., A note on Haar-like measure for group-extremal semigroups, Proc. Am. Math. Soc. *17* (1966b), 1079–1082.

Freidberg, M., Some examples of clans, Semigroup Forum *4* (1972), 156–164.

Gierz, G., K. H. Hofmann, K. Keimel, J. D. Lawson, M. Mislove, and D. Scott, A Compendium of Continuous Lattices, Springer-Verlag, New York, 1980.

Graham, G. E. Differentiable semigroups, in Lecture Notes in Mathematics 998, Springer (1981), 57–127.

Herrlich, H., and G. E. Strecker, *Category Theory*, Allyn and Bacon, Boston, 1973.

Hildebrant, J. A., Extending congruences on factors of ideally compactifiable semigroups, Semigroup Forum *12* (1976), 245–250.

Hildebrant, J. A., Ideal extensions of compact reductive semi-groups, Semigroup Forum *25* (1982), 283–290.

Hildebrant, J. A., The translational degree of a semigroup Semigroup Forum *30* (1984), 331–349.

Hildebrant, J. A., J.D. Lawson and Yeager, D. P. The translational hull of a topological semigroup, Trans. Am. Math. Soc. *221* (1976), 251–280.

Hilgert, J., and K. H. Hofmann, Lie theory for semigroups, Semigroup Forum *30* (1984a), 243–251.

Hilgert, J., and K. H. Hofmann On Sophus Lie's fundamental

theorems, III, Preprint *799* Technische Hochschule Darmstadt, no 799, 1984b.

Hilgert, J., and K. H. Hofmann, Lie semialgebras are real phenomena, Math. Ann. *270* (1985), 97–103.

Hinman, B. Products of threads, Semigroup Forum *1* (1974), 1–20.

Hofmann, K. H., Locally compact semigroups in which a subgroup with compact complement is dense, Trans. Am. Math. Soc. *106* (1963a), 19–51.

Hofmann, K. H., Homogeneous locally compact groups with compact boundary, Trans. Am. Math. Soc. *106* (1963b), 52–63.

Hofmann, K. H., and R. P. Hunter, On a centralizer result of Hunter's, Semigroup Forum *6* (1973), 365–372.

Hofmann, K. H., and J. D. Lawson, The local theory of semigroups in nilpotent Lie groups Semigroup Forum, *23* (1981a), 343–357.

Hofmann, K.H., and J. D. Lawson, *Foundations of Lie Semigroups*. Lecture notes in Mathematics 998, Springer (1981b), 128–201.

Hofmann, K. H., and J. D. Lawson, Divisible subsemigroups of Lie groups J. London Math. Soc. *27* (1983a), 427–434.

Hofmann, K. H., and J. D. Lawson, On Sophus Lie's fundamental theorem I. Indag. Math. *45* (1983b), 453–466. On Sophus Lie's fundamental theorem II. Indag. Math. *46* (1984), 255–265.

Hofmann, K. H., and M. Mislove, Lawson semilattices do have a Pontryagin duality, in *Proc. Lattice Theory Conf.*, U. Houston, 1973, 200–205.

Hofmann, K. H., and M. Mislove, Epics of compact Lawson semilattices are surjective Arch. Math. *26* (1975), 337–345.

Hofmann, K. H., M. Mislove, and A. R. Stralka, Dimension raising maps in topological algebra Math. Zeit., *135* (1973), 1–36.

Hofmann, K. H., M. Mislove, and A. R. Stralka, *The Pontryagin Duality of Compact O-dimensional Semilattices and its Applications*. Springer-Verlag Lecture Notes in Math. 396, 1974.

Hofmann, K. H., M. Mislove, and A. R. Stralka, On the dimensional capacity of semilattices Houston J. Math. *1* (1975), 43–55.

Hofmann, K. H., and P. S. Mostert, *Elements of Compact Semigroups*. Merill, Columbus, Ohio. 1966.

Hofmann, K. H., and P. S. Mostert, Problems about compact semigroups Semigroups (K. W. Foley, ed.) Academic Press, 1969.

Hofmann, K. H, and A. R. Stralka, Mapping cylinders and compact monoids Math. Ann. *205* (1973a), 219–239.

Hofmann, K. H., and A. R. Stralka, Push-outs and strict projective limits of semilattices Semigroup Forum *5* (1973b), 243–262.

Hofmann, K. H., and A. R. Stralka, The algebraic theory of Lawson semilattices-Applications of Galois connections to compact semilattices Diss. Math *137* (1976), 1–54.

Horne, J. G., Real commutative semigroups on the plane I, II, Trans. Am. Math. Soc. *104* (1962a), 17–23.

Horne, J. G., Semigroups on a half-plane, Trans. Am. Math. Soc. *105* (1962), 9–20.

Horne, J. G., The boundary of a one-parameter group in a semigroup, Duke Math. J. *31* (1964), 109–117.

Houston, R. *Cancellative Semigroups on Manifolds*, Dissertation, University of Houston, 1973.

Hudson, A. L., Some semigroups on the two-cell, Proc. Am. Math. Soc. *10* (1959), 648–655.

Hudson, A. L., Example of a non-cyclic continuum semigroup S with 0 and S = ESE, Proc. Am. Math. Soc. *14* (1963), 648–653.

Hudson, A. L. and P. S. Mostert, A finite dimensional homogeneous clan is a group An. of Math. *78* (1963), 41–46.

Hunter, R. P., On the semigroup structure of continua Trans. Am. Math. Soc. *93* (1959), 356–368.

Hunter, R. P., Note on arcs in semigroups Fund. Math *49* (1961), 233–245.

Hunter, R. P., On the structure of homogroups with applications to the theory of compact connected semigroups Fund. Math. *52* (1963), 69–102.

Hunter, R. P., Compact semigroups with low dimensional orbit space, Proc. Am. Math. Soc. *40* (1973), 277–279.

Hunter, R. P., Certain idempotents lying in the centralizer of the group of units, Proc. Am. Math. Soc. *71* (1978), 339–344.

Hunter, R. P., Toral subgroups lying in the centralizer of the group of units, Proc. Am. Math. Soc. *79* (1980), 113–121.

Hunter, R. P., Some remarks on subgroups defined by the Bohr compactification, Semigroup Forum, *26* (1983), 125–137.

Hunter, R. P. and N. J. Rothman, Characters and cross sections for certain semigroups Duke Math. J. *29* (1962), 347–366.

Hurewicz, W. and H. Wallmann, *Dimension Theory*, Princeton University Press, Princeton, N. J., 1941.

Husain, T., *Introduction to Topological Groups*, Saunders, Philadelphia, 1966.

Kelley, J. L., *General Topology*. Van Nostrand, Princeton, N. J., 1955.

Koch, R. J., On monothetic semigroups, Proc. Am. Math. Soc. *8* (1957a), 397–401.

Koch, R. J., Note on weak cutpoints in clans Duke Math. J. *24* (1957b), 611–616.

Koch, R. J., Arcs in partially ordered spaces Pac. J. Math. *9* (1959), 723–728.

Koch, R. J., Weak cutpoint ordering in hereditarily unicoherent continua Proc. Am. Math. Soc. *11* (1960), 679–681.

Koch, R. J., Threads in compact semigroups Math. Zeit. *86* (1964), 312–316.

Koch, R. J., Connected chains in quasi-ordered spaces Fund. Math. *56* (1965), 245–249.

Koch, R. J., Some open questions in topological semigroups, An. Acad. brasil Cienc., *41* (1969), 19–20.

Koch, R. J., Compact connected spaces supporting topological semigroups Semigroup Forum *1* (1970), 95–102.

Koch, R. J., and L. F. McAuley, Semigroups on trees Fund. Math., 50 (1962), 341–346.

Koch, R. J., and L. F. McAuley, Semigroups on continua ruled by arcs Fund. Math. *56* (1964), 1–8.

Krein, M., and D. Milman, On extreme points of regular convex sets Studia Math., 9 (1940), 133–137.

Krule, I. S. Structs on the 1-sphere Duke Math. J., 24 (1957), 623–626.

LaMartin, W., On the foundations of k-group theory Louisiana State Univ. at New Orleans manuscript.

Langlands, R. P., On Lie semi-groups Canad. J. Math. *12* (1960), 668–693.

Lau, A. Y. W., Concerning costabiliy of compact semigroups Duke Math. J. *39* (1972a), 657–664.

Lau, A. Y. W., Small semilattices Semigroup Forum *4* (1972b), 150–155.

Lau, A. Y. W., Costability in SEM and TSL Semigroup Forum *5* (1973a), 370–372.

Lau, A. Y. W., Coverable semigroups Proc. Am. Math. Soc. *38* (1973b), 661–664.

Lau, A. Y. W., The boundary of a semilattice on an n-cell Pac. J. Math. *56* (1975), 171–174.

Lawson, J. D., *Vietoris Mappings and Embeddings of Topological Lattices*. Dissertation, University of Tennessee, 1967.

Lawson, J. D., Topological semilattices with small semilattices J. London Math., 2 (1969a), 719–724.

Lawson, J. D., A generalized version of the Vietoris-Begle Theorem, Fund. Math. *LXV* (1969b), 65–72.

Lawson, J. D., Lattices with no interval homomorphisms Pac. J. Math. *32* (1970a), 459–465.

Lawson, J. D., The relation of breadth and codimension in topological semilattices Duke Math. J. *37* (1970b), 207–212.

Lawson, J. D., The relation of breadth and codimension in topological semilattices II Duke Math. J. *38* (1971), 555–559.

Lawson, J. D., Dimensionally stable semilattices Semigroup Forum *5* (1972), 181–185.

Lawson, J. D., Intrinsic lattice and semilattice topologies in *Proc. Lattice Theory Conf.*, U. Houston, 1973a, 206–260.

Lawson, J. D., Intrinsic topologies in topological lattices and semilattices Pac. J. Math. *44* (1973b), 593–602.

Lawson, J. D., Additional notes on continuity in semitopological semigroups Semigroup Forum *12* (1976), 265–280.

Lawson, J. D., Compact semilattices which must have a basis of subsemilattices J. London Math. Soc. *16* (1977), 369–371.

Lawson, J. D., J. R. Liukkonen, and M. W. Mislove Measure algebras of semilattices with finite breadth Pac. J. Math. *69* (1977), 125–139.

Lawson, J. D., and B. L. Madison, Peripherial and inner points Fund. Math. *69* (1970a), 253–266.

Lawson, J. D., and B. L. Madison, Peripherality in semigroups Semigroup Forum *1* (1970b), 128–142.

Lawson, J. D., and W. Williams, Semilattices and their underlying spaces Semigroup Forum *1* (1970), 209–223.

Lea, J. W., Jr., An embedding theorem for compact semilattices Proc. Am. Math. Soc. *34* (1972), 325–331.

Lea, J. W., Jr., and A. Y. W. Lau, Codimension of compact M-semilattices Proc. Am. Math. Soc. *52* (1975), 406–408.

Madison, B. L., A note on local homogeneity and stability Duke Math. J. *36* (1969a), 61–64.

Madison, B. L., Semigroups on coset spaces, Duke Math J. *36* (1969b), 61–63.

Madison, B. L., and J. Selden, Clans on group-supporting spaces Proc. Am. Math. Soc. *18* (1967), 540–545.

McCharen, J. D., *Maximal Elements in Compact Semigroups.* Dissertation, Louisiana State University, 1969.

McCharen, J. D., Semigroups on finitely floored spaces Trans. Am. Math. Soc. *156* (1971), 85–89.

McCharen, J. D., An application of peripherality to compact semigroups Semigroup Forum 8 (1974), 56–64.

Michael, E., Topologies on spaces of subsets Trans. Am. Math. Soc., 71 (1951), 151–182.

Mislove, M. W., The existence of Irr (X) Semigroup Forum, *1* (1970), 243–248.

Mislove, M. W., The existence and structure of Irr (X) Semigroup Forum *4* (1972), 1–33.

Mostert, P. S., Plane semigroups Trans. Am. Math. Soc. *103* (1962), 320–328.

Mostert, P. S., Compact subgroups of contractible semigroups are not self-linked Am. J. Math. *85* (1963), 47–48.

Mostert, P. S., Comments on some Wallace's problems on topological semigroups Coll. Math. *10* (1963b), 221–225.

Mostert, P. S., and A. L. Shields, On continuous multiplications on the two-sphere Proc. Am. Math. Soc. 7 (1956). 942–947.

Oberhoff, K., Doctoral Dissertation, University of Houston, 1973.

Paalman-De-Miranda, A. B., *Topological Semigroups*. Math. Centre Tracts, 2nd Ed., Math. Centrum Amsterdam, 1970.

Pym, J. S., Idempotent measures on semigroups, Pac. J. Math. *12* (1962), 685–698.

Petrich, M., The translational hull in semigroups and rings Semigroup Forum *1* (1970), 283–360.

Petrich, M., *Intrduction to Semigroups*. Merill, Columbus, Ohio, 1973.

Poguntke, D., Epimorphisms of compact groups are onto Proc. Am. Math. Soc. *26* (1970), 503–504.

Poguntke, D., Well-bounded semigroups in connected groups Semigroup Forum, 15 (1977), 159–167.

Pontryagin, L. S., *Topological Groups*, Gordon and Breach, New York, 1961.

Rhodes, J., Decomposition semilattices with applications to topological lattices Pac. J. Math. *44* (1973), 299–307.

Rosen, W. G., On invariant means over compact semigroups Proc. Am. Math. Soc. 7 (1956), 1076–1082.

Rosenblatt, M., Limits of convolution sequences of measures on a compact topological semigroup, J. Math. Mech. *9* (1960), 293–306.

Ruppert, W., *Compact Semitopological Semigroups: An Intrinsic Theory* Lecture Notes, Springer Verlag, New York, 1984.

Selden J., A note on compact semigroups Notices Am. Math. Soc. *8* (1961), 588.

Spanier, E. H., *Algebraic Topology*. McGraw Hill, New York, 1966.

Stepp, J. W., Semilattices which are embeddable in a product of min intervals Semigroup Forum 2 (1971), 80–82.

Stepp, J. W., Topological semilattices which are embeddable in topological lattices J. London Math. Soc. 7 (1973), 76–82.

Stepp, J. W., Algebraic maximal semilattices Pac. J. Math. *58* (1975a), 243–248.

Stepp, J. W., The free compact lattice generated by a topological semilattice J.f.d. reine u. angew. Mathematik, *273* (1975b), 77–86.

Stralka, A. R., The congruence extension property for compact topological lattices, Pac. J. Math., 38 (1971), 795–802.

Stralka, A. R., The lattice of ideals of a compact semilattice Proc. Am. Math. Soc. *33* (1972), 175–180.

Stralka, A. R., Congruence extension and amalgamation in CL Semigroup Forum, *13* (1977), 355–375.

Strauss, D. P., Topological lattices Proc. London Math. Soc. *18* (1968), 217–230.

Tychonov, A., Ein Fixpunktsatz Math. Ann. 111 (1935), 767–776.

Wallace, A. D., Cohomology dimension and mobs Summa Brasil. Math. *3* (1953), 45–54.

Wallace, A. D., Partial order and indecomposability Proc. Am. Math. Soc. *6* (1955), 780–781.

Wallace, A. D., Struct ideals Proc. Am. Math. Soc. *6* (1955), 634–638.

Wallace, A. D., Acyclicity of compact connected semigroups Fund. Math. *50* (1961a), 99–105.

Wallace, A. D., A theorem on acyclicity Bull, Am. Math. Soc. *67* (1961b) 123–124.

Wallace, A. D., Problems on semigroups Coll. Math. *8* (1961c), 223–224.

Wallace, A. D., Problems concerning semigroups Bull. Am. Math. Soc. *68* (1962), *68* (1962), 447–448.

Ward, L. E. Jr., Partially ordered topological spaces Proc. Am. Math. Soc. *5* (1954), 144–161.

Ward, C. E., Jr., Completeness in semilattices Canad. J. Math. (1958), 578–582.

Williams, W. W., Semilattices on Peano continua Proc. Am. Math. Soc. *49* (1975), 495–500.

Symbols

Index

cent. In hair color, skin color, and eye color 75 per cent were "medium" or "dark." Less than 17 per cent were narrow-headed. As Huxley and Haddon say: "The study of Dr. Hrdlička's work will leave little doubt that . . . the Nordic element in the 'Old American' is small." [1]

In all the American racist volumes there was an immediate political objective: revision of the immigration laws. The American temper had changed since the days when our motto was "No distinctions of race, creed, or color" and we offered an "asylum for the oppressed" and wrote enthusiastically about "the Melting Pot." It was becoming harder to offer opportunity to all Americans, and the social engineering that America needed was to be had only at a price. Because of social conditions in the United States there was no doubt that immigration could no longer be left wide open. The only point at issue was the basis on which choice should be made. Grant's *Passing of the Great Race* was written in 1916, and by 1921 a hurried piece of legislation, the Quota Act, was rushed through Congress to check the rapid increase of immigration that followed the First World War. Subsequent acts have modified percentages and changed the dates used for reckoning quotas, but they have followed the original principle. This principle was to admit new immigrants in numbers calculated at a certain percentage—3 per cent in 1921, 2 per cent in 1924—of the American foreign-born at certain dates—1910 in the Act of 1921, 1890 in the Act of 1924. The total number admitted in any year was fixed in 1924 at 150,000. In 1929 the "national origin" provision, which depends on a more complicated calculation, went into effect. Immigrants from independent countries of the Americas and those from Canada are exempt from quota restrictions.

---

[1] Huxley, J. S., and Haddon, A. C., *We Europeans,* New York, Pelican Books, 1939, p. 132.

If American thinking had not been confused by racist dogmas, the immigration regulations might have been drawn up on a socially more advantageous basis. Health and educa-tion are not determined by "national origins"; they are indi-vidual. In view of the cost of assimilating non-English-speaking, cheap-labor groups we might have announced frankly our preference for the educated. We might have chosen to admit emigrants from countries whose social order and standard of living are comparable to our own. Princi-pally, however, the fixed annual number admitted was a shot in the dark. With every change in the economic condition of America, the social advantage or disadvantage of additional manpower varies. During the depression of the last decade the Immigration Service has actually tried to balance man-power and employment by free interpretation of the phrase "liable to become a public charge." Adjustment to economic conditions in America has, however, been left to adminis-trative interpretation; it has never been recognized in the law of the land or placed in the hands of a fact-finding commis-sion.[1]

The racist literature of the United States [2] deals hardly at all with our great national racial problem, the Negro. Our treatment of the Negro conforms so closely to the predilec-tions of these authors that they doubtless had little to suggest. On the other hand they made the most of the opportunity to seize upon a racial basis to differentiate the still unassimilated laborer from the earlier and now more prosperous settlers. Their constant injunction is that Old America should limit

[1] For an excellent discussion of the problems of minority groups, see Donald Young, *American Minority Peoples,* New York, 1932.

[2] Grant, Madison, *The Passing of the Great Race,* New York, 1916. Burr, Clinton Stoddard, *America's Race Heritage,* New York, 1922. Stoddard, Lothrop, *The Revolt Against Civilization; the Menace of the Under Man,* New York, 1922. Gould, Charles W., *America: A Family Matter,* New York, 1922. Osborn, Henry Fairfield, *Man Rises to Parnassus,* New York, 1927.

immigration on a "racial" basis and should keep its blood free from mixture with that of the inferior non-Nordics we have carelessly admitted. Racism in America turned out to be no more than a spectacle of immigrants of one decade condemning to everlasting inferiority the immigrants of a later decade. It is the part of wisdom to wait a little longer before we commit ourselves to such judgments. A Norman in the time of Ivanhoe could have written of the impossibility of civilizing the Saxons with much better justification than does Madison Grant of non-Nordics in the 1920's in America, but to what purpose? History has long since reversed such a judgment, and to Madison Grant himself to be an Anglo-Saxon is the proudest boast. Americans of the future may likewise boast of heritages that today appear no more promising than that of Anglo-Saxon seemed not so long ago to the Norman.

Racism and Nationalism

By the beginning of the twentieth century the nations of Europe were drawn up against each other in increasingly bitter conflict. Nationalism was the juggernaut before which all lesser causes became unimportant. Class rivalries and minority conflicts were crushed before it at every crisis. When in the 1890's Gobineau's *Essay* was resuscitated from comparative oblivion and its dogmas passionately and popularly espoused, it was not as a gospel of class but as a gospel of national patriotism.

If pure racial heredity for a class in modern Europe or America was an impossible claim, pure racial heredity for a nation was a fantastic one. With European rules of property entailed in the family line, the privileged classes had a certain family continuity at least in one male line, and in spite of the fact that *any* ancestor is as important in the eyes of the biologist as the one who gives the surname, nevertheless this lent a certain verisimilitude to hereditary claims of the individual. With a nation, however, the verisimilitude vanishes. The popularizing of the doctrine had nevertheless been made easier both by increasing familiarity with the slogans when they were still class doctrines and by the uncritical notion that every group that differed was a "race." If Frenchmen and Germans differed, by that token they were different races.

Racism became a national battle cry in this era of nationalism. In "fatherlands" in need of a common rallying cry it provided a pedigree and a bond any man could understand and take pride in. Racism therefore became a babel of voices. The French, the Germans, the Slavs, the Anglo-Saxons— each produced their literary and their political spokesmen proving that to their "race" alone from the beginning of European history the triumphs of civilization had been due. Each laid violent hands on the facts of race and distorted them to contrary racist conclusions. Racism in its national phase lost any pretense of scientific objectivity.

There had been, of course, patriotic racist pronouncements almost from the time of Darwin. But they were scattered and casual. The first wave of national racism occurred, significantly enough, in France immediately after her defeat and humiliation by Germany in 1870. German armies had invaded France and take Paris, and along with that triumph Bismarck had succeeded in unifying the kingdoms and grand duchies west of the Rhine into the unified German nation. France had for the time being lost her place as a great European power; and internal conflicts, which had weighed so heavily with Gobineau, were overshadowed by a humiliation the whole nation had experienced together. The new character of the groups in conflict immediately brought forth its counterpart: a change in racist theories. Gobineau's exaltation of the Aryans (Teutons) had given an equal place in the sun to both France and Germany, whether defeated or victorious, if they kept pure their fair, long-headed supermen. The French of 1871 found this pronouncement unsatisfactory, and they were not long in remedying it. Quatrefages, the Director of the National History Museum in Paris, published *La Race Prussienne*,[1] in which he singled out Bismarck's conquering kingdom of Prussia and provided it with a racial ancestry entirely distinct from that of France. The inhabitants of Prussia, wrote Quatrefages, were not Aryans at all. To judge of their race one must study the Finns, that tall, fair, broad-headed race to the north of Prussia. The Finns had mixed with Slavs, representatives of the old Asiatic invaders of Europe, and it was this race which inhabited the whole of Prussia. In overrunning the high civilization of France they were but once more the scourge of Europe.

The racial gulf between France and Germany was argued also in a quite different fashion. The dean of anthropometric scholars in France, the indefatigable Broca, published five volumes [2] containing the skull measurements of both living and dead, and showing—what was already well known—the numerical predominance of broad-heads in France. France, Broca proclaimed, was a nation of Gallic (read *Alpine, Celtic*) broad-heads, and he reversed Gobineau's pronouncement of their inferiority. The broad-heads, he stated, had undoubtedly larger and better brains than the long-heads. Thus the Germans might pride themselves on their Nordic blood, but the French should pride themselves on their Gallic blood. The difficulty, which Broca's theory of French Gallicism did nothing to remove, is that the Germans are also predominantly broad-headed.

Both Broca and Quatrefages were pioneers in accurate an-

---

[1] English translation: Quatrefages, Jean-Louis Armand de, *The Prussian Race*, London, 1872. Tr. by Isabella Innes.
[2] Broca, Paul, *Mémoires d'Anthropologie*, Paris, 1871.

thropometric measurement of great populations, and they contributed much to our knowledge of European physical types. In a fashion unknown to Gobineau they used actual measurements in their arguments. Their researches on *race* advanced knowledge; the racist conclusions they drew were a quite different matter. All objective investigation indicates that an equally good brain can be housed in a broad or a long skull case, and, besides, the distribution of these physical types is quite similar in Germany and in France. On these precarious foundations, however, a chasm was fixed between the hated enemy and their own suffering nation. The racist theories of Broca and Quatrefages showed, not for the last time, how race data can be interpreted according to the pressing political needs of the moment.

Broca's exaltation of the broad-heads became the popular watchword of France during the whole lifetime of the "generation of 1870." In art and literary criticism, in political pronouncements, the cult of Celticism (read *Gallic, Alpine*) became a mystic faith. Under its favored designation of Celticism it allowed for racial ties with England, then growing in popularity in France, and dug deeper the channels of France's eastern barrier, the Rhine. Historians joined also; the dean of French historians, Fustel de Coulanges, proved that Germanic influences had had no part in forming the civilization of France.

On the other side of the Rhine the Germans were not slow to adopt their own racial theories. They had no need, as the French had, to change Gobineau's categories, and it was Germany which first made his work politically important. Richard Wagner, in his role as a passionate German nationalist, found the Count's *Essay* after his own heart and provided means for popularizing his writings in Germany. It was not until after Gobineau's death, however, that the *Gobineau Vereinigung* was founded in Germany in 1894, and not until

1899 that Wagner's son-in-law, Houston Chamberlain, one of Gobineau's earlier youthful disciples, published *Foundations of the Nineteenth Century* [1]—a work that made Gobinism a paramount cult in Germany.

The two bulky volumes of the *Foundations* seem today among the most confused, pretentious, and overwritten books that racism has produced, but they were welcomed in Germany with signal honors. The Kaiser read them aloud to his sons, had them distributed to officers of the Army, and directed that they be displayed in libraries and bookshops throughout Germany. The work went through edition after edition. Its contentions became part of the folk thought of the German nation.

The *Foundations* criticizes Gobineau severely, yet the racist position is much the same in the two authors. The situation to which racist theories had to be applied, however, had changed, and this led, as it always has in the history of racism, to new identifications of ancient and modern "races." The early Germanic tribes, which represented the superman to Gobineau, had left their heirs, he believed, among the aristocracy of many European nations; these same early Germanic tribes were, for Chamberlain, on the other hand, the settlers and defenders of the nation now united under the name of Germany. He called them the Teutons, but they were not merely the blond long-headed Nordics; if they had been, the German nation could not be as a whole the heirs of these predestined conquerors. Germans are, it is well known, some of them blond, some brunet, some long-headed, and some—the majority—broad-headed. Chamberlain's "Teutons" therefore are not blond and long-headed, nor dark and short-headed; they are both. Measurements of skull or tabulation of hair

---

[1] Chamberlain, Houston Stewart, *Die Grundlagen des Neunzehnten Jahrhunderts*, Munich, 1899. English translation: *The Foundations of the Nineteenth Century*, London, 1911, 2 vols. Trans. by John Lees.

color were not called for in his scheme. "Teutons" were not merely the early Germanic tribes Tacitus had described; they were Celts and Slavs as well. "The Celts, Slavs, and Teutons are descended from a single pure stock," [1] and therefore any triumph of the Teutons proper is a triumph for all the Chosen People. In this way Chamberlain reworked Gobineau's racist theories so that no German need be excluded. He fitted his praise to the German nation, and in that nation he found this blood of the Chosen People in its greatest purity. Mixture of blood among his three chosen stocks had prevented sterility and made for German greatness.

If physical characteristics do not identify Chamberlain's Great Race, upon what does he rely? This race alone understands the principle of leadership; it gives unfaltering loyalty to the leader of its choice. If he finds this trait among Italians or Frenchmen, he discovers them too to be Teutons in whatever country they were born. Their presence in these other countries only proved to Chamberlain that what greatness these nations had achieved was due to German blood; he claimed as Teutons Louis XIV, Dante, Michelangelo, Marco Polo, and Jesus Christ. His great concern was to define race so that it could rule out no member of the German nation: "Whoever reveals himself German by his acts, whatever his genealogical tree, is a German." In these pronouncements *race* ceases to have any assignable meaning, but such is obviously the price that must be paid for trying to draw up racist theories that can be applied to the mongrel nations of Europe in the twentieth century. In Chamberlain, this Nemesis overtook the gospel of racism.

He expounded anti-Semitism in the same manner. The *Foundations* stated all the racist pronouncements against the Jews which, in the past decade, we have come to associate with the Nazi dogmas. Chamberlain, however, did not dis-

---

[1] *Ibid.*, Vol. I, p. 499, note.

tinguish Semites by physical traits or by genealogy; Jews, as he knew, cannot be accurately separated from the rest of the population in modern Europe by tabulated anthropomorphic measurements. But they were enemies because they had special ways of thinking and acting. "One can very soon become a Jew . . . it needs only to have frequent intercourse with Jews, to read Jewish newspapers, etc." [1] Chamberlain is therefore the most frank of the prewar racists. Carrying out their arguments to their necessary conclusions, he disavows race completely and boasts that it is irrelevant to the racist position. In the interval between two world wars racists have repeated Chamberlain's self-contradiction whenever it was to their advantage to do so.

Racist literature in Germany became more and more inspirational, less and less hampered by facts, as the First World War drew near; by 1914 racism had become a nationalistic faith. After the First World War and the fall of the Weimar Republic, a defeated and disrupted Germany made racism the basis of national policy. It was not so difficult as it might seem to change the German racist theories from the boast of all-conquerors to the uses of a humiliated and despairing people. When Hitler wrote *Mein Kampf* in prison in the 1920's, he indicated the line along which this transformation was to be accomplished. Prewar Germany had ignored the racial basis of nationality, "the one and only law which makes life possible on this earth"; it had nurtured the viper Judaism in its bosom, and the Jews had been responsible for national defeat. Therefore the whole involved problem of who was Nordic, who Slav, and who Alpine in Germany was politically irrelevant; the enemy was the Jew and the Jew could be identified through his genealogy. For difficult cases Nazi theory still fell back on Chamberlain's pronouncement that a man might be a true German without a German genealogy; they called

---

[1] *Ibid.*, Vol. I, p. 491.

it "a German soul in a non-German body." But this evasion was saved for exceptional cases. The basis of racism in all other cases was genealogy—a genealogy in which there was no Jewish parent or grandparent. In this form racism became the basis of National Socialism. The program was stated in 1920 in the first draft of the Nazi program by the then unknown party leaders headed by Adolf Hitler, and included: Citizenship and public office are possible only to those of German blood (i.e., to none with Jewish blood); non-citizens are to be deported if any true Germans are unemployed, and in any case are to remain in Germany only as guests under special laws; immigration of all with alien blood to be prohibited, etc., etc.

Immediately upon Hitler's assumption of power in 1933 laws began to be passed putting into effect different items of this program, and scattered anti-Semitic persecutions soon occurred. It was not until the autumn of 1935, however, that the comprehensive rulings known as the Nuremberg Laws deprived all Jews of the right of citizenship, prohibited marriages between Jews and German non-Jews, and made a criminal offense of extra-marital relations between them. In the same month all Jewish children were removed from the elementary schools. A year later the expropriation, without recompense, of Jewish property and banking accounts was begun, and in 1937 this was systematically prosecuted with the object of eliminating Jews from trade and commerce. In 1938 outbursts against the Jews became general, and mass arrests took place in Berlin. All the world knows the pogroms that simultaneously occurred throughout Germany on November 10 of that year, and the edict which made all damage done during these outbreaks collectable claims against the Jews, plus a fine upon them of one billion marks. By this time the emigration of helpless and poverty-stricken Jews from Germany and Austria had become an international problem, and early in 1939 the Jewish community in Berlin received orders from the police to produce daily the names of one hundred Jews who would then receive two weeks' notice to leave the country. No provisions were made to finance this emigration. In Nazi-dominated parts of Europe the doctrines of racism had borne their bitter fruit.

Racism in the Third Reich, however, is not only a matter of anti-Semitism. From the first it involved also a program of Pan-Germanism—"Union," as the 1920 platform stated, "of all Germans in a Greater Germany." Germans lived not only in Germany and Austria; there were thirty million scattered throughout the world. They were "as good as we are" and they were by the ineradicable fact of blood members of the German nation. There are some seven million German-Americans, and any of these—or any Germans living under other governments—were branded as traitors if they assisted "opponents of the Third Reich," among whom the Nazis have long counted the United States.

Racism in the Third Reich has been altered to meet each new wind of political expediency. Chamberlain held that the Teuton was racially Christian, and he heaped panegyrics upon Christianity; Alfred Rosenberg, editor-in-chief of official newspapers and specifically in charge of racial indoctrination, pronounced the Christian church the chief menace to true Nordics, who will come into their own only when they have reasserted their old militant paganism and thrown off the Jewish Asiatic Catholic dominance to which they have been subjected in the Church.[1] He discovers a racial antipathy in the Nordics to the decadent words of the Sermon on the Mount.

Political developments, however, have led to even more fundamental changes in orthodox racism. Chamberlain, as

---

[1] Rosenberg, Alfred, *Der Mythus des Zwanzigsten Jahrhunderts*, Munich, 1935.

we have seen, based the greatness of Germany on the inter-mixture by marriage of Teutons, Celts, and Slavs—all "de-scended from a single pure stock." But the Third Reich's holy opposition to Russian Communism from 1934 to 1939 made the Slavs unacceptable as members of the Chosen People. They became in Nazi propaganda enemies not only in ideology but by heredity. This view was dropped even before the signing of the non-aggression pact in August 1939, and German silence on this score was one of the reasons on which some close observers based their belief that such a treaty was under consideration.

Germany's alliance with Italy raised a similar difficulty. Orthodox racism of the prewar and First World War period had been full of contempt for the Mediterranean race, but the Rome-Berlin Axis had to be given a racial basis. Much was made, therefore, of the German-ness of Northern Italy and the fact that classic German racists had ascribed all achievements beyond the Alps to infiltrations of northern blood; Chamberlain and others had outdone themselves in claiming as "Nordics" such Italians as Dante, Petrarch, Giotto, Leonardo, and Michelangelo. The same Italy which in 1915 France had welcomed as an ally because they both were racially Latin, Germany now welcomed on the basis of their common Teutonic blood.

The alliance with Japan was a more difficult matter. Hitler excepts the Japanese when he strikes out at non-Aryans, and Japanese residents of Germany are not subject to the racial laws of the Third Reich. They may therefore marry with German Aryans without polluting the pure blood extolled by the Nazis. Hans Gunther, who under the Nazi regime is Professor of Anthropology at the University of Jena, believes that Nordics were among the ancestors of the Japanese, and Dr. Alfred Rosenberg, "inspector-general of Nazi mental training," laid down, as a teaching officially sanctioned in

German schools, that the biological guarantee of Germany's leadership is shared by the Japanese. No travesty of anthropomorphic facts is too startling for propaganda to announce if the propaganda is backed by force of arms and concentration camps.

Racialism has become involved in scientific absurdities under the Third Reich, and it is obviously only a front used to justify negotiations and persecutions of the moment. Germany's invasion of Russia made Russians again Germany's "racial" enemies. Because of Norway's resistance to Nazi terrorism Norwegians are now officially proclaimed in Berlin to be non-Nordic. Therefore no one can say what racist theories will be current in Germany within the next few years. If the future of racism is like its past, these theories will depend not on any scientific facts but on what treaties are signed or not signed and on what power politics are in the ascendant.

Wherever we study racism, not only in the Third Reich, there are similar evidences that racist doctrines are invoked for political ends. Nations are hailed now as blood brother, now as destined foe, according to political alignments in peace and in war. In a world as yet unthreatened by the First World War, Carlyle and the historian J. R. Green accounted the valiant Germanic tribes as the ancestors of the English; in 1914 "the Germans," according to English pronouncements, "were what they were fifteen centuries ago, the barbarians who raided our ancestors and destroyed the civilization of the Roman Empire." They became "the Huns," the Mongols from the barbarous East. But Russia was in 1914 on the side of the Allies and racism therefore did obeisance to the affinities of the Celtic soul and the Slavic soul.

The history of national racism, wherever one looks, is the history of chauvinism. In a world which knew the history of Western civilization and the facts of race and wished to distinguish jingoism from fact, such racism would fall on deaf ears. Arrogance and panic, however, are eager to satisfy themselves with an easy and comforting oratory, and the oratory has been provided for them. Desperate peoples, too, are satisfied with a victim, and racism, telling them on the one hand that they are the heirs of the ages, has pointed out to them, on the other, a degenerate breed to extirpate. Racism, seen in its perspective of fifty years, has stemmed not from the sciences—which have repudiated it, and which, indeed, racism has constantly distorted in its pronouncements—but from politics.

Racism in its nationalistic phase, therefore, has been a politician's plaything. It has been bandied about by both enemies against each other even when these are, by anthropomorphic measurements, of similar racial composition; it has been used to discover racial brotherhood where the allies concerned are racially distinct. It is a dangerous plaything, a sword which can be turned in any direction to condemn the enemy of the moment. The inescapable conclusion from a consideration of its history is that these racist claims are a front designed to hide self-seeking aggressions and alliances. They are camouflage. For practical guidance in the world of affairs, we should do well therefore to go behind the racists' slogans and look squarely at the conflict they are trying to foment. Conflicts are sometimes justified, and we may perhaps decide the particular conflict is necessary. But we shall not have decided the matter on the dubious grounds of racism.

WHAT THEY SAY

[Before the French Revolution], however much men of different races may have striven with one another, it was seldom any sense of racial opposition that caused their strife.

They fought for land. They plundered one another. They sought glory by conquest. In none of these cases did the thought of racial distinctions come to the front.

> James Bryce, *Race Sentiment as a Factor in History*. Creighton Lecture. London, 1915, pp. 25, 26.

Racial relations today present more dangerous features in the field of interhuman relations than any other point of conflict. Nowhere are mob passions, prejudices, and fears so easy to evoke and so difficult to check.

> H. Kohn, "Race Conflict." *Encyclopædia of the Social Sciences,* Vol. XIII, 1934, p. 41.

All reputable anthropologists condemn the malignant nonsense about racial psychology which is preached and published by those who try to justify the oppression of ethnic minorities. Political theories about race are nothing more than instruments of propaganda, devised for the child minds of totalitarian populations.

> E. A. Hooton, *Twilight of Man*. New York, G. P. Putnam's Sons, 1939, p. 129.

[Racism] is a method of bolstering up self-esteem and lust for power by means of beliefs which have nothing in their favor except that they are flattering.

> Bertrand Russell, "The Ancestry of Fascism," in: *In Praise of Idleness*. New York, W. W. Norton & Co., 1935, p. 114.

At the best, however, belief in race dogma is just the same as national chauvinism, a symptom of immaturity, lack of experience, and in general of an intellectually poor individuality.

> Friedrich Hertz, *Race and Civilization*. New York, Macmillan Co., 1928, p. 323.

VIII. WHY THEN RACE PREJUDICE?

As WE HAVE SEEN, all scientific knowledge of race contradicts the idea that human progress has been the work of one race alone or can safely be entrusted to a program of racial hygiene in the future. No great civilization has been the work of a pure race, and neither history nor psychology, biology nor anthropology can render decisions about the future destiny of any present human breed. Racism has been a travesty of scientific knowledge and has served consistently as special pleading for the supremacy of any group, either class or nation, to which the pleader himself belonged and in whose permanent place in the sun he desired to believe.

Why then does racism have such social importance in our times? No discussion of race and racism can be complete without raising this problem; it is the really burning question, for upon our answer depend the measures we can trust to bring about a cure.

In answering this question we do not need to depend on fine-spun theories or self-communings; history has given the answers many times. We need only to obtain a little perspective. We have seen that racist dogmas as they are stated today are modern. But they express an old human obsession and only the "reasons why" have been altered. This old human obsession is that my group is uniquely valuable and, if it is weakened, all valuable things will perish. It were better therefore that a million perish than that one jot or tittle of that unique value should be lost. It becomes my divine mission to extirpate the challenger in whatever field.

The fields change, however. When one field has been won and tolerance and co-operativeness established in what was before an armed camp, we look back upon the episode as an example of human aberration. We think we are different and feel that progress has really been achieved—until other generations arise to look back upon us and decide that we have only shifted mutual intolerance to another area of life. For centuries the battlefield was religion. The Inquisition was not pure barbarism; it was the claim to unique value worked out with all its implications in a field where today we are willing to follow the precept of live and let live. We cannot see racism in perspective without reviewing the occasions and consequences of this earlier arrogance. The fact that it is in the field of religion instead of in the field of race is a reflection of the times; from every other point of view religious persecutions and racial persecutions duplicate one another. Their proponents claimed similar sacred missions; they killed and looted and temporarily enriched themselves. From the standpoint of history both set up false fronts that served political purposes; they destroyed brilliant civilizations. In that one matter in which they differ, religion as over against race, the earlier persecution was at least as justified as the latter. The medieval world, convinced that man's existence was an infinitesimal episode in his everlasting life, thought it was common humanity to kill the Antichrist that would lead thousands of souls to damnation. Today we judge this a fallacy, but we must not underestimate the worthy motives of those who believed that they alone had received the divine command; they were not actuated solely by arrogance but by their duty to keep the world faithful to the word of God and to ensure salvation to as many souls as possible. In many churchmen this must have been a worthy emotion, just as today we recognize that patriotism or pride of class is a worthy emotion. However, the judgment of history is that, when either of these worthy emotions is carried into a campaign of extermination of all who belong in other camps, the exterminators suffer with the exterminated and the result is social tragedy.

It was so in the Inquisition. Between 1200 and 1250 the Roman Church was at the apex of its political and temporal power, and these were the great years of the Inquisition. Heresy hunting was, like Jew-baiting in this decade in Germany, an eruption of minority persecution. It held out the same short-range advantages to the persecutors; it could be used as a front for political purposes; the confiscation of the victims' property enriched the persecutors; and the campaign of hate distracted attention from real issues. The real issues, as they appear in the perspective of history, were two. The first was the issue of freedom of conscience, a freedom which all the tortures of the Inquisition were powerless to uproot and which eventually triumphed in spite of bishops and of kings. The second was the worldliness and in some cases the corruption of the Catholic clergy of the period. Even in the highest Council of the Church itself this had been for some time a grave issue, and under Hildebrand (Gregory the Great) and the monk Bernard of Clairvaux there had been valiant efforts toward reform. The times, however, were not auspicious, and the heretics took up the cry of licentiousness against the Church. In stamping out the heretics, the Church embarked upon a campaign of extirpation that absorbed the attention of the faithful and postponed reform in its own ranks.

As a front for political purposes the Inquisition was used

in southern France to break the opposition to the growing power of the Capetian kings, and in Florence its terrible severities under Fra Ruggieri crushed also the Ghibelline revolt. Wherever the Inquisition flourished—in France, in Italy, and in Spain—it made common cause with power politics. The full extent of this common cause depended upon the practice of confiscating the heretics' property. The Inquisition is linked in popular thought with the burning of heretics and the use of torture to obtain confessions, but the confiscation of property was sociologically more important. Originally such property confiscated by the Inquisition belonged not to the Church but to kings and secular rulers; the right of the Papacy, and hence of the Inquisitors, to a share of these riches was not accepted until almost 1250, and the lion's share went always to secular authorities. Heresy hunting was profitable, and all those who sought riches and power eagerly took advantage of the opportunity, masking their satisfactions behind the dogma that the heretics were guilty of treason against the Almighty.

The most celebrated campaign of the Inquisition "in the name of God" was against the heretics of southern France in the first half of the thirteenth century. These heretics were known as the Albigenses and their home in Provence was a region on which the Roman Church had a comparatively slight hold. In those days Provence had little in common with northern France, and her barons were not vassals of the French king. The house of Toulouse in southern France had had an especially brilliant history. For two centuries its court had been famous for its love of art and literature, for its wealth and gallantry, and it had established its sovereignty throughout half of Provence. Its cities were the most wealthy and independent in all of France, and their culture was greatly influenced by interchange of goods and ideas with the Saracens of Palestine and the Moors of Spain

—cultures in many ways more enlightened than any others in the Western World at that time.

The heresy of the Albigenses was one of the many medieval cults of Manichaeism which taught the strictest asceticism in order that man might free himself from original evil. Manichaean cosmology was an all-embracing dualism of good and evil, of light and darkness, and only by eating the light contained in plants and by eschewing the darkness in meat, only by eliminating the darkness of sensual acts, could righteousness be achieved. "Finished" ascetics, as in many Oriental religions, became divinities and objects of worship to the laity. The dualism of these heresies was simple to grasp and offered an explanation of the evils of the world which had a strong appeal in those troubled times. But we know little of the teachings of the Albigensian sect; most of our knowledge is of their protest against the corruption of the contemporary clergy of the Church. Though Provence lay between great Catholic strongholds to the south and to the north, within its territories the Church was weak; the roots of Provençal culture were not in Rome. The rising burgher class in the towns especially espoused the heresy, and the growing independence of this class made the threat increasingly serious to the Church which was then at the height of its temporal power. The Papacy ordered the faithful clergy of northern France to preach a campaign of extermination against heretical Provence, and the crusade became one of the most implacable of religious wars. Its conclusion established the Capetian kings of northern France as monarchs in Provence after mass executions had decimated the independent burghers of the cities and had destroyed the civilization that had flourished in southern France. The burning of heretics continued for a hundred years, and at last the cult was exterminated.

The Inquisition did not survive into the modern period,

but religious persecution did. One of the longest and most disastrous of these conflicts occurred in France in the sixteenth and seventeenth centuries. French Protestants of that time were called Huguenots; by the middle of the sixteenth century they had grown greatly in numbers. Like the Albigensian heretics they were mainly prosperous bourgeois, and the bourgeois of the sixteenth century were opposed to concentration of power in the hands of the French kings. The bloody wars of a generation (1562–1593) were fought in the name of religion, but they masked a conflict which was in great part economic and political. After the renegade Huguenot leader, Henry of Navarre, was crowned king of France as Henry IV in 1594, the Edict of Nantes proclaimed full civil rights for the Protestants without withdrawing these from the Catholics. It was a signal victory. The law of the land now guaranteed religious and political freedom but, as has happened before and since that time, conflict continued. The Crown was Catholic and the Catholic clergy never accepted the Edict of Nantes. Cardinal Richelieu was the greatest power in France; he was both Cardinal and member of the royal council. His domestic policy was to concentrate power in the hands of the king, and to this the Huguenots were opposed. Therefore his internal policy was dominated by his ruthless opposition to the Huguenots, whom he could persecute in the name of religion. Louis XIV, after the death of Richelieu, exercised these royal powers to the full; his dream of absolute monarchy could be realized only if the Huguenots were removed. He carried on a legal persecution, discriminating against them in the exercise of their religion and their civil rights, and the terrible *dragonnades* used torture to compel their acceptance of the "king's religion." It was then, in 1685, that Louis XIV revoked the Edict of Nantes, declaring it was now unnecessary since all his subjects were Catholics. The Protestants emigrated or were sent to the galleys. His act left Louis absolute monarch and enriched his coffers with the expropriated wealth of the Huguenots. It also bled France of more than 400,000 of its inhabitants, intelligent and courageous people who enriched with their abilities the countries which received them.

The Albigensian crusade and the expulsion of the Huguenots are only two high spots in the long story of the suppression of minority groups before the rise of racism.

This suppression of minorities has been continued in the persecutions and nationalistic wars of the twentieth century. In the thirteenth century and in the sixteenth, as in the world today, new economic and social necessities were starting new ferments. Groups arose which opposed some aspect of the old order. The party in power answered by using torment, death, and confiscation of property. Parties in power can always do this, but in the eyes of history these suppressions have purchased an empty triumph. The great period of the Inquisition marked the downward-turning point in the temporal power of the Church no less than the ruin of Provençal civilization, and the Huguenot expulsion gave France only the disastrous and temporary splendor of the reign of Louis XIV. Persecution stopped neither the growing demand for freedom of conscience nor the rise of the bourgeoisie.

For a theory of racism there are two conclusions to be drawn from the whole matter. The first is that, in order to understand race persecution, we do not need to investigate race; we need to investigate *persecution*. Persecution was an old, old story before racism was thought of. Social change is inevitable, and it is always fought by those whose ties are to the old order. These ties may be economic or they may be religious, as in medieval Europe, or those of social affiliation, as with Roman patricians. Those who have these ties will consciously or unconsciously ferret out reasons for believing that their group is supremely valuable and that the new claimants threaten the achievements of civilization. They will raise a cry of rights of inheritance or divine right of kings or religious orthodoxy or racial purity or manifest destiny. These cries reflect the temporary conditions of the moment, and all the efforts of the slogan-makers need not convince us that any one of them is based on eternal verities. The battle cries of Nordicism belong with "Keep Cool with Coolidge" and "He Kept Us Out of War" of American presidential campaigns, and with slight changes in social necessities they will be as evanescent. All slogans are useful in the degree to which they express the faiths and discontents of the hour. Religious varieties were politically useful in eras and regions which had powerful religious interests; when these were overshadowed by secular privileges and when cleavages along religious lines became less important, religious slogans no longer justified the persecution of minorities as they had in earlier days.

Racial slogans serve the same purpose in the present century that religious slogans served before, that is, they are used to justify persecution in the interests of some class or nation. This racial slogan is peculiarly congenial to our times. Science is a word to conjure with in this century; unfortunately it is often used to conjure. It is not alone racism that has turned to so-called science for its arguments. A manufacturer of cosmetics conducted not long ago an investigation of various advertisements of his wares. He found that the two words which had most sales-appeal were "immediately" and "scientific." Every rouge, every face powder must claim a "scientific" uniqueness, and by this ballyhoo millions are impressed. It was the same with fake medicines, with drug-store drinks, and with health foods until it became necessary to defend the public by federal supervision of manufacturers' claims. The slogan of "science" will sell most things today, and it sells persecution as easily as it sells rouge.

The scientist repeatedly points out that the advertised rouge is indistinguishable from others or even that he has found it especially harmful in a laboratory test; he points out that no race has a monopoly of abilities or of virtues and that, as science, the racists' claims have no validity. For the scientist, science is a body of knowledge; he resents its use as a body of magic. But he knows that *scientific* is the word our civilization conjures with—in no matter what cause.

The choice of racial slogans to justify conflict is rooted in still another manner in the conditions of the modern age. Racial reasons for persecution are convenient just because in Western civilization today so many different breeds live in close contact with one another. The racist cries are raised not because those who raise them have any claim to belong to pure races, but because they do not; in other words, because today several ethnic groups occupy one city or one state, or states that share in one civilization are engaged in nationalistic wars. Hence comes the paradox that has been so often pointed out: that it is the most mongrel peoples of the world who raise the war cry of racial purity. From the point of view of race, this makes nonsense, but from the point of view of persecution it is inevitable. No group raises battle cries against people whose existence is of no moment to it; for conflict to arise, there must first be contact. Racial slogans arose therefore in Europe in class and national conflicts. The old religious slogans for persecution had lost their hold, and the racists evolved in their stead a bastard version of contemporary science. Racism remains in the eyes of history, however, merely another instance of the persecution of minorities for the advantage of those in power.

Once we have recognized that race conflict is only the justification of the persecution that is popular at the moment, the strangest paradox in all racist theory becomes clear. The racists have over and over again derived race prejudice from a race repulsion instinctive in mankind, and historians and biologists and anthropologists have as repetitiously pointed out that such a theory is impossible in view of the universal mixture of races. "Why, if Nature abhors race-crossing, does she do so much of it?" [1] But repulsion to inter-marriage accompanies any conflict of two groups, however the groups may be defined. They need not be racial. The patricians of Rome recoiled from marriage with plebeians in the same way, the Catholics of France from marriage with the Huguenots. It is not that man has a set of instincts which make only his own race sexually attractive, but that in-groups are unwilling to give status to the outsider. They do not want to share prerogatives with him. If this in-group is defined racially as Anglo-Saxons have defined it in their contact with native peoples of the world, their desire to maintain the in-group will bring about selective mating in marriage, but it notoriously does not prevent mating out-side of marriage. The great numbers of half-castes in India and mulattoes in America are testimony to the fact that the antipathy is not instinctive aversion to members of another race.

Those theorists also who have explained race prejudice by visible racial differences are similarly confused. They have said that race prejudice is caused by obvious and striking contrasts in face and color. They are, however, mistaking a momentary feature of persecution for a causal one. There was no differentiating skin color or nose shape in a Hugue-not, or in the Albigensian victims of the Inquisition. On the other side of the picture, poverty sets groups as visibly apart as the color of their hair or the shape of their heads. Groups may be set apart by any number of things besides race—by whether they go to Mass or by whether they drop their *h*'s.

---

[1] Castle, W. E., "Biological and Social Consequences of Race-Crossing," *American Journal of Physical Anthropology,* Vol. IX, pp. 145–146.

Members of a primitive tribe have been known to kill at sight members of a neighboring tribe of the same race and language because they felt that the way they carried their burden baskets was an insult to human beings. Not the fact of "visibility" of skin color but the fact that racial characteristics are transmitted over so many generations makes racial prejudice a new problem in the world. A man can stop going to Mass or a Huguenot can take the sacrament because "Paris is worth a Mass" or the heroine of *Pygmalion* learn to enunciate her mother tongue in the Oxford fashion, but too dark a Negro cannot "pass" and not even his children's children may be born light enough to do so. This is a problem of relative permanence of distinctions, not specifically of "visibility." In the long course of history persecution has been now more, now less intense; but these variations do not correlate with the presence or absence of racial visibility.

Mistaken explanations of the nature of race prejudice are of minor importance so long as they are concerned with theoretical points like instinctive antipathies or the role of racial visibility. There is a far more important issue. The fact that to understand race conflict we need fundamentally to understand *conflict* and not *race,* means something much more drastic. It means that all the deep-seated causes of conflict in any group or between groups are involved in any outbreak of race prejudice. Race will be cried up today in a situation where formerly religion would have been cried up. If civilized men expect to end prejudice—whether religious or racial—they will have to remedy major social abuses, in no way connected with religion or race, to the common advantage. Whatever reduces conflict, curtails irresponsible power, and allows people to obtain a decent livelihood will reduce race conflict. Nothing less will accomplish the task.

For the friction is not primarily racial. We all know what

the galling frictions are in the world today: nationalistic rivalries, desperate defense of the status quo by the haves, desperate attacks by the have-nots, poverty, unemployment, and war. Desperate men easily seize upon some scapegoat to sacrifice to their unhappiness; it is a kind of magic by which they feel for the moment that they have laid the misery that has been tormenting them. In this they are actively encouraged by their rulers and exploiters, who like to see them occupied with this violence, and fear that if it were denied them they might demand something more difficult. So Hitler, when his armament program cut consumers' goods and increased hours of work and lowered real wages, exhorted the nation in 1938 to believe that Germany's defeat in 1919 had been due to Jewry, and encouraged racial riots. And this served two purposes: It gave an undernourished people an outlet harmless to the government, and it allowed the government treasury to appropriate to itself the wealth of the Jews.

In this sequence of events the Third Reich is but following a long series of precedents in European anti-Semitism. During the Middle Ages persecutions of the Jews, like all medieval persecutions, were religious rather than racial. Intermarriage between Jews and Gentiles was condemned, not as a racist measure, but in the same manner as marriages between Catholics and heretics were condemned. The pogroms of the time of the Crusades were carried out by stay-at-home mobs imitating the Crusaders in avenging the death of Christ; the mobs killed Jews, the Crusaders fought the Arabs and Turks. The link between Jews and Turks was not racial; in the period of the Crusades the two were equated because the first had crucified Christ and the second owned his tomb. Nor were persecutions other than those set in motion by the Crusaders directed toward eliminating a racial breed; apostate Jews purchased safety. A renegade

Jew denounced or concealed his religion, not his race. The Popes and rulers favorable to the Jews promulgated laws directing that "they should not be baptized by force, constrained to observe Christian festivals nor to wear badges." Even up to the First World War some German racists advocated as the cure for conflict, not extinction of the Jewish race, but a racial merger. This was especially true of the great nationalist historian Treitschke, who was one of Germany's foremost advocates of racist salvation at the turn of this century.

As racist persecutions replaced religious persecutions in Europe, however, the inferiority of the Jew became that of *race*. By the 1800's a tidal wave of pogroms and persecutions swept over large parts of Europe. To the people it everywhere appeared that the bourgeoisie were in the saddle, and the Jews, owing to earlier segregation in city ghettos and to restrictions against land-owning, were all bourgeoisie. They were hated for this reason, and persecution was reinforced by the old tradition of religious animosity against the Jews. Racial anti-Semitism was all too easy to arouse. In Germany in the eighties an anti-Semitic demagogue of evil repute was cynically encouraged by members of the Conservative Party in order to strengthen with his following their opposition to the Social Democrats; synagogues were burned and violence against the Jews went unpunished. The charge of Jewish ritual murder was revived. In France, the anti-Semitic movement came to a climax in the 1890's with the famous Dreyfus affair. It marks probably the climax of prewar anti-Semitism in Europe. The reactionary party was most strongly represented in the Army, and the "framing" of a prominent Jewish staff officer, Captain Alfred Dreyfus, and his conviction of treason on forged evidence, were the occasion for a year-long conflict that rocked the nation. To the honor of France, the plot was laid bare, Dreyfus was exonerated, and it was shown that those who were really guilty of the treason had attempted to hide themselves behind a Jew because of popular anti-Semitism.

The more closely one studies European anti-Semitism in its modern racial guise, the less it appears that the conflict is racial; it is the old problem of unequal citizenship rights. Whenever one group, whether industrial workers or a religious sect or a racial group, is discriminated against before the law or in equal claims to life, liberty, and jobs, there will always be powerful interests to capitalize on this fact and to divert violence from those responsible for these conditions into channels where it is relatively safe to allow. In the case of the Jews we inherit from the old era of religious persecution all the necessary shibboleths of hate, and these are easily turned to account in a new setting. In addition there is exceptional profit; unlike most discriminated-against minorities, the Jews often provide rich contraband and are therefore marked objects for persecution to a poverty-stricken government or populace.

The cure for anti-Semitism, therefore, logically lies, as in all minority conflicts, in the extension to all men of full citizenship rights and of full opportunity to make good in any field. There would have been no Dreyfus case if certain traitors had not felt that a framed Jew would be found guilty by the courts. There would have been no nationwide pogroms in Germany in 1938 if all those who took part in them had known the state would hold them accountable. It is not only for the sake of the persecuted that the full rights of minorities need to be maintained. The minorities may be only martyrs, but the persecutors revert to savagery. If we are unwilling or unable to pay the price of equality in human rights, we, the persecutors, suffer brutalization in ourselves whenever we fall into the trap set for us.

The case of the Negro since the Civil War in America

points the same social lesson. The only trustworthy objective in any color-line program is the ultimate elimination of legal, educational, economic, and social discriminations. The fact that such elimination is not accepted even as an ultimate objective in most parts of the South is due to the persistence of slave-owner attitudes on the one hand and, on the other, to the degrading conditions under which great numbers of Negroes have lived in the United States. Granted that great numbers of Negroes are not ready for full citizenship, the social conditions which perpetuate their poverty and ignorance must be remedied before anyone can judge what kind of citizens they might be in other, more favorable circumstances. To be able to live a decent life and be respected for it, without being subjected to a blanket damnation that one's personal life cannot remove, is a human right, the granting of which would have immense social repercussions.

In periods and places where social institutions have made this possible for the Negro in the New World, the results have been incomparably better than those in the United States since the Civil War. Lord Bryce, an excellent observer, said of Brazil: "Brazil is the one country in the world, besides the Portuguese colonies on the east and west coasts of Africa, in which a fusion of the European and African races is proceeding unchecked by law or custom. The doctrines of human equality and human solidarity have here their perfect work. The work is so far satisfactory that there is little or no class friction. The white man does not lynch or maltreat the Negro; indeed I have never heard of a lynching anywhere in South America except occasionally as part of a political convulsion. The Negro is not accused of insolence and does not seem to develop any more criminality than naturally belongs to any ignorant population with loose notions of morality and property. What ultimate effect the intermixture of blood will have on the European element in

Brazil I will not venture to predict. If one may judge from a few remarkable cases it will not necessarily reduce the intellectual standard." [1]

Such conditions were possible in Brazil only because of the extreme lack of racial discrimination which the Portuguese everywhere showed in their post-Columbian colonization; with the growing influence of non-Portuguese cultures in modern Brazil, the Negro has to some extent suffered. With growing discrimination against his race, the usual effects have followed, small though these consequences are in Brazil in comparison with the United States. But while discrimination was at a minimum, the social results were good.

To minimize racial persecution, therefore, it is necessary to minimize conditions which lead to persecution; it is not necessary to minimize race. Race is not in itself the source of the conflict. Conflict arises whenever any group—in this case, a race—is forged into a class by discriminations practiced against it; the race then becomes a minority which is denied rights to protection before the law, rights to livelihood and to participation in the common life. The social problem does not differ whether such a group is racially distinguished or whether it is not; in either case the healthy social objective is to do away with minority discriminations.

We are so far from doing this in the modern world that it is likely to seem a program impossible of achievement. Even so, this is not the total program for a world free of race conflict. It is not enough merely to legislate human rights for the minorities. The majorities, also—the persecutors— must have solid basis for confidence in their own opportunity to live in security and decency. Otherwise, whatever the laws, whatever the guarantees, they will find out a victim

---

[1] Bryce, James, *South America, Observations and Impressions*, New York, 1914, pp. 477, 480.

and sacrifice him as a scapegoat to their despair. Everything that is done in any nation to eliminate unemployment, to raise the standard of living, to ensure civil liberties, is a step in the elimination of race conflict. Whatever is done to fasten fear upon the people of a nation, to humiliate individuals, to abrogate civil liberties, to deny coveted opportunities, breeds increased conflict. Men have not, for all their progress in civilization, outgrown the hen yard; a hen who is pecked at by a cock attacks, not the cock, but a weaker hen; this weaker hen attacks a still weaker, and so on down to the last chicken. Man too has his "pecking order," and those who have been victims, even though they belong to the "superior race," will require victims.

The truth of the matter is that these two aspects of a program for preventing the ravages of racism—democratic opportunity for the privileged and for the underprivileged —cannot be separated from one another. They are web and woof. One of the great political advantages of racist slogans is that the underprivileged may use them. Therefore the unemployed and the low-income groups can vent, through this alleged racist "superiority," the hatred that is engendered by their fear and insecurity. Studies in America have many times shown that anti-Semitism is strongest among low-income groups and that the high peaks of racial persecution have coincided with the low troughs of depression periods. While we raise Negro standards of living, of health, and of education in the South, therefore, it is necessary also to raise the standards of the Southern poor whites. Until we have "made democracy work" so that the nation's full manpower is drafted for its common benefit, racist persecution will continue in America. Until housing and conditions of labor are raised above the needlessly low standards which prevail in many sections of the country, scapegoats of some sort will be sacrificed to poverty. Until the regulation of industry has enforced the practice of social responsibility, there will be exploitation of the most helpless racial groups, and this will be justified by racist denunciations.

Hard-boiled economists and statesmen recognize today the shortsightedness of policies which allow such conditions to continue and to become intensified. Those who fight to perpetuate them are repeating the errors of the Albigensian crusade and the Huguenot expulsion; they are gaining a false and temporary advantage at the expense of their own permanent welfare. National prosperity, however thin you cut it, has two surfaces: ability to sell means ability to buy; employment means production. Whatever groups battle with each other, under conditions of modern industry and finance, the most important condition of either one's getting more is that the other shall also get more. Since their conflict is truly suicidal, it is necessary for the benefit of the contestants themselves that farsighted regulations should be imposed on both parties.

In the last decade we have grown to recognize much more fully the responsibility that rests on the state for achieving satisfactory national conditions, and from the standpoint of history it is likely that this role of the state will in the long run be extended rather than curtailed. A democratic state, when it lives up to its minimum definition at all, is the one institution which represents all the parts of the body politic. It can propose for itself programs which will eventually benefit the whole body. It is hard to see how this responsibility for the whole can be taken today except by the national government, and in the past decade state regulation has increased, national treasuries all over the Western World have been opened for the relief of the unemployed, and compulsory old-age insurance is in operation in many nations. These and other national undertakings can be used to minimize economic discrimination. Equality in the matter of civil liberties is closely bound up with such programs, and so long as civil liberties are made more, rather than less, equal for different groups, there is no historical reason for fearing the increased role of the state. For the true goal in any program for a better America is that all men may be able to live so that self-respect is possible and so that they may have confidence that prosperity will spread its benefits widely over the population.

The cultural anthropologist has the best reason in the world to know that conflict is eliminated only as men work together for common benefits, and obtain them in common. In most of the tribes the anthropologist knows, he can study side by side two different codes of ethics: one is that of open-handed hospitality and liberality and sharing, along with condemnation of aggressions like stealing and murder; the other is death at sight, torture, and the exaltation of robbery. The first code a man applies to those whose economic and social activities benefit him; these form an in-group within which none but moral reprobates are penalized. No matter who is successful in the hunt, the whole in-group benefits; any special skills any man may possess are an asset to the group as a whole. The priests conduct ceremonies for the good of the tribe and for common advantages like increase of plants and animals; warriors defend the little group against predatory outsiders. The second code a man applies to tribes with whom his tribe makes no common cause. No activities of theirs feed or house or bless or defend him. They are outside the pale. It is only a question of whether he kills his enemies first or they kill him.

The in-group code of ethics arises, however, only as the institutions of a society provide for shared advantages. When increase of food supply is not a common benefit, but something one man must get at the expense of another; when supernatural power is not used for general blessings, like rain, which falls on all, but for charms to use for personal ends against a neighbor; when legal or economic or political institutions put one man at the mercy of his neighbors, persecution develops. The gain or loss of all men is no longer my own gain or loss and the tribe is no longer a unit within which in-group ethics operate. The persecution that develops is most often sorcery. Sorcery is a very evil thing and when society does not officially punish it the victim has no redress. Unchecked sorcery societies are like modern nations with Ogpus and Gestapos, and they act out in deeds Hitler's dictum: "We need hatred, hatred, and then more hatred."

In-group ethics is therefore a reflection of the fact that all members share in their tribal enterprises and do actually profit from one another's activities. In-group mutual support is as native to the human race as out-group hostility; it is not something precarious and achieved only by isolated individuals at the end of a long social evolution. It arose long before the higher ethical religions with their teachings of altruism and duty. It occurs automatically whenever the social order makes it advantageous. It is at home among the lowest savages, and the one essential contribution modern civilization has made has been to enlarge the size of the in-group. In this there has been incomparable progress. Millions today recognize their common cause as citizens of a great nation, or as members of a party, or as financiers, or as workers, whereas in past history some little territory might be divided into a dozen hostile groups recognizing no common bonds. Today the increasing complexity of the processes of production, the ease of transportation, the interdependence of financial systems have brought it about that people in the remotest part of civilization suffer from catastrophe in another part.

The very progress of civilization, therefore, has laid the foundation for a vast extension of in-group mutual dependency and mutual support. Mankind has not yet adjusted its institutions to the real requirements of the world it has created, and this cultural lag today threatens the very bases of international life. Many serious students of human affairs have been driven to despair. The world of our fathers, they conclude, has been destroyed because it tried to ignore the real facts of human nature; it tried to impose a peaceful social order on a predatory animal. The lesson we should learn from recent events, they say, is that man is by nature a beast of prey who will always tear and rend his weaker neighbors; we must recognize that wars and racial persecutions are inevitable in human destiny. To the anthropologist such a counsel of despair is demonstrably false. In-group ethics are as "innate" as out-group ethics, *but they occur only when certain social conditions are fulfilled*. We cannot get in-group ethics without meeting those conditions. In our own country this means that a better America will be one which benefits not some groups alone but all citizens; so long as there is starvation and joblessness in the midst of abundance we are inviting the deluge. To avert it, we must "strongly resolve" that all men shall have the basic opportunity to work and to earn a living wage, that education and health and decent shelter shall be available to all, that regardless of race, creed, or color, civil liberties shall be protected.

The elimination of race conflict is a task of social engineering. But what of education? It is often said that our school systems must make themselves responsible for ending race prejudice, and attempts have been made to achieve tolerance by special instruction. This is of great importance, but we should be quite clear about the limits of its effectiveness; otherwise, in the end we shall cry that we were betrayed because it has not succeeded. All education, whether of children or of adults, is important and necessary because it makes for an enlightened mind and for unbiased impulses.

These are essential because without them discriminations may not be done away with at all and barriers to opportunity may never be thrown down. But good impulses are socially effective only when they have accomplished these results. "Hell is paved with good intentions"—intentions which were blindly regarded as ends in themselves and not as mere preliminaries. This is a platitude, but one which is often forgotten in discussions of the role of our schools in racial matters. If we are to make good use of the great powers of education in combating racism, two goals should be kept clearly distinct. On the one hand, it is desirable to teach in the regular social studies the facts of race and of the share of different races in our civilization. On the other hand, it is necessary to hold up ideals of a functioning democracy; it is necessary to help children to understand the mutual interdependence of different groups; it is necessary to encourage comparison of our social conditions with conditions which are better than ours as well as with those that are worse. It is necessary that they should be taught to think of unsatisfactory conditions not as inescapable facts of Nature, but as ones which with effort can be done away with. Only through such education can school instruction lay the basis for the amelioration of race conflict. We cannot trust to teaching them about the glories of Chinese civilization or the scientific achievements of the Jews. That is worth doing, but if we leave it at that and expect them to become racially tolerant we have deceived ourselves. The fatal flaw in most arguments which would leave to the schools the elimination of race conflict is that they propose education *instead* of social engineering. Nothing but hypocrisy can come of such a program.

The program that will avail against racism is called today "making democracy work." In so far as it is achieved in America it will produce the kind of behavior it has always produced in a mutually supporting in-group. Change, we must recognize, is always difficult and produces dislocations. But if we know the direction in which we must move, we can resolve to pay the necessary costs of change. The Arabians have a proverb: " 'What will you have?' said the Prophet, 'take it and pay for it.' " We must pay for a democracy that works, but fortunately in this case we can reassure ourselves with the knowledge that, even in financial accounting, government investments in rehousing and rebuilding America, in soil conservation, in health and education, and in increasing the nation's purchasing power through insurance benefits, pay their own way with handsome returns. A price is exacted also for a social order like Nazi Germany, and that price, in lowered standard of living, in brutalization, in denial of human rights, in sabotage of science and the intellectual life, is higher than any costs of democracy. In persecuting victims, the Nazis were themselves victimized.

Our Founding Fathers believed that a nation could be administered without creating victims. It is for us to prove that they were not mistaken.

WHAT THEY SAY

In the gain or loss of one race all the rest have equal share.

James Russell Lowell in *The Crisis.*

There is no irrepressible conflict between Oriental and Western civilizations. On the contrary they are complementary to each other, not necessarily competitive.

Paul Samuel Reinsch, *Intellectual and Political Currents in the Far East.* New York, Houghton Mifflin Co., 1911, p. 35.

Every effort of the Negro to move, to raise and improve his social status, rather than his condition, has invariably met with opposition, aroused prejudice and stimulated racial animosities. Race prejudice, so conceived, is merely an elementary expression of conservatism.

> R. E. Park, "Bases of Race Prejudice." *Annals of the American Academy,* Vol. CXL, Nov. 1928, p. 13.

Race thus has a profound social significance. . . . It is made the symbol of cultural status and thus serves to justify the exploitation of the weaker group with the inevitable political and cultural consequences. Being a symbol of cultural status it serves automatically to classify individuals, and so to retard their advance by limiting their freedom and determining the cultural values to which they have access.

> E. B. Reuter, *American Race Problem.* New York, T. Y. Crowell Co., 1927, p. 34.

The philosophical implication of race-thinking is that by offering us the mystery of heredity as an explanation, it diverts our attention from the social and intellectual factors that make up personality.

> Jacques Barzun, *Race, A Study in Modern Superstition.* New York, Harcourt, Brace and Co., 1937, p. 282.

For the combating of racism before it sinks its ugly fangs deep in our body politic, the scientist has a special responsibility. Only he can clean out the falsities which have been masquerading under the name of science in our colleges, our high schools and our public prints. Only he can show how groundless are the claims that one race, one nation or one class has any God-given right to rule.

> Henry A. Wallace, in an address delivered at the World's Fair, New York, October 14, 1939.

Anti-alien campaigns of whatever nature are a sickening travesty of Americanism. We can contribute nothing of more value to a sick world than proof that men and women of different racial origins can get along together peaceably and democratically. Go far enough back and we are all aliens.

New York Times, Editorial, December 7, 1939.

The Races of Mankind

Resolutions and Manifestoes of Scientists

Index

NOTE ON *The Races of Mankind*

"The Races of Mankind" has become a household phrase.

It all started on October 25, 1943, with the publication of a pocket-size, green-jacketed 32-page pamphlet by the Public Affairs Committee, Inc., non-profit, educational organization of 30 Rockefeller Plaza, New York City.

Ruth Benedict and Gene Weltfish, both of the Department of Anthropology of Columbia University, prepared this simple exposition of the facts of science about race. A committee of the American Association of Scientific Workers, including L. C. Dunn, Zoology; Otto Klineberg, Psychology; and Marion Smith, Anthropology, gave assistance in a supervisory capacity.

Publication day was quiet, the press paid little attention; churches, schools, organizations, and the YMCA-USO began to use the pamphlet in modest numbers. But soon things began to happen.

During January 1944 newspapers throughout the United States headlined the story that the USO had "banned" *The Races of Mankind*.

With editorial writers, columnists, and radio commentators still taking sides vehemently, the little pamphlet hit another storm: In March distribution of 55,000 copies by the U.S. Army Morale Division was blocked when Representative Andrew May said that if the Army used the pamphlet someone would get in trouble. In April a special House Military Affairs Sub-Committee charged that the pamphlet was filled with "all the techniques . . . of Communistic propaganda." Countered Frederick Woltman, New York *World Telegram* authority:

If it doesn't watch out, the House Military Affairs Committee is going to wake up some morning to discover it has accused Alfred

P. Sloan, Jr., chairman of General Motors; Matthew Woll, foremost anti-Red in the American Federation of Labor; the YWCA, Girl Scouts, Junior League and Baptist Sunday School Board of spreading "Communist propaganda."

In addition to the controversy carried on in press and radio, hundreds of individuals, men and women from all parts of the United States, expressed vigorous opinions, both pro and con. Almost overnight about 200,000 agate lines of press comment appeared. Radio voices were raised louder. Thousands of people who otherwise would never have heard about *The Races of Mankind* sent in their dimes for copies of the pamphlet. Almost all the letters received by the Public Affairs Committee praised "the statement of the facts of race as science knows them."

The Races of Mankind was translated into seven foreign languages. Arrangements were made for a comic strip feature.

The creative use made of the pamphlet by churches (all denominations and faiths), schools, and civic, educational and religious organizations speaks loudest for the excellence of *The Races of Mankind*. Among the outstanding educational materials developed from the pamphlet are the traveling exhibit prepared by the Cranbook Institute of Science, Bloomfield Hills, Michigan; "Meet Your Relatives," a lively musical comedy prepared by Mrs. Alice B. Nirenberg and pupils of Public School No. 6, New York City; and *The Races of Mankind* film strip, "We Are All Brothers— What Do You Know About Race?" produced by New Tools for Learning, New York City. Currently, an educational motion picture in animated cartoon technique is being prepared.

Total distribution of the pamphlet reached almost three-quarters of a million; orders for copies of the pamphlet continue steadily. The Public Affairs Committee's experience with *The Races of Mankind* pamphlet (No. 85 in the Public Affairs series of pamphlets on current economic and social issues) shows that America is not afraid to examine and to discuss its problems.

—VIOLET EDWARDS

The Races of Mankind

BY RUTH BENEDICT AND GENE WELTFISH

The World Is Shrinking

Thirty-five nations are now united in a common cause—victory over Axis aggression, the military destruction of fascism. This is the greatest fighting alliance of nations in history. These United Nations include the most different physical types of men, the most unlike beliefs, the most varied ways of life. White men, yellow men, black men, and the so-called "red men" of America, peoples of the East and the West, of the tropics and the arctic, are fighting together against one enemy.

Every morning in the newspapers and on the bulletin boards we read of yesterday's battles in Russia, in China, in Italy, in the Solomon Islands, and in New Guinea. One day's hop in a plane can carry us across the oceans. Our supply ships go to every corner of the globe. On the radio we hear men reporting on the spot from Cairo and Australia. Burma is much closer to us today than New Orleans was to Washington at the time of the War of 1812. Distance then was a hard fact; it had not been scaled down by the triumphs of human invention.

This war, for the first time, has brought home to Americans the fact that the whole world has been made one neighborhood. All races of man are shoulder to shoulder. Our armed forces are in North Africa with its Negro, Berber, and Near-East peoples. They are in India. They are in China. They are in the Solomons with its dark-skinned, "strong"-haired Melanesians. Our neighbors now are peoples of all the races of the earth.

For Americans this is not so new an experience as it is to people of most nations. In our country men of different color, hair texture, and head shape have lived together since the founding of our nation. They are citizens of the United States. Negroes and Whites, Indians, Mexicans, Chinese, and people from the European nations are all taxable, subject to the draft and to the other laws of the land. They are part of our great national community. History today is only bringing together on a world scale races which have been brought together on a smaller scale here in America.

Americans know better than most how much hard feeling there can be when people of different races and nationalities have to live together and be part of one community. They know that there is often conflict. Today when what we all want more than anything else is to win this war, most Americans are confident that, whatever our origins, we shall be able to pull together to a final victory. Hitler, though, has always believed we were wrong; he has believed that hard feeling would break out and leave us defeated. He has been sure that he could "divide and conquer." He has believed that he could convince non-White races in Asia and Africa that this is a "white man's war." He has believed especially that America was a no man's land, where peoples of all origins were ready to fall to fighting among themselves. He believes that this is a front on which we are doomed to lose the battle. It is certainly a front no less important in this war than the Production Front and the Inflation Front.

Science and the Race Front

In any great issue that concerns this war we turn to science. When we need new fuels, substitutes for rubber, lighter metals, or new plastics, we ask scientists to tell us what is possible and what is impossible. The chemists tell us how to make the plastics we need, and the physicists tell us how to detect and locate an approaching airplane, and the engineers tell us how to build a better fighting plane. When we are faced with war shortages, they tell us what essential materials we have been throwing out on the dump heap.

We need the scientist just as much on the race front. Scientists have studied race. Historians have studied the history of all nations and peoples. Sociologists have studied the way in which peoples band together. Biologists have studied how man's physical traits are passed down from one generation to the next. Anthropologists have studied man's bodily measurements and his cultural achievements. Psychologists have studied intelligence among different races. All that the scientists have learned is important to us at this crucial moment of history. They can tell us: "this is so," "this is not so," "this occurs under certain conditions," or "this occurs under opposite conditions."

This booklet cannot tell you all that science has learned about the races of mankind, but it states facts that have been learned and verified. We need them.

One Human Race

The Bible story of Adam and Eve, father and mother of the whole human race, told centuries ago the same truth that science has shown today: that all the peoples of the earth are a single family and have a common origin. Science describes the intricate make-up of the human body: all its different organs co-operating in keeping us alive, its curious anatomy that couldn't possibly have "just happened" to be the same in all men if they did not have a common origin. Take the structure of the human foot, for instance. When you list all the little bones and muscles and the joints of the toes, it is impossible to imagine that that would all have happened twice. Or take our teeth: so many front teeth, so many canines, so many molars. Who can imagine finding the same arrangements in two human species if they weren't one family?

The fact of the unity of the human race is proved, therefore, in its anatomy. It is proved also by the close similarity in what all races are physically fitted for. No difference among human races has affected limbs and teeth and relative strength so that one race is biologically outfitted like a lion and another biologically outfitted like a lamb. All races of men can either plow or fight, and all the racial differences among them are in nonessentials such as texture of head hair, amount of body hair, shape of the nose or head, or color of the eyes and the skin. The White race is the hairiest, but a white man's hair isn't thick enough to keep him warm in cold climates. The Negro's dark skin gives him some protection against strong sunlight in the tropics, and white men often have to take precautions against sunstroke. But the war has shown that white men can work and fight even in a tropical desert. Today white men in hot countries wear sun helmets and protect themselves with clothes and rub their skin with suntan oil. Very dark-skinned people in the north, too, can add cod-liver oil and orange juice to their diet, and, if they need to, take a vitamin pill or two. The shape of the head, too, is a racial trait; but whether it is round or long, it can house a good brain.

The races of mankind are what the Bible says they are—brothers. In their bodies is the record of their brotherhood.

WHAT ARE RACE DIFFERENCES?

The greatest adventure story in the history of the world is the spread of early man to all corners of the globe. With crude tools, without agriculture, without domesticated animals except the dog, he pressed on, from somewhere in Asia, to the tip of Africa, to the British Isles, across Bering Strait into America and down to Cape Horn. He occupied the islands of the Pacific and the continent of Australia. The world had a small population then, and many of these pioneers were for centuries as separated from other peoples as if they lived on another planet. Slowly they developed physical differences.

Those who settled nearer the equator, whether in Europe, Asia, or in the Americas, developed a darker skin color than those who settled to the north of them. People's hair is often the same over great areas: frizzly hair, lank hair, wavy hair. Europeans remained quite hairy, but in some parts of the world body hair almost disappeared. Blue eyes appeared in the north. In some places in Asia a fold of skin developed over the inner corner of the eye and produced what we call a slant eye.

All these distinctive traits made it easy to recognize people as belonging to different parts of the world. In each place the people got used to looking at one another. They said, "Our men are really men. Our women are beautiful. This is the way people should look." Sometimes they liked the appearance of their close neighbors. But strangers seemed odd and queer. Strangers wore funny clothes and their manners were bad. Even more important, strangers did not look the way people should. Their noses were too flat or too pointed. Their skin was "a sickly white" or "a dirty black." They were too fat or too short. Everywhere in the world men and women used the standard of their own people to judge others and thought that people who differed from this standard looked funny or ugly.

All Peoples Much the Same

After the discovery of America by Columbus, Europeans began traveling to every quarter of the globe, and all the new peoples they met were complete strangers to them. For one thing, the Europeans couldn't understand their languages. They looked and acted strange. Europeans thought they were different creatures and named a lot of different "races." Gradually the Europeans described each one as having a skin color, kind of hair, kind of lips, height, and head shape that was peculiar to that "race." Nowadays we know that this was a false impression.

Height

Take height, for example. There are tall and short people almost everywhere in the world. Near the sources of the Nile, the Shilluk Negroes are 6 feet 2 inches; their neighbors, the brown pygmies, are 4 feet 8 inches. In Italy, a six-footer and a five-footer could both be native Italians for generations back. Among the Arizona Indians, the Hopi Pueblos are 5 feet 4 inches; their Mohave neighbors are nearly 6 feet.

A report of the Selective Service System of November 10, 1941, showed that registrants examined for the U. S. Army varied in height from 4 feet 6 inches to 7 feet 4 inches. This represents the extremes of height anywhere in the world. The Army's limits for acceptance, from 5 feet to 6 feet 6 inches, would include most men the world over.

Shape of Head

Take the shape of the head as another example. In West Africa there are more long heads; in the Congo, more round. Among the American Indians, as well as in the population of Europe, both the longest and the roundest heads are to be found, and in Asia Minor long heads and round heads appear among very close relatives.

Or let us take the brain itself. Because the brain is the thinking organ, some scientists have tried to find differences in the size and structure of the brain among different groups of people. In spite of these efforts, using the finest microscopes, the best scientists cannot tell from examining a brain to what group of people its owner belonged. The *average* size of the brain is different in different groups, but it has been proved over and over again that the size of the brain has nothing to do with intelligence. Some of the most brilliant men in the world have had very small brains. On the other hand, the world's largest brain belongs to an imbecile.

Blood the Same

For ages men have spoken of "blood relations" as if different peoples had different blood. Some people have shouted that if we got into our veins the blood of someone with a different head shape, eye color, hair texture, or skin color, we should get some of that person's physical and mental characteristics.

Modern science has revealed this to be pure superstition. All human blood is the same, whether it is the blood of an Eskimo or a Frenchman, of the "purest" German "Aryan" or an African pygmy—except for one medically important difference. This medical difference was discovered when doctors first began to use blood transfusion in order to save life. In early attempts at transfusion it was discovered that "agglutination" or clumping together of the red cells sometimes occurred and caused death. Gradually investigators learned that there are four types of blood, called O, A, B, and AB, and that although blood type O can be mixed successfully with the other three, none of these can be mixed with one another without clumping.

These four types of blood are inherited by each child from its forebears. But Whites, Negroes, Mongols—all races of man have all these blood types. The color of their skin does not tell which blood type they have. You and an Australian bushman may have the same blood type. Because you inherit your bodily traits from your many different ancestors, you may have a different blood type from your mother or your father or your brothers and sisters. You may have eyes like your mother's, teeth and hair like your father's, feet like your grandfather's, and a blood type like your great-grandmother's.

Today on the battlefronts doctors are giving blood "plasma" infusions without regard to race or blood type. Plasma is what is left after the red and white cells or corpuscles are removed from the blood contributed to the Blood Bank. Plasma from several different persons is mixed together and is used to restore any wounded man, whether he is white or yellow or black.

Color

Finally, let us take skin color, the most noticeable of the differences between peoples. Few traits have been used as widely to classify people. We all talk about Black, White, and Yellow races of man.

In the world today the darkest people are in West Africa, the lightest people in northwest Europe, while in southeast Asia are men with yellowish-tan skins. Most people in the world, however, are not of these extremes but are in-betweens. These in-betweens probably have the skin shades that were once most common, the white, yellow, and dark brown or black being extreme varieties.

Recently scientists found that skin color is determined by two special chemicals. One of these, *carotene,* gives a yellow tinge; the other, *melanin,* contributes the brown. These colors, along with the pinkish tinge that comes when the blood vessels show through, give various shades to the human skin. Every person, however light or dark his skin may appear, has some of each of these materials in his skin. The one exception is the albino, who lacks coloring substances—and albinos appear among dark- and light-skinned peoples alike. People of browner complexions simply have more *melanin* in their skin, people of yellowish color more *carotene*. It is not an all-or-nothing difference; it is a dif-

MOST PEOPLE IN THE WORLD HAVE IN-BETWEEN-COLOR SKIN.

ference in proportion. Your skin color is due to the amount of these chemicals present in the skin.

HOW ARE RACES CLASSIFIED?

The three primary races of the world have their strongest developments in areas A, B, and C on the map on this page. In these parts of the world most of the inhabitants not only have the same skin color but the same hair texture and noses. A is the area of the Caucasian race, B of the Mongoloid race, C of the Negroid race.

The Caucasian race inhabits Europe and a great part of the Near East and India. It is subdivided in broad bands that run east and west: Nordics (fair-skinned, blue-eyed, tall, and long-headed) are most common in the north; Alpines (in-between skin color, often stocky, broad-headed) in the middle; Mediterraneans (slenderer, often darker than Alpines, long-headed) in the south. The distribution of racial subtypes is just about the same in Germany and in France; both are mostly Alpine and both have Nordics in their northern districts. Racially, France and Germany are made up of the same stocks in just about equal proportions.

American Indians are Mongoloid, though they differ physically both among themselves and from the Mongols of China.

The natives of Australia are sometimes called a fourth primary race. They are as hairy as Europeans, and yet they live in an area where other peoples have very little body hair.

Aryans, Jews, Italians are *not* races. Aryans are people who speak Indo-European, "Aryan" languages. Hitler uses the term in many ways—sometimes for blond Europeans, including the Scandinavian; sometimes for Germans, whether blond or brunet; sometimes for all who agree with him politically, including the Japanese. As Hitler uses it, the term "Aryan" has no meaning, racial, linguistic, or otherwise.

Jews are people who acknowledge the Jewish religion. They are of all races, even Negro and Mongolian. European Jews are of many different biological types; physically they resemble the populations among whom they live. The so-called "Jewish type" is a generalized type common in the Near East in countries bordering on the Mediterranean. Wherever Jews are persecuted or discriminated against, they cling to their old ways and keep apart from the rest of the population and develop so-called "Jewish" traits. But these are not racial or "Jewish"; they disappear under conditions where assimilation is easy.

Italians are a nationality. Italians are of many different racial strains; the "typical" South Italian is a Mediterranean, more like the Spaniard or the Greek or the Levantine Jew than the blond North Italian. The Germans, the Russians, and all other nations of Europe are *nations,* not races. They are bound together, not by their head shape and their coloring, but by their national pride, their love of their farms, their local customs, their language, and the like.

Racial Mixture

As far back in time as the scientist can go he finds proof that animals and men moved about in the world. There were different kinds of animals, and many of them went great distances. But wherever they went, the different kinds could not breed together. A tiger cannot mate with an elephant. Even a fox and a wolf cannot mate with each other. But whenever groups of people have traveled from one place to another and met other people, some of them have married and had children.

At first men had to travel by foot. It took them a long time but they got almost all over the world that way. Long ago when people knew only how to make tools out of stone, the Cro-Magnons lived in Europe. Waves of migration came in from the east and the southeast. These new people settled down, bred with the Cro-Magnons, and their children were the ancestors of modern Europeans. Since then there have been many migrations from Asia and northern Africa.

Later men tamed the horse. They built carts and rode horse-back. They built great boats, which were rowed by hundreds of men. They could go faster and travel farther than ever before. The Phoenicians went on trading expeditions through the Mediterranean. The Romans went to Spain and up along the coast to the British Isles. Then the Huns swept in from Asia through central Europe and destroyed the Roman Empire. The Tartars came in from the east. They threatened to conquer all of Europe but were defeated in one of the greatest cavalry engagements of all time. The Mohammedans captured all of North Africa; they took Spain and went on up into France across the Pyrenees.

Thousands of Negro slaves have been brought into Europe at various times. Where are they now? Peoples have come and gone in Europe for centuries. Wherever they went, some of them settled down and left children. Small groups were absorbed into the total population. Always the different races moved about and intermarried.

We are used to thinking of Americans as mixed. All of us have ancestors who came from regions far apart. But we think that the English are English and the French are French. This is true for their nationality, just as we are all Americans. But it is not true for their *race*. The Germans have claimed to be a pure German race, but no European is a pure anything. A country has a population. It does not have a race. If you go far enough back in the populations of Europe you are apt to find all kinds of ancestors: Cro-Magnons, Slavs, Mongols, Africans, Celts, Saxons, and Teutons.

It is true, though, that people who live closer together intermarry more frequently. This is why there are places like Alsace-Lorraine, where Germans and French have intermarried so much that the children cannot tell whether they are German or French and so call themselves Alsatians. Czechoslovakia included old Bohemia which had a population of Nordics and semi-Asiatics and Slavs. After World War I the Germans and the Czechs along the border between the two countries intermarried so often that the Germans of this section got to look like Czechs and the Czechs began to speak German. But this did not make the two countries love each other.

People of every European nation have racial brothers in other countries, often ones with which they are at war. If at any one moment you could sort into one camp all the people in the world who were most Mediterranean, no mystic sense of brotherhood would unite them. Neither camp would have language or nationality or mode of life to unite them. The old fights would break out again unless social conditions were changed—the old hatred between national groups, the old antagonisms between ruler and ruled and between the exploiter and the exploited.

The movements of peoples over the face of the earth inevitably produce race mixture and have produced it since before history began. No one has been able to show that this is necessarily bad. It has sometimes been a social advantage, sometimes a running sore threatening the health of the whole society. It can obviously be made a social evil, and, where it is so, sensible people will avoid contributing to it and grieve if their children make such alliances. We must live in the world as it is. But, as far as we know, there are no immutable laws of Nature that make racial intermixture harmful.

Racial Superiorities and Inferiorities

When they study racial differences, scientists investigate the way by which particular traits are passed on from parents to children. They measure head form and identify skin color on a color chart. They map out the distribution of different kinds of hair or noses in the world. Scientists recognize that these differences do not themselves show better or worse qualities in peoples, any more than bay horses are better than black ones. They know that to prove that a bay horse is superior to a black one you have to do more than identify its skin color on a color chart; you have to test its abilities.

Science therefore treats human racial differences as facts to be studied and mapped. It treats racial superiorities as a separate field of investigation; it looks for evidence. When a Nazi says "I am a blue-eyed Aryan and you are non-Aryan," he means "I am superior and you are inferior." The scientist says: "Of course. You are a fair-haired, long-headed, tall North European (the anthropological term is Nordics, not Aryans), and I am a dark-haired, round-headed, less tall South European. But on what evidence do you base your claim to be superior? That is quite different."

Race prejudice turns on this point of inferiority and superiority. The man with race prejudice says of a man of another race, "No matter who he is, I don't have to compare myself with him. I'm superior anyway. I was born that way."

It is the study of racial superiorities and inferiorities, therefore, which is most important in race relations. This investigation, to have any meaning at all, must get evidence for and against the man who says, "I was *born* that way. My race is proof that I am the better man." It must be an investigation of what is better and what is worse in traits passed down by inheritance. Such traits are, by definition, racial. The first thing we want to know scientifically is what traits a man is born with and what things happen to him after he is born. If he is lucky after he is born, he will have good food, good care, good education, and a good start in life; these are not things of which he can boast: "I was *born* that way."

A man learns the language he speaks. If he'd been born of Nordic parents and brought up from infancy in China, he'd speak Chinese like a native and have as much difficulty learning Swedish when he was grown as if he'd been born of Chinese parents. He wasn't "born" to speak Cockney English or to speak with a Brooklyn accent; he speaks the way people around him speak. It's not a racial trait; he didn't inherit it.

Customs Not Racial

Differences in customs among peoples of the world are not a matter of race either. One race is not "born" to marry in church after a boy-and-girl courtship, and another race to marry "blind" with a bride the groom has never seen carried veiled to his father's house. One race is not "born" equipped to build skyscrapers and put plumbing in their houses and another to run up flimsy shelters and carry their water from the river. All these things are "learned behavior," and even in the white race there are many millions who don't have our forms of courtship and marriage and who live in shacks. When a man boasts of his racial superiority and says that he was "born that way," perhaps what he's really saying is that he had a lot of luck after he was born. A man of another race might have been his equal if he'd had the same luck in his life. Science insists that race does not account for all human achievements.

What About Intelligence?

The most careful investigations of intelligence have been made in America among Negroes and Whites. The scientist realizes that every time he measures intelligence in any man, black or white, his results show the intelligence that man was born with *plus* what happened to him since he was born. The scientist has a lot of proof of this. For instance, in the First World War, intelligence tests were given to the American Expeditionary Forces; they showed that Negroes made a lower score on intelligence tests than Whites. But the tests also showed that Northerners, *black and white,* had higher scores than Southerners, *black and white.* Everyone knows that Southerners are inborn equals of Northerners, but in 1917 many Southern states' per capita expenditures for schools were only fractions of those in Northern states, and housing and diet and income were far below average, too. Since the vast majority of Negroes lived in the South, their score on the intelligence test was a score they got not only as Negroes, but as Americans who had grown up under poor conditions in the South. Scientists therefore compared the scores of Southern Whites and Northern Negroes.

MEDIAN SCORES ON A.E.F. INTELLIGENCE TESTS

Southern Whites:

Mississippi	41.25
Kentucky	41.50
Arkansas	41.55

Northern Negroes:

New York	45.02
Illinois	47.35
Ohio	49.50

Negroes with better luck after they were born got higher scores than Whites with less luck. The White race did badly where economic conditions were bad and schooling was not provided, and

Negroes living under better conditions surpassed them. *The differences did not arise because people were from the North or the South, or because they were white or black, but because of differences in income, education, cultural advantages, and other opportunities.*

Scientists then studied gifted children. They found that children with top scores turn up among Negroes, Mexicans, and Orientals. Then they went to European countries to study the intelligence of children in homelands from which our immigrants come. Children from some of these countries got poor scores in America, but in their homeland children got good scores. Evidently the poor scores here were due to being uprooted, speaking a foreign language, and living in tenements; the children were not unintelligent *by heredity*.

Character Not Inborn

The second superiority which a man claims when he says, "I was born a member of a superior race," is that his race has better *character*. The Nazis boast of their racial soul. But when they wanted to make a whole new generation into Nazis they didn't trust to "racial soul"; they made certain kinds of teaching compulsory in the schools, they broke up homes where the parents were anti-Nazi, they required boys to join certain Nazi youth organizations. By these means they got the kind of national character they wanted. But it was a planned and deliberately trained character, not an inborn "racial soul." In just the same way the Japanese have bred a generation of ruthless fighters. Fifty years ago Europeans who lived in Japan used to describe them as "butterflies flitting from flower to flower," incapable of "the stern drives" of Western civilization. Since 1900 the "butterflies" have fought six times overseas, and they are desperate and ruthless fighters. In a generation the butterflies have become game cocks. But their *race* has not changed. The same blood still flows in their veins. But spiritually they are more like the Germans than they are like their racial brothers, the peace-loving Chinese.

It can go the other way, too. In 1520 the ancient Mexicans were like the Germans. They talked like Nazis, thought like them, in many ways felt like them. They, too, believed war to be man's highest mission. They, too, trained their children for it, placing their boys in great state schools where they learned little else but the glories of battle and the rituals of their caste. They, too, believed themselves invincible, and against small, defenseless villages, they were. But they were defeated in battle by the Spaniards with the help of the peoples whom the Aztecs had oppressed; their leaders were killed, their temples destroyed, their wealth pillaged, and their power broken. The Mexican peasant, who still speaks the Aztec language and in whose veins still runs the blood of Aztec conquerors, no longer dreams of glorious death in battle and eternal life in an Indian Valhalla. He no longer goes on the warpath, no longer provokes war with peaceful villages. He is a humble peon, wishing only to be left in peace to cultivate his little field, go to church, dance, sing, and make love. These simple things endure.

Americans deny that the Nazis have produced a national character superior to that of Goethe's and Schiller's day, and that the ruthless Japanese of today are finer human beings than in those generations when they preferred to write poetry and paint pictures. Race prejudice is, after all, a determination to keep a people down, and it misuses the label "inferior" to justify unfairness and injustice. Race prejudice makes people ruthless; it invites violence. It is the opposite of "good character" as it is defined in the Christian religion—or in the Confucian religion, or in the Buddhist religion, or the Hindu religion, for that matter.

Civilization Not Caused by Race

History proves that progress in civilization is not the monopoly of one race or subrace. When our white forebears in Europe were rude Stone Age primitives, the civilizations of the Babylonians and the Egyptians had already flourished and been eclipsed.

There were great Negro states in Africa when Europe was a sparsely settled forest. Negroes made iron tools and wove fine cloth for their clothing when fair-skinned Europeans wore skins and knew nothing of iron.

When Europe was just emerging from the Middle Ages, Marco Polo visited China and found there a great civilization, the like of which he had never imagined. Europe was a frontier country in those days compared with China.

Since the beginning of history an unusual collection of fortunate circumstances has been present sometimes among one race, sometimes among another. Up to now, every great center of civilization has had its day and has given place to others. The proud rulers of yesterday become the simple peasants of another era. The crude people who once threatened the great cities become later the kings and emperors in the same country. The peoples change, but the old arts of life are, for the most part, not permanently lost. They pass into the common heritage of mankind.

Inventions pass, too, from one continent to another when people trade with each other. This has happened since the dawn of history. About 5000 years ago, when Europe was on the frontiers of the civilized world, Asiatics came to trade in Europe and North Africa in great caravans. They followed the main rivers—the Nile into North Africa, the Danube into Europe, and the Tigris and Euphrates Rivers out of Asia. People from all over came in contact with one another and compared notes on what they knew. In this way they pooled their knowledge, and out of this combined knowledge came the great inventions of civilization—massive building and the arts of metallurgy, chemistry, writing, medicine, and mathematics; transportation on wheels. The idea of printing and the use of movable type are old Chinese inventions, and our power engines depend upon a knowledge of explosives that the Chinese worked out with firecrackers.

When Columbus discovered America, corn, "Irish" potatoes, tobacco, and "Boston" beans were unknown in Europe. They had been developed by American Indians. Within ten years corn was being planted in Central Asia and in the interior of Africa, and African tribes today think that corn was given them by their own gods "in the beginning."

All races have made their contributions to human knowledge. Those who have lived at the crossroads of the world have invented most; those who have lived isolated on islands or at the tip ends of continents have been content to earn their livelihoods by old traditional methods. There was, for them, no "necessity" to be "the mother of invention" after they had devised a way to live on the land.

Peoples who came into contact with strangers, however, gave what arts of life they had and took what the strangers had. These contributions to civilization accumulated over the centuries and on this accumulation new discoveries are based. We are all the gainers.

The United States is the greatest crossroads of the world in all history. People have come here from every race and nation, and almost every race in the world is represented among our citizens. They have brought with them their own ways of cooking food, so that our "American" diet is indebted to a dozen peoples. Our turkey, corn, and cranberries come from the Indians. Our salads we borrowed from the French and Italians. Increasingly in recent years we have enriched our tables with soups from Russia, vegetables from Italy, appetizers from the Scandinavian countries, seafoods from the Mediterranean lands, chile and tortillas from Mexico, and so on almost endlessly. At the same time, everywhere we have gone in the world, we have popularized ice cream, beefsteak, breakfast cereals, corn on the cob, and other foods that are called "American."

Industry in the United States has taken the hand-skills of our immigrants and made machines to do the work; without their skills we should not have known how. Our music, our buildings have developed from patterns brought to our shores or learned from every quarter of the world. Our country would be poorer in every phase of its culture if different cultures had not come together here, sharing and learning the special contributions each had to offer.

THE FUTURE OF RACE PREJUDICE

Nevertheless there is race prejudice in America and in the world. Race prejudice isn't an old universal "instinct." It is hardly a hundred years old. Before that, people persecuted Jews because of their religion—not their "blood"; they enslaved Negroes because they were pagans—not for being black.

Looking back now, moderns are horrified at all the blood that was shed for centuries in religious conflicts. It is not our custom any more to torture and kill a man because he has a different religion. The twenty-first century may well look back on our generation and be just as horrified. If that century builds its way of life on the Atlantic Charter—for the whole world—our era will seem a nightmare from which they have awakened. They will think we were crazy. "Why should race prejudice have swept the Western World," they will say, "where no nation was anything but a mixture of all kinds of racial groups? Why did nations just at that moment begin talking about 'the racial purity' of their blood? Why did they talk of their wars as racial wars? Why did they make people suffer, not because they were criminals or double-crossers, but because they were Jews or Negroes or non-Nordic?"

We who are living in these troubled times can tell them why. Today weak nations are afraid of the strong nations; the poor are afraid of the rich; the rich are afraid they will lose their riches. People are afraid of one another's political or economic power, they are afraid of revenge for past injuries, they are afraid of social rejection. Conflict grows fat on fear. And the slogans against "inferior races" lead us to pick on them as scapegoats. We pin on them the reason for all our fears.

Race Prejudice Not Inevitable

Freedom from fear is the way to cure race prejudice. When aggressions like those of the Axis are made impossible by guarantees of collective security, those guarantees must cover countries of all races. Then Nazi race tactics will be outmoded. In any country every legal decision that upholds equal citizenship rights without regard to race or color, every labor decision that lessens the terror of being "laid off" and gives a man self-respect in his employment, every arrangement that secures the little farmer against losing his acres to the bank—all these and many more can free people from fear. They need not look for scapegoats.

The Russian nation has for a generation shown what can be done to outlaw race prejudice in a country with many kinds of people. They did not wait for people's minds to change. They made racial discrimination and persecution illegal. They welcomed and honored the different dress, different customs, different arts of the many tribes and countries that live as part of their nation. The more backward groups were given special aid to help them catch up with the more advanced. Each people was helped to develop its own cultural forms, its own written language, theater, music, dance, and so on. At the same time that each people was encouraged in its national self-development, the greatest possible interchange of customs was fostered, so that each group became more distinctively itself and at the same time more a part of the whole.

The Russians have welcomed cultural *differences* and they have refused to treat them as *inferiorities*. No part of the Russian program has had greater success than their racial program.

What Is Being Done?

In the United States a considerable number of organizations are working for democratic race equality. To mention only a few: The East-West Association has done some splendid work in emphasizing the importance of racial understanding, especially between Asiatic and Western peoples. The China Institute is active in promoting the work of Chinese students in America, and the Phelps-Stokes Foundation has brought many African students here, cementing the relation between the two continents.

The Council Against Intolerance in America has a continuous program in the schools. The Council on Intercultural Relations has done much to emphasize the Negro's contribution to American culture. The Bureau for Intercultural Education interprets the contributions made to America by many different races and nationalities. The Rosenwald Foundation has sponsored Southern Negro schools, elementary, high school, and college, in order to make up for the deficiencies of Southern Negro education. It has also pressed for Negro housing and health projects in the North. The National Association for the Advancement of Colored People arranges publicity and fosters public education through periodicals, the radio, and special publications. It fights cases of discrimination in the courts and tries to get effective laws passed for the protection of Negro rights. The National Urban League helps Negroes who move from rural districts to the cities to find industrial work and proper living conditions.

The Churches

Many church bodies have done much to help people realize that ideas of race superiority or inferiority are un-Christian. The Department of Race Relations of the Federal Council of the Churches of Christ in America and the National Conference of Christians and Jews have encouraged collaboration among church leaders interested in interracial co-operation. During World War II, the Executive Committee of the Council called on all local churches to eliminate racial discrimination in their own practices. Church bodies of all faiths have encouraged education for tolerance.

Commission on Interracial Co-operation

For some twenty years White and Negro leaders of the South have co-operated actively through the Commission on Interracial Co-operation in establishing local committees of both Whites and Negroes. This commission has promoted mutual respect and understanding. In many local areas, small groups have worked patiently to increase interracial co-operation.

By Unions

Among the unions we find that the National Maritime Union has fought and won the right of Negroes to serve as skilled workers instead of in menial jobs only. Today mixed crews on freighters, tankers, and merchant ships are doing a magnificent job without friction. The *Booker T. Washington* with its Negro captain, Hugh Mulzac, is a notable example. The United Auto Workers has an interracial committee with Walter Hardin, a veteran Negro official, as its chairman. At first white workers resisted the right of Negroes to do more skilled kinds of work. For example, when Negroes were first placed on machines previously manned by white operators, a work stoppage shut down a whole section of the Packard plant. R. J. Thomas, the president of the union, ordered the white strikers to return to work or suffer loss of union membership and employment. Within a few hours the strikers were back, with the recently promoted Negroes still at their machines.

Besides the National Maritime Union and the Auto Workers, a number of other unions have taken the lead in promoting interracial understanding. They include the International Ladies Garment Workers, the Amalgamated Clothing Workers, the United Electrical Radio and Machine Workers, the Marine Shipbuilding Workers, and the United Rubber Workers. In the Birmingham, Alabama, area there are more than a hundred union locals with both White and Negro members, and the Southern Tenant Farmers Union has a mixed membership.

The Government

From the time of Lincoln's Emancipation Proclamation to the present day, the national and state governments have passed laws to carry forward the principles of our Declaration of Independence and our Constitution. In June 1941 President Roosevelt took direct action in his Executive Order No. 8802 toward eliminating discrimination in employment in plants with war contracts. The Fair Employment Practices Committee was set up and held public hearings in Los Angeles, Chicago, New York, and Birmingham. When an individual applied for a job in a plant doing war work and was refused for reasons of prejudice—because he was a Negro, a Jew, or a naturalized citizen—he could bring his case before the committee, who then called the company to a public hearing. This committee is now part of the War Manpower Commission.

The Negro Manpower Commission of this same body is headed by an able Negro economist and maintains a staff of Negro field representatives attached to the U. S. Employment Service. They also work through the regional offices of the Social Security Board to detect cases of racial discrimination.

The Bureau of Indian Affairs under Commissioner Collier should be mentioned here as a government bureau with a long record of successful effort for the adjustment of a racial minority.

But at best the government can act only as a policeman, finding a wrongdoer here and there. Only the people themselves can really end racial discrimination, through understanding, sympathy, and public action. But there is evidence that the American people as individuals are beginning to think and to act. One hundred thousand Americans have petitioned the War Department to have at least one division in the Army containing both Negroes and Whites. A separate petition was signed by American white men of draft age who asked to be assigned to such a division—many of these were Southerners.

Community Activities

In Houston, Texas, the mayor and a group of prominent citizens advertised in the local papers that no disturbance would be tolerated that would blacken the reputation of Houston when the Negroes of that city celebrated Juneteenth Day in honor of the emancipation of the slaves. It began with the statement, "Don't do Hitler's work," and warned citizens not to repeat rumors. The celebration was peacefully carried out. It is unfortunate that in Beaumont, Texas, similar effective action was not undertaken and a serious riot occurred.

Just Folks

In the most disastrous of recent riots in Detroit, a number of obscure bystanders performed heroic actions.

A white passenger on a street car spoke to the mob and dissuaded them from searching the car.

Two women, a mother and daughter, realizing that the Negro passenger was in danger, sheltered him so that when the rioters looked into the car he was effectively hidden.

In a bus going South recently the white passengers all remained standing rather than occupy the "white" seats of a Jim Crow bus.

During the recent disturbances in New York's Harlem, a group of Negroes stood in front of the restaurant of a white proprietor who had been their friend and in this way protected it from being broken into and destroyed by the mob.

In the last analysis these homely incidents tell the real story. They tell us that the conscience of America is aroused, that there is work to be done, and that some of us are already trying to do it.

The Challenge

With America's great tradition of democracy, the United States should clean its own house and get ready for a better twenty-first century. Then it could stand unashamed before the Nazis and condemn, without confusion, their doctrines of a Master Race. Then it could put its hand to the building of the United Nations, sure of support from all the Yellow and the Black races where the war is being fought, sure that victory in this war will be in the name, not of one race or of another, but of the universal Human Race.

FOR FURTHER READING

ABC's of Scapegoating. Chicago, Central Y.M.C.A. College. 1944. 25¢

Americans All. A Short History of American Jews. Chicago, Anti-Defamation League. 1943. 10¢

Benedict, Ruth. *Race: Science and Politics.* New York, Viking Press. Revised edition, 1943. $2.50

Brown, Earl, and Leighton, George R. *The Negro and the War.* Public Affairs Pamphlet No. 71. 1942. 10¢

Embree, Edwin R. *American Negroes: A Handbook*. New York, John Day. 1942. Cloth, $1; paper, 40¢

Livingston, Sigmund. *Must Men Hate?* New York, Harper & Bros. 1944. $2.50

McWilliams, Carey. *Brothers Under the Skin*. Boston, Little, Brown. 1943. $2.50

Myrdal, Gunnar. *The American Dilemma; The Negro Problem and Modern Democracy*. New York, Harper & Bros. 1944. $7.50

Resolutions and Manifestoes

of Scientists

RESOLUTION OF
THE AMERICAN ASSOCIATION OF UNIVERSITY PROFESSORS
(Passed unanimously, December 28, 1938)

BE IT RESOLVED: that the American Association of University Professors at its annual meeting of 1938, believing that the primary duty of the college and university is the search for and diffusion of truth, express its abhorrence at the action of totalitarian regimes which prevent the accomplishment of this duty by persecuting teachers on account of their race, religion, or political ideals; and that it express its sympathetic approval of its colleagues living under such regimes who, even in apparent silence, are protesting against the action of their governments.

RESOLUTION OF
THE AMERICAN ANTHROPOLOGICAL ASSOCIATION
(December 1938) [1]

Whereas, The prime requisites of science are the honest and unbiased search for truth and the freedom to proclaim such truth when discovered and known; and,

Whereas, Anthropology in many countries is being conscripted and its data distorted and misinterpreted to serve the cause of an unscientific racialism rather than the cause of truth;

---

[1] *Science,* Vol. 89, No. 2298, January 13, 1939.

Be it resolved, That the American Anthropological Association repudiates such racialism and adheres to the following statement of facts:

(1) Race involves the inheritance of similar physical variations by large groups of mankind, but its psychological and cultural connotations, if they exist, have not been ascertained by science.

(2) The terms "Aryan" and "Semitic" have no racial significance whatsoever. They simply denote linguistic families.

(3) Anthropology provides no scientific basis for discrimination against any people on the ground of racial inferiority, religious affiliation or linguistic heritage.

PSYCHOLOGISTS' STATEMENT (EXCERPTS) AT THE ANNUAL
MEETING OF THE AMERICAN PSYCHOLOGICAL ASSOCIATION

(December 1938) [1]

THE current emphasis upon "racial differences" in Germany and Italy, and the indications that such an emphasis may be on the increase in the United States and elsewhere, make it important to know what psychologists and other social scientists have to say in this connection.

In the experiments which psychologists have made upon different peoples, no characteristic, inherent psychological differences which fundamentally distinguish so-called "races," have been disclosed. This statement is supported by the careful surveys of these experiments in such books as *Race Psychology* by Professor T. R. Garth of the University of Denver, *Individual Differences* by Professor Frank S. Freeman of Cornell University, *Race Differences* by Professor Otto Klineberg of Columbia University, and *Differential Psychology* by Dr. Anne Anastasi of Barnard College. There is no evidence for the existence of an inborn Jewish or German or Italian mentality. Furthermore,

---

[1] A statement prepared by the Executive Council of the *Society for the Psychological Study of Social Issues,* representing an organization of more than 400 professional psychologists.

there is no indication that the members of any group are rendered incapable by their biological heredity of completely acquiring the culture of the community in which they live. This is true not only of the Jews in Germany, but also of groups that actually are physically different from one another. The Nazi theory that people must be related by blood in order to participate in the same cultural or intellectual heritage has absolutely no support from scientific findings.

Psychologists look elsewhere for the explanation of current racial hatred and persecution. It is certain that the Nazi race theories have been developed not on the basis of objective fact, but under the domination of powerful emotional attitudes. A well-known psychological tendency leads people to blame others for their own misfortunes, and the Nazis have found in the Jew a convenient psychological scapegoat for their own economic and political disabilities. In certain Czechoslovakian localities as well, Jews are now being blamed for the dismemberment of the country. There can be no doubt that economic factors are also directly involved, as the recent enormous levy on Jewish capital in Germany has amply demonstrated. Theories of Jewish plots and machinations are an excuse, a rationalization, for the expropriation of badly needed property. This attitude is not new nor is it restricted to Central Europe.

Racial and national attitudes are psychologically complex, and cannot be understood except in terms of their economic, political and historical backgrounds. Psychologists find no basis for the explanation of such attitudes in terms of innate mental differences between racial and national groups. The many attempts to establish such differences have so far met failure. Even if successful they would offer no justification for repressive treatment of the type now current in Germany. In the scientific investigations of human groups by psychologists, no conclusive evidence has been found for racial or national differences in native intelligence and inherited personality characteristics. Certainly no individual should be treated as an inferior merely because of his membership in one human group rather than another. Here in America, we have clear indications of the man-

ner in which members of different racial and national groups
have combined to create a common culture.

Council Members:

F. H. ALLPORT, Syracuse University
GORDON ALLPORT, Harvard University
J. F. BROWN, Kansas University
HADLEY CANTRIL, Princeton University
L. W. DOOB, Yale University
H. B. ENGLISH, Ohio State University
FRANKLIN FEARING, University of California, Los Angeles
GEORGE W. HARTMANN, Columbia University
I. KRECHEVSKY, University of Colorado
GARDNER MURPHY, Columbia University
T. C. SCHNEIRLA, New York University
E. C. TOLMAN, University of California

BIOLOGISTS' MANIFESTO (EXCERPTS) AT
THE SEVENTH INTERNATIONAL GENETICS CONGRESS, EDINBURGH
(*August 28–30, 1939*) [1]

THE question "how could the world's population be improved
most effectively genetically" raises far broader problems than the
purely biological ones, problems which the biologist unavoidably
encounters as soon as he tries to get the principles of his own
special field put into practice. For the effective genetic improvement of mankind is dependent upon major changes in social
conditions, and correlative changes in human attitudes. In the
first place there can be no valid basis for estimating and comparing the intrinsic worth of different individuals without economic and social conditions which provide approximately equal
opportunities for all members of society instead of stratifying
them from birth into classes with widely different privileges.

The second major hindrance to genetic improvement lies in
the economic and political conditions which foster antagonism
between different peoples, nations and "races." The removal of
race prejudices and of the unscientific doctrine that good or bad

---

[1] *Journal of Heredity*, Vol. 30, No. 9, September 1939.

genes are the monopoly of particular peoples or of persons with features of a given kind will not be possible, however, before the conditions which make for war and economic exploitation have been eliminated. This requires some effective sort of federation of the whole world, based on the common interests of all its peoples.

Thirdly, it cannot be expected that the raising of children will be influenced actively by considerations of the worth of future generations unless parents in general have a very considerable economic security and unless they are extended such adequate economic, medical, educational and other aids in the bearing and rearing of each additional child that the having of more children does not overburden either of them. As the woman is more especially affected by child bearing and rearing she must be given special protection to ensure that her reproductive duties do not interfere too greatly with her opportunities to participate in the life and work of the community at large. These objects cannot be achieved unless there is an organization of production primarily for the benefit of consumer and worker, unless the conditions of employment are adapted to the needs of parents and especially of mothers, and unless dwellings, towns and community services generally are reshaped with the good of children as one of their main objectives. . . .

The day when economic reconstruction will reach the stage where such human forces will be released is not yet, but it is the task of this generation to prepare for it, and all steps along the way will represent a gain, not only for the possibilities of the ultimate genetic improvement of man, to a degree seldom dreamed of hitherto, but at the same time, more directly, for human mastery over those more immediate evils which are so threatening our modern civilization.

(original signers)

F. A. E. CREW, F.R.S.	J. S. HUXLEY, F.R.S.
J. B. S. HALDANE, F.R.S.	H. J. MULLER
S. C. HARLAND	J. NEEDHAM
L. T. HOGBEN, F.R.S.	

Index